Computer Programming In The BASIC Language

Neal Golden

HARCOURT BRACE JOVANOVICH
New York   Chicago   San Francisco   Atlanta   Dallas   *and*   London

About the Author

Brother Neal Golden, S.C.
Chairman, Department of Mathematics
and Computer Science
Brother Martin High School
New Orleans, Louisiana

PICTURE AND ART CREDITS

Frontispiece: Xerox Corporation
Alan Dunn, © 1968, The New Yorker Magazine, Inc. p. 39.
Anatolia Budilova, SMENA, January 1972. p. 85.
Deborah Addison. p. 236.

Printed in the United States of America

ISBN 0-15-359088-2

PREFACE

As the title suggests, *Computer Programming in the BASIC Language* is a high school course in BASIC programming. The first four chapters may also be used at the junior high level.

Computers have become part of everyday living. Therefore any student should know what a computer can do and what it cannot do. In particular, a student's knowledge of programming reinforces his mathematical and scientific training.

This text may be used in various ways:

1. As a course in itself;

2. As an adjunct to a particular mathematics, science, or business course (for example, algebra one, physics, or business mathematics). The only mathematical prerequisite for use of *Computer Programming in the BASIC Language* is a half year of algebra; that is, enough time to become familiar with the use of variables and operations with them.

3. As part of a four-, five-, or six-year sequence in which students gradually and systematically gain more and more programming experience in conjunction with their regular mathematics courses.

The "Rounds"

The heart of the text is the *Rounds of Program Assignments* or, briefly, *"Rounds"* with one round at the end of each chapter. Except for Round One, which consists of flowcharting problems, the rounds provide students a variety of problems to which they can apply the programming techniques they have learned in each chapter. Thus, Chapter Two covers the elementary BASIC needed for Round Two, Chapter Three the BASIC needed for Round Three, and so forth. All together there are over 550 problems in Rounds Two through Seven.

To make assignments easier, Rounds One through Five are grouped by subject matter. Algebra one, geometry, algebra two, and advanced mathematics appear as subject areas in all five rounds. ("Advanced mathematics" includes trigonometry, complex numbers, analytic geometry, vector algebra, probability, sequences and series, and calculus.) Rounds Four and Five include problems from number theory; Round Four also contains a list of business problems, and Round Five has a statistics category.

Round Six, on matrices, is not subdivided since matrices are not a common topic in algebra one, geometry, or algebra two. It is assumed that a class attempting that round either has taken matrices in a mathematics course or else has studied Chapter Six.

Round Seven, the last in the book, is also not subdivided since the problems there are in an advanced category (for example, game simulations such as blackjack, dice, poker, baseball, and tic-tac-toe) and usually do not fit into any particular mathematics classification.

Within a round each subject category (for example, algebra one) contains problems ranging in difficulty from relatively easy to challenging. The subject divisions are not rigid. For example, an algebra one class may also be assigned selected geometry or algebra two problems. Naturally, the teacher of the advanced mathematics class has the biggest advantage since he or she has the entire list of problems to choose from. Problems should be assigned in accordance with each student's talent, background, and interest. An alternate approach is to assign a program to a group of four or five students.

Within each lesson, exercise sets are grouped in categories labeled 'A,' 'B,' and 'C' in order of increasing difficulty. All students should be able to do the 'A' exercises, most of which can be handled orally in class. 'B' exercises either are more challenging or else involve material not essential to the minimum course. 'C' exercises are either highly challenging or of the "look-ahead" variety that leads students into concepts presented later in the text. All but two lessons have **A** exercises, and all but nine have **B** or **C** exercises.

Teacher's Manual/Solution Key

Accompanying this text is a *Teacher's Manual/Solution Key (with Sample Chapter Tests)*. It discusses the philosophy and use of the text in more detail and provides complete answers to the exercises within each chapter. The booklet contains a set of sample chapter tests, one for each chapter, as well as answers to these tests.

There is a discussion of every round exercise. Attention is given to such matters as the mathematics involved, similarities to other problems, and suggested formats for the output. The programs discussed are based upon those prepared by students. As a direct result of this fact the author has paid special attention to the most common pitfalls that students are likely to make. In addition to a discussion of each problem, an actual program is usually shown, either in its entirety or with the principal steps displayed. Where appropriate, a printout of a run of the program is also shown.

Finally, the author wishes to thank the many students who were involved in the piloting of the various versions of the manuscript. It was the day-to-day classroom experiences with these students (beginning in 1967) that gave final form to the manuscript. Particular individuals owed a debt of gratitude are Brother Flavian, S.C., and Brother Remigius, S.C., administrators with foresight who cooperated fully with the author in establishing this computer course at Brother Martin High School. I am also indebted to Brother Anthony, S.C., who contributed many ideas to the organization of the course.

CONTENTS

SIGMA 5 Computer System *(Photo courtesy Xerox Data Systems)*

In the left foreground is the printer (output). The young lady sits at the teletypewriter which is used as a console for this system (input/output). Behind her is the central processing unit, which also houses memory (main storage). On the right the gentleman removes a disk pack from the auxiliary storage device. Further on the right are magnetic tape drives (input/output). In the right foreground, side-by-side, are, on the left, the card reader (input) and, on the right, the card punch (output). The cables connecting the devices are under the floor. Sigma computer systems are often used for timesharing applications.

1

COMPUTER SYSTEMS; FLOWCHARTING

1-1 FUNDAMENTAL CONCEPTS OF COMPUTER SYSTEMS

You have probably seen movies, TV shows, or cartoons that portray a computer in operation. They usually show a big box with blinking lights, whirling tapes, rows of buttons, and slots for input-output. Actually, a *computer* is not a single box, but a set of electronically connected boxes, each unit performing a particular function. All units are coordinated by the *central processing unit* (CPU) of the system. In fact, it is better to think in terms of a *computer system* rather than just a computer.

Whether a computer system is large or small it must encompass the following functions.

- **(a)** input
- **(b)** storage
- **(c)** processing
- **(d)** output

However, the machinery or *hardware* of the system is useless by itself. There has to be some way to tell the units what to do and when to do it. Thus, it is necessary to have *software* or *programs*.

> A **program** is a planned sequence of instructions that tells a computer system what steps to perform in order to produce a desired output.

In this book you will learn how to write programs in the BASIC language. "BASIC" is an abbreviation for "Beginners' All-purpose Symbolic Instruction Code." There are also other popular programming languages. FORTRAN ("FORmula TRANslator") is the most widely used language for scientific programming. COBOL ("COmmon Business-Oriented Language") is the most prominent language for business applications. Other languages are: APL ("A Programming Language"), PL/1 ("Programming Language 1"—a combination of FORTRAN and COBOL), and ALGOL ("ALGOrithmic Language").

We now return to the four components of a computer system.

(**a**) INPUT: We must distinguish between an input *medium* and an input *device*. An input device converts data from an input medium into a form that the computer can use.

Examples of input media are punched cards, magnetic tapes, and punched paper tape. Examples of input devices are card readers, teletypes, magnetic tape drives, and paper tape readers. A familiar input device is the typewriter, which is often attached to the console of a computer, sometimes with a television-like screen attached.

(**b**) STORAGE: When a program is fed into a computer, it must be stored, as must the data to be used in computation. Also, intermediate results that are obtained during the course of a computer run must be held for use later in the procedure.

There are two kinds of storage.

Memory or **main storage** is used for temporary storage of programs, input data, intermediate results, and output results. **Auxiliary storage** is used for permanent data files and for programs that are used often.

Auxiliary storage capacity is found mainly in large systems.

(**c**) PROCESSING: The heart of a computer system is the Central Processing Unit, or CPU. It is ironic that although it controls all the activity mentioned above, the CPU gives no external evidence of its work— no blinking lights or whirling tapes.

The Central Processing Unit consists of two sections.

The **control unit** coordinates all activity, very much like a traffic policeman at a busy intersection.
The **arithmetic-logical unit** performs all calculations and, under program control, makes decisions based on the results of its computations.

Some of the computations of the arithmetic-logical unit are simple arithmetic calculations, while others have the effect of comparing the results of calculations.

(**d**) OUTPUT: The input media mentioned earlier can also be used for output. Examples of output devices are card punches, magnetic tape drives, and paper tape punches.

An output device that prints data in an easily read form is the **line printer,** which prints an entire line at once. Some such printers attain speeds of over 2000 lines per minute.

EXERCISES 1-1

A Classify each item 1 through 14 below as (**a**) input, (**b**) storage, (**c**) processing, or (**d**) output. If an item comes under more than one category, then note all categories that apply.

1. punched cards
2. magnetic tape drives
3. teletype
4. paper tape reader
5. control unit
6. auxiliary storage
7. memory
8. arithmetic-logical unit
9. magnetic tape
10. console typewriter
11. card reader
12. line printer
13. punched paper tapes
14. card punch

In Exercises 15 through 18 fill in the missing blanks.

15. The four functions which any computer system must perform are __?__ , __?__ , __?__ , and __?__ .

16. The most common input media are __?__ , __?__ , and __?__ .

17. A (n) __?__ is a planned sequence of instructions telling the computer what steps to perform.

18. A computer system consists of __?__ , the electronic units themselves and __?__ , the programs which direct the system.

1-2 THE SYMBOLS OF FLOWCHARTING

Before writing a program, a programmer usually prepares a flowchart for the problem to be solved. A **flowchart** is a step-by-step outline of the procedure to be followed by the computer. These are the symbols.

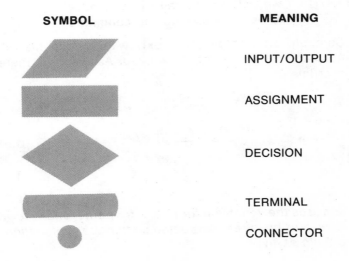

SYMBOL	MEANING
	INPUT/OUTPUT
	ASSIGNMENT
	DECISION
	TERMINAL
	CONNECTOR

Example: Compute the average of three numbers.

Solution:

Flowchart 1–1

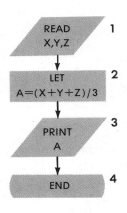

Comments:

The programmer chooses three letters (X, Y, and Z) to represent the numbers to be averaged.

The computing step uses the standard formula for finding an average, the programmer electing to call the answer "A." You may assume that the computer can perform the usual operations of addition, subtraction, multiplication, division, raising to a power, and taking a root.

Since card punches, teletypes, and other input equipment print capital letters, letters are always capitalized in flowcharts.

Note that in a flowchart:

1. Arrows connect the symbols to show the flow of steps.

2. It is customary to chart the steps downward. However, we sometimes will chart the steps from left to right.

3. Inside each symbol is written a direct command to the computer.

   (a) For INPUT we will use the READ command.
   (b) For ASSIGNMENT we will use the LET command.
   (c) For OUTPUT we will use the PRINT command.
   (d) For TERMINAL we must use the END command.

Example: Compute an employee's weekly wage, given his rate-per-hour and number of hours worked. Assume that there is no overtime pay.

Solution: *Flowchart 1–2*

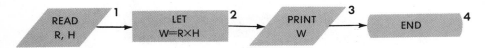

Comment:

The flowchart uses the variable R for rate, H for hours, and W for weekly wage. The flowchart boxes are numbered so that the explanation below can refer to them easily.

It is important to understand how variables are used in programming. A variable is the name of a particular location in the memory of the computer. In Flowchart 1-2 on page 4 the command in box 1, "READ R,H," causes two values to be obtained from a data list. In the BASIC language, which we shall study in this book, the data are usually listed in a DATA statement in the program itself and entered via a teletype terminal. But for the flowchart it is sufficient to understand that the two values are read and stored, respectively, in memory locations designated "R" and "H." Storage positions have numerical addresses within the machine but in languages such as BASIC and FORTRAN the programmer needs only to use variables such as R and H. When the computer moves to box 2, it obtains the values stored in locations R and H, multiplies them, and stores them in a location named "W." Box 3 causes the value in W to be printed on an output device (printer, card punch, magnetic tape drive, teletype, etc.).

The rectangle (see Box 2) is called an **assignment box** because it causes the value obtained from the right side of "=" to be *assigned* to the storage location named by the variable on the left side. Thus, "=" should be thought of as a left-pointing arrow. Thus,   LET W $=$ R $\times$ H has the effect   W $\leftarrow$ R $\times$ H   , that is, "let the value obtained by multiplying R and H be *assigned* to the location W." Some books actually use "$\leftarrow$" in place of "=" in assignment boxes of flowcharts, but since the BASIC language uses "=," we use "=" in flowcharts in this text. In view of the above discussion, it is clear that "=" does not have the same meaning in BASIC as it does in an algebraic equation.

EXERCISES 1-2

A   Write the letter that corresponds to each symbol.

1.

2.

3.

4.

5.

(a) Connector
(b) Decision
(c) Input/Output
(d) Assignment
(e) Terminal

In Exercises 6 through 8 a flowcharting problem is stated and part of the flowchart shown. Complete the flowchart.

Example:

Compute a baseball player's batting average, given his number of at-bats and number of hits.

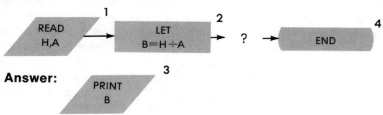

Answer:

6. Compute the geometric mean of two positive numbers.

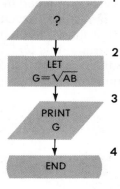

7. Read two real numbers; multiply them and divide the result by two.

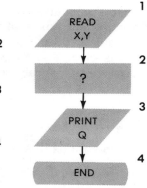

8. Compute the annual simple interest on a given invest- ment if the rate is 6%.

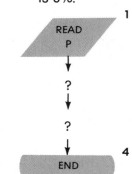

What is wrong in each of the following flowchart boxes?

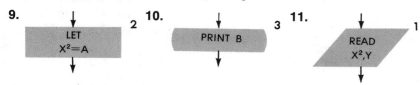

9.
LET
$X^2 = A$

10.
PRINT B

11.
READ
X^2, Y

B Flowchart each of the following problems.
12. Compute the perimeter of a rectangle, given the length and width.
13. Compute the area of a circle, given the radius. (Note: use an approximation such as 3.14159 for pi.)

1-3 FLOWCHARTS INVOLVING DECISIONS

Example: Read a real number x. If x is nonnegative, give its square root. If x is negative, print "NO REAL SQUARE ROOT."

Solution: *Flowchart 1-3*

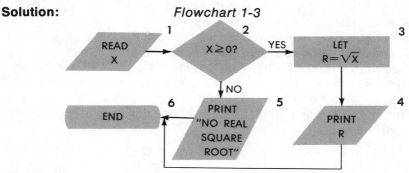

Comment:

We assume that the hardware of the computer can compare numbers and answer questions such as "x ≥ 0?"

It must always be clear which direction to take when executing the steps of a flowchart. The answer to the decision box must be *yes* or *no*.

The logic of a flowchart can be followed by using a **trace**. In Table 1-1 below we follow the flowchart of the square root problem twice, first using x = 16 and then using x = −5.

Table 1-1   Trace 1: Assume 16 input as x.

Step Number	Flowchart Box Number	Values of Variables		Test	Yes or No?	Output
		x	R			
1	1	16				
2	2			$16 \geq 0?$	Yes	
3	3		4			
4	4					4
5	END					

Trace 2: Assume −5 input as x.

Step Number	Flowchart Box Number	Values of Variables		Test	Yes or No?	Output
		x	R			
1	1	−5				
2	2			$-5 \geq 0?$	No	
3	5					NO REAL SQUARE ROOT
4	END					

Note the difference between the two PRINT steps of Flowchart 1-3 on page 7 (box 4 and box 5). PRINT R causes the current *value* in the memory location named R to be printed on an output device. PRINT "NO REAL SQUARE ROOT" results in the *message* NO REAL SQUARE ROOT being printed as the output of the program. The two types of output can be combined. For example, box 4 in the square

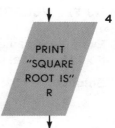

root flowchart could be changed to the one shown above. If, as in Trace 1 on page 7, x = 16, then box 4, as revised, would result in the output   SQUARE ROOT is 4   . The quotation marks are used in the program to begin and end the message. They are not actually printed as part of the output.

The PRINT boxes in Flowcharts 1-1 and 1-2 on page 4 could be similarly amended to those shown at the right.

Example:

Read a real number; print whether it is positive, negative, or zero.

Solution: *Flowchart 1-4*

Note that the program does not require three decisions. If x is not greater than zero and not less than zero, the computer can automatically print "zero" since there is no other possibility left.

The decisions of the program could have been stated differently or in a different order. As long as the yes and no branches of the two decisions lead to the correct print statements, the program will work.

Let us now trace Flowchart 1-4 using the data list: 7, −5, 0.

Table 1-2 Trace of Flowchart 1-4

Trace 1: Input 7 for x.

Step Number	Flowchart Box Number	Value of Variable x	Test	Yes or No?	Output
1	1	7			
2	2		7 > 0?	Yes	
3	3				
4	END				POSITIVE

Trace 2: Input −5 for x.

Step Number	Flowchart Box Number	Value of Variable x	Test	Yes or No?	Output
1	1	−5			
2	2		−5 > 0?	No	
3	4		−5 < 0?	Yes	
4	5				
5	END				NEGATIVE

Trace 3: Input 0 for x.

Step Number	Flowchart Box Number	Value of Variable x	Test	Yes or No?	Output
1	1	0			
2	2		0 > 0?	No	
3	4		0 < 0?	No	
4	6				
5	END				ZERO

EXERCISES 1-3

A Trace each flowchart for the data values listed. Refer to Table 1-1 on page 7.

1. DATA: 10, −5

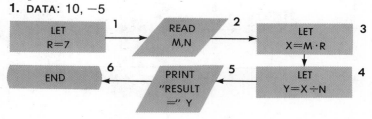

Trace each flowchart for each set or sets of data values listed above the flowchart. Refer to Table 1-1 on page 7.

2. DATA: 10, 4   **3.** DATA: 5   **4.** DATA: -2

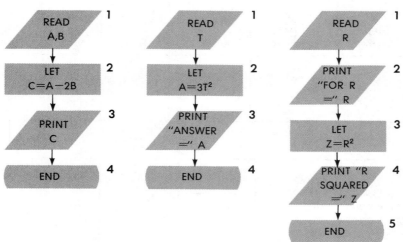

5. DATA: 8, 2   **6.** DATA: -5, 0

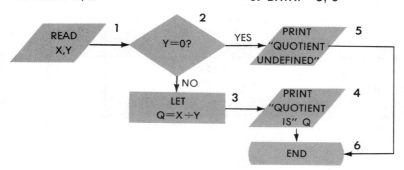

7. DATA: 7, -3 **8.** DATA: -4, -5 **9.** DATA: -1, 6

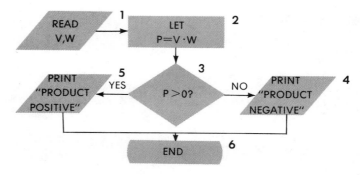

In Exercises 10 through 13 draw a portion of a flowchart that does what is stated.

Example: If $x > 10$, then print x; otherwise, assign x to y.

Solution:

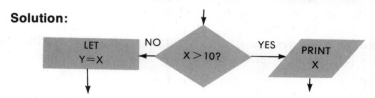

10. If $A^2 = s$, then print "SQUARE ROOT IS" A; otherwise, print "NO SQUARE ROOT."
11. Read M; if M $= 100$, then END; otherwise, let $y = 2M$.
12. If D > 0, print "YES"; if D ≤ 0, print "NO".
13. Check if $x = 0$. If it does, print "ZERO". If it does not, test if $y = 0$.

Galileo discovered that the relationship between the distance an object falls and the time it takes to fall is defined by $d = 16t^2$, where t is given in seconds and d in feet.
14. Complete the flowchart below which reads a value for t, computes d, and prints t and d.

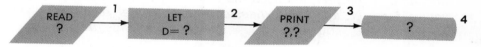

15. Trace the completed flowchart for these data values: 1, 2, 3, 4.

B Draw a flowchart for each of the following exercises.
16. Read two unequal real numbers x and y. Print either "$x < y$" or "$y < x$."
17. Read real numbers A and B. Then print "$A < B$," "$A = B$," or "$A > B$."
18. Read three real numbers. Determine which is the largest. (Note: The computer can compare only *two* numbers at a time.)
19. Read three positive real numbers. Decide whether these three numbers could represent the lengths of the sides of a triangle.
20. Read three numbers A, B, and C, representing the lengths of the sides of a triangle. Determine if the triangle is ISOSCELES, EQUILATERAL, or SCALENE.
21. Change the wage problem of Flowchart 1-2 on page 4 as follows: input an employee's hourly rate and the number of hours worked the past week. Assume that any hours worked beyond forty are overtime hours for which he is paid double his regular rate.

1-4 PROCESSING MORE THAN ONE SET OF DATA

Rarely is a program written to process only one set of data. Computers are most often used for simple tasks that are performed many times. For that reason we take a second look at some of the programs already flowcharted in order to extend them to many sets of data.

Example: Find the average of sets of three numbers, where the number of sets is not known in advance.

Solution: *Flowchart 1-5*

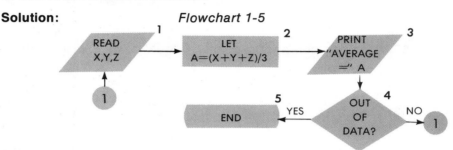

Comment:

The OUT OF DATA *decision is performed internally within the machine. In the program itself the data are listed. When the string of values for* X, Y, *and* Z *is exhausted, the computer receives a "*YES*" answer to the* OUT OF DATA? *question and ends the program.*

Here is a trace using data values 10, 8, 12, −2, 5, 7, 88, 90, 92.

Table 1-3 Trace of Flowchart 1-5

Step Number	Flowchart Box Number	Values of Variables				Test	Yes or No?	Output
		X	Y	Z	A			
1	1	10	8	12				
2	2				10			
3	3							AVERAGE = 10
4	4					Out of Data?	No	
5	1	−2	5	7				
6	2				3.33333			
7	3							AVERAGE = 3.33333
8	4					Out of Data?	No	
9	1	88	90	92				
10	2				90			
11	3							AVERAGE = 90
12	4					Out of Data?	Yes	
13	END							

A variable in a flowchart (that is, a memory location) can have only one value at a time. Whenever a new value is assigned to the variable, the previous value is lost.

Here are the general principles governing flowchart construction.

1. INPUT: Examples of correct READ boxes are shown below. You can see that the general form consists of the word READ followed by a list of variables.

When a READ box is executed, one or more values are obtained from a data list and entered into the location(s) named by the variable(s) in the list following the word READ. The previous contents of the locations are destroyed. A READ step has the same effect as an assignment box except that one or more variables are assigned values taken from a data list.

As the trace in Table 1-3 on page 12 implies, the first execution of the READ instruction causes the required number of values to be taken from the beginning of the data list and stored in the memory locations specified by the variables in the READ list. A "pointer" inside the computer keeps track of the position of the first unused value in the data list so that the next time a READ box is executed, the next data values in sequence are selected. If there are no more items in the data list or if there are not enough for all the variables in the READ command, the OUT OF DATA? question yields a "YES" answer and the program is terminated. For example, if the input list for the program on the previous page was 10, 8, 12, −2, 5, 7, 88, 90, 92, 46, 73, the number triplets (10, 8, 12), (−2, 5, 7), and (88, 90, 92) would be processed as in the trace. But since there are only two values left in the data list, there are not enough items for the three variables in the READ box and the OUT OF DATA? test would produce a "YES" result and end the program.

Arithmetic expressions may never appear in a READ box.

2. ASSIGNMENT: The general form of the assignment box is shown at the right. Other examples are shown below.

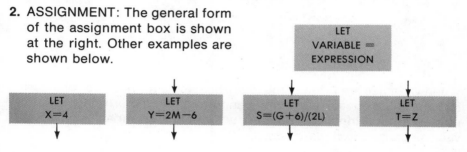

It has already been pointed out that the $=$ in an assignment box has the effect of $\leftarrow$ so that the general form can be thought of as variable $\leftarrow$ expression. As the examples illustrate, "expression" could be a constant, a variable, or a combination of constants, variables, and operations.

Carrying out an assignment command involves three steps.

(a) The current values of any variables appearing in the expression to the right of $=$ are obtained from memory.

(b) If the right-hand expression is more complicated than a simple constant or a single variable, then this expression is evaluated, that is, all operations performed and one value obtained for the expression.

(c) The value of the expression is then assigned to the variable (i.e., stored in the memory location) on the left-hand side of the $=$.

An assignment step, like a READ, is destructive; that is, each time a new value is assigned to a variable, the previous value of that variable is lost and no longer available in memory. (If for some reason that value will be needed later in the program, a new variable should be introduced and the value "copied" into the new location where it can be held until needed.)

Using a variable in the expression to the right of $=$ in a LET step does not harm the value of that variable. For example, if the statement W = R × H is executed, W receives a new value but (for the moment at least) the values in R and H remain the same.

3. OUTPUT: The general forms of the output command are illustrated at the right. The two forms may also occur in combination.

Examples of legitimate PRINT boxes follow.

When variables are listed in the PRINT box, the current values of the variables are obtained from memory and printed in the order listed on an output device. Printing is nondestructive since no variables have their values changed in the process.

4. DECISIONS: The general form of the decision symbol is

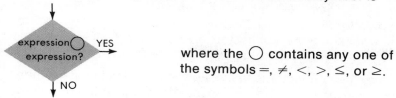

where the $\bigcirc$ contains any one of the symbols $=$, $\neq$, $<$, $>$, $\leq$, or $\geq$.

The YES and NO branches may exit from any two of the three other points of the diamond. As in the assignment box, "expression" means a constant, a variable, or a combination of constants, variables, and operations. Here are further examples of valid decision boxes.

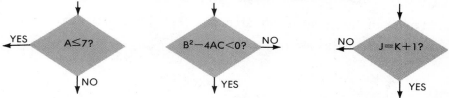

Execution of the decision box involves these steps.

(a) Obtain from memory the current values of any variables in the box.
(b) Evaluate (if necessary) the expressions on either side or both sides of the relation using the values of the variables found in (a).
(c) Test the truth or falsity of the statement appearing in front of the question mark in the decision box.
(d) Choose the appropriate exit path depending on the result of the test in (c).

Note, first, that no variables change their values as a result of the execution of a decision box. Second, expressions are permitted on both sides of the relation symbol in a decision box, whereas in an assignment command, an expression is permitted only on the right side of $=$. Third, the statement in the decision box may be an inequality but the statement in an assignment box always uses $=$.

5. TERMINAL: The only form of the terminal symbol that we will use is the one shown at the right. The effect of this box is to halt execution of the program.

There may be no "dead ends" in a flowchart. Regardless of the number of decisions and the number of possible paths through the flowchart, every branch must ultimately connect to the END statement (often through the OUT OF DATA? step, though not necessarily). If the program is logically sound, END will always be the last statement executed.

6. CONNECTOR: This symbol is always used in pairs. The general form is shown by the pair →⊖ and ←⊖ where — represents a numeral or letter. Flowchart 1-5 on page 12 used ①. Ⓐ is another good choice. If additional connectors are needed, ②, ③, ④, etc., or Ⓑ, Ⓒ, Ⓓ, etc., can be used.

The purpose of the connector is to link flowchart boxes in cases where it would be inconvenient or (in complicated programs) impossible to draw a connecting arrow segment. If a lengthy flowchart must be continued on a second page, connectors are needed at the end of the first page and the beginning of the second to show the linkage.

EXERCISES 1-4

A For each box state whether it is a valid flowchart box. If not, explain why.

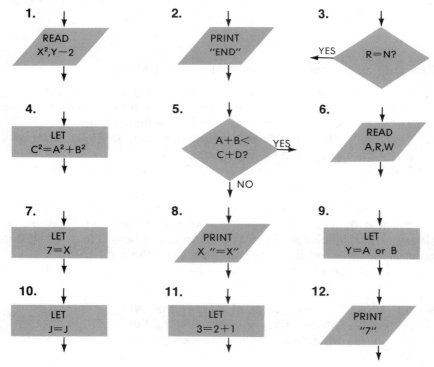

1. READ $X^2, Y-2$

2. PRINT "END"

3. YES ← $R=N$?

4. LET $C^2=A^2+B^2$

5. $A+B < C+D$? YES → / NO ↓

6. READ A,R,W

7. LET $7=X$

8. PRINT X "=X"

9. LET $Y=A$ or B

10. LET $J=J$

11. LET $3=2+1$

12. PRINT "7"

13. Do the assignment boxes below accomplish the same result? If not, explain the differences in the execution of the two boxes.

LET $A=B$ ¹ LET $B=A$ ²

Trace each flowchart for the data listed. See Table 1-2 on page 9.

14. DATA: 10, 20, 5, −2, 0, 11

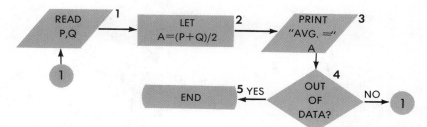

15. DATA: 7, 4, 4, 8, 5, 5

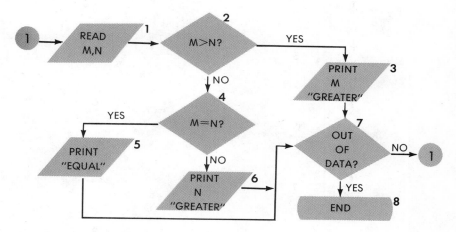

16. DATA: 7, 4, 4, 8, 5, 5

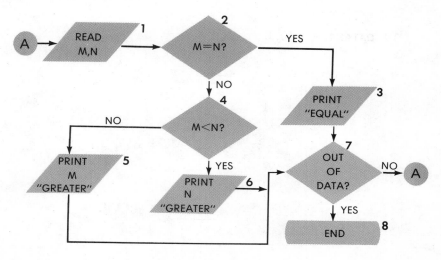

Trace each flowchart for the data listed. See Table 1-2 on page 9.

17. DATA: 2, 7, 5, −4   **18.** DATA: 2, 7, 5, −4

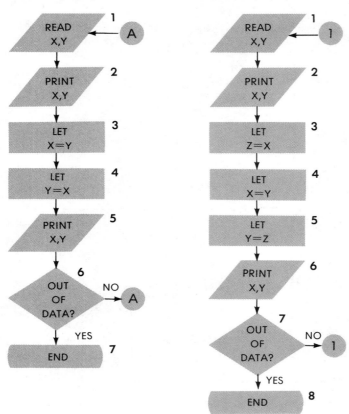

19. DATA: 4, −3, 10, 0

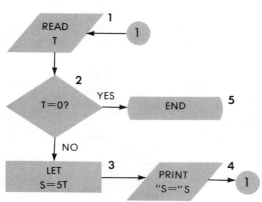

Suppose that you are given two rational numbers A and B (with A < B) and a third rational number C. Decide whether C is "between" A and B; that is, determine whether A < C < B.

20. Complete the flowchart below for this problem.

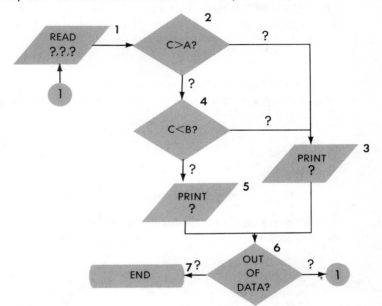

21. Trace the completed flowchart for these data values: 1, 2, 1.3, .7, .8, .9, 2.02, 2.07, 2.01.

22. Copy the flowchart symbols given and fill in the boxes for the following problem. "Accept any two nonzero real numbers and print the quotient of the greater divided by the smaller."

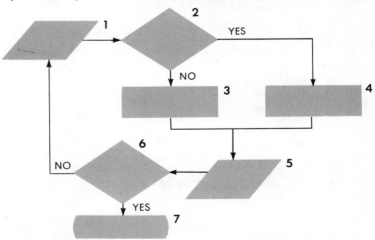

B Flowchart each of these problems to handle as many sets of data as needed.

23. Compute the area of each of a set of rectangles.
24. Compute the area of each member of a set of triangles.
25. Compute the circumference of each member of a set of circles.
26. Compute the pay of each of a set of employees. (See Ex. 21, p. 11.)

C Do the following assignment boxes make sense? If not, explain why. If they are valid, what would be the result of each?

27.

LET
J=J+1

28.

LET
J=J×2

Trace each flowchart for the data listed.

29. DATA: 4, −2, 7, 6, 0
30. DATA: 7, 6, 6, 7, 9, −7, −8, 3, 0, 14, 10, 5

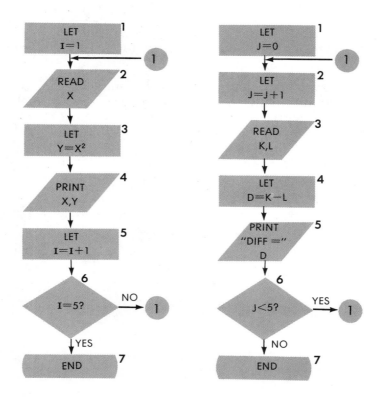

1-5 ADDITIONAL FLOWCHART PROBLEMS

Example: Read the coordinates of a point in the *xy*-plane. Decide the number of the quadrant in which the point lies. Assume that the point is not on an axis.

Solution: *Flowchart 1-6*

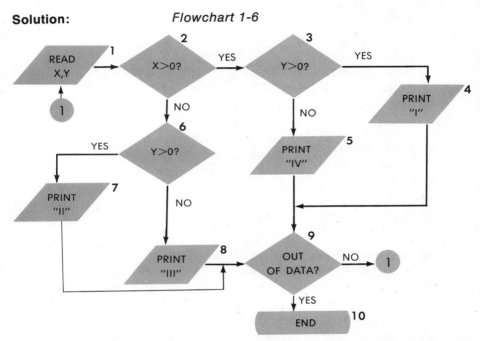

Note that it was necessary to place the decision "Y > 0?" at two points in the flowchart. After x and Y are read, x is tested to decide if it is positive or negative. Regardless of the outcome of this decision, Y must then be checked. Thus "Y > 0?" appears twice in the program but with different outcomes: I or IV in one case and II or III in the other. Of course, one of these decisions could just as logically have been worded "Y < 0?" (with the YES and NO outcomes reversed).

CAUTION: In algebra, coordinates are written as an ordered pair, in parentheses, as in (*x, y*). The computer does not have to *know* that x and Y form an ordered pair. To the machine x and Y are just numbers.

An ordered pair could be printed with a PRINT box like the one shown at the right. The open parentheses, comma, and closed parentheses are dictated to the computer between quotation marks.

Make sure that the number of quotation marks in a PRINT box is *even*. In complicated output boxes such as the one just shown, it is easy to omit an open or closed parentheses.

EXERCISES 1-5

A   **1.** Trace Flowchart 1-6 on page 21 for this list of data values: 2, 4, −1, −6, 10, −5, −5, 32.

What erroneous output will result from Flowchart 1-6 from each data pair below? (The output is erroneous since Flowchart 1-6 is not meant to handle zero coordinates.)

2. 0, 6   **3.** −2, 0   **4.** 0, 0   **5.** 0, −9   **6.** 7, 0

Consider $y - 6 < 7x + 3$ and a replacement set $\{(1, \ 15), (-2, \ 6), (1, \ 30), (-5, \ -20)\}$. The flowchart shown at the right should use each pair from the replacement set as data and determine which pairs are solutions of the inequality.

7. Complete the flowchart shown on the right.

8. Trace the completed flowchart for the given replacement set.

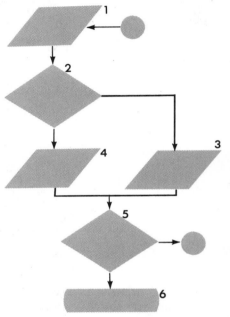

B   In Exercises 9 through 11 a problem is stated and a flowchart shown for that problem. Identify and correct any error(s) in each flowchart.

9. Read two numbers; double the larger and print the result.

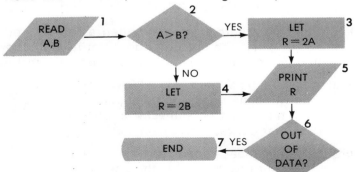

10. Given a real number, determine if it is positive, negative, or zero.

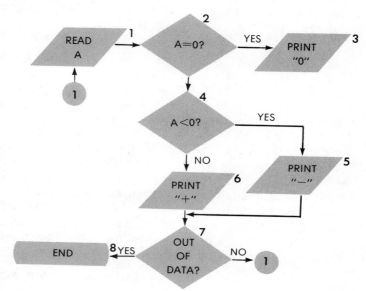

11. Read a real number. If it is not zero, print its reciprocal.

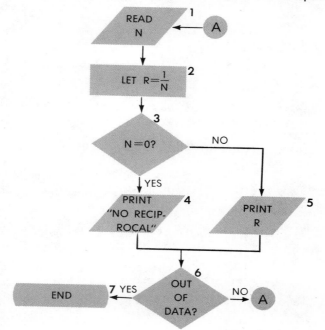

12. The "slope-intercept form" of a linear equation is $y = Mx + B$ where M is the slope and B, the y-intercept. Suppose you are to design a flowchart which, given M and B, prints the equation of the line. Consider the print box below.

For M $= 2$ and B $= 7$, this print box would give as its output Y $= 2x + 7$. For M $= -2$ and B $= 7$, the output would be Y $= -2x + 7$. Now suppose that M $= 2$ and B $= -7$. The step would produce Y $= 2x + -7$. The double sign before the 7 is awkward. We would prefer printing just Y $= 2x - 7$. A different PRINT box is needed to handle negative values for B. Similarly if B $= 0$, we do not wish to print Y $= 2x + 0$ but instead just Y $= 2x$. Design a flowchart to accept M and B and print the equation "neatly" without double signs or needless zeros. (Is there any value of M that should be specially handled?)

For each box state whether it is a valid output box. If not, explain why.

13. PRINT (−A)

14. PRINT "X="

15. PRINT "("X,Y")"

16. PRINT "("X,Y")"

17. PRINT "X+Y=" Z

18. PRINT A"+"B"I"

19. Trace the flowchart below. DATA: 10, 90, 43, 11

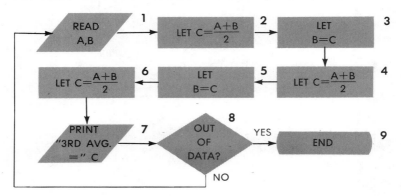

C Use the flowchart below for Exercises 20 through 22.

20. Trace the flowchart. No data are needed.

21. Would the flowchart produce the same output if boxes 7 and 8 were reversed so that box 8 would come before box 7?

22. The flowchart automatically starts I at 0 and J at 1. The algorithm could be made more flexible by allowing the two starting values to be input from data. Explain how the flowchart below can be modified to allow this flexibility.

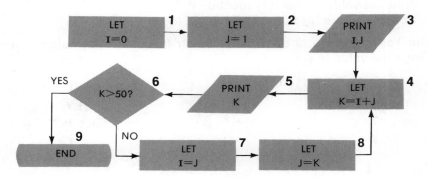

CHAPTER REVIEW

For each box state whether it is a valid flowchart box. If not, explain why.

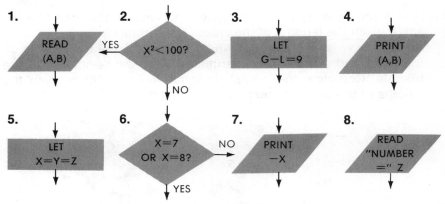

Construct a section of a flowchart that does what is stated each time.

9. If M = N, then print "ZERO"; otherwise, print "NOT ZERO".

10. Read X and Y. If X > Y, let Z = X; if X ≤ Y, assign Y to Z.

11. If $x^2 + 4x = 7$ is true, print X "IS A ROOT"; if it is false, END.

12. Read I then read Y. If Y = I, print "FOUND"; if Y ≠ I, read a new value of Y.

13. Print Y. If I > 10, go to the OUT OF DATA? decision box; otherwise read Y.

Draw a flowchart box to execute each task.
14. Input values for the variables R, Y, and Z.
15. Test whether x is greater than 7.
16. Halt the program.
17. Assign to Y the sum of twice x and 7.
18. Output the message   HELP!
19. Take the square of the number in location M and copy this square into location T.
20. Print the value in memory location P.
21. Accept a value for the variable K.

Write *Yes* or *No*, to show whether each flowchart box below would change the value in Q .

22.

READ
Q

23.

PRINT
Q

24.

LET
R=Q+7

25.

Q=10? → YES

NO

26.

LET
Q=R+7

27.

LET
R=5Q

28. Hero's (or Heron's) Formula is used to compute the area of a tri-angle given the lengths of the sides. The formula is
Area $= \sqrt{s(s-a)(s-b)(s-c)}$ where *a*, *b*, and *c* are the lengths of the sides and *s* is the "semiperimeter" (half the perimeter) of the triangle. Complete the partial flowchart below which, given the lengths of the sides, computes and prints the area.

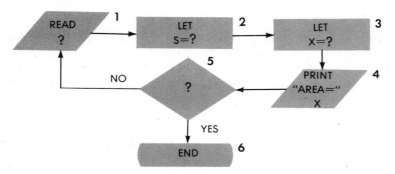

READ ? 1
LET S=? 2
LET X=? 3
PRINT "AREA=" X 4
? 5
NO
YES
END 6

29. Trace the flowchart that you completed in Exercise 28. Use the fol-lowing data list: 5, 4, 3, 4, 4, 6.

*ROUND ONE: *FLOWCHARTS FOR STUDENT ASSIGNMENT*

GENERAL INSTRUCTIONS:

1. In each exercise on pages 27 through 33, draw a flowchart to handle as many sets of data as needed.

2. Include steps in the flowchart to handle all possibilities.

3. Trace the flowchart for a variety of data values. The data should be chosen so that each box of the flowchart is executed at least once.

4. Regardless of the number of paths through the flowchart, the trace should process at least three sets of data.

ALGEBRA ONE

1. Read a real number. Print the number and its absolute value. (Assume that there is no "built-in" way for the computer to take the absolute value of a number.)

2. Find the slope of the line through two given points in the coordinate plane. Include the possibility that the slope may be undefined.

3. Input two real numbers. Without actually multiplying the numbers, determine whether their product is positive, negative, or zero.

4. Accept the coordinates of two points on the real number line. Subdivide the line segment determined by these two points into four equal subsegments. Print the coordinates of the endpoints of each segment.
Example: Suppose the given points are 0 and 1. The endpoints of the subdivisions are 0, .25, .5, .75, and 1.

5. Read the coordinates of a point in the *xy*-plane. Decide the number of the quadrant in which the point lies or, if it lies on an axis, decide whether it lies on the *x*-axis, on the *y*-axis, or on both.

6. Assume that the cost, not including tax, for sending a telegram from Chicago to Los Angeles is $2.10 for the first fifteen words or less, plus $0.15 for each additional word beyond fifteen. Design a flowchart which, given the number of words in a telegram (Chicago-Los Angeles), computes the cost.

7. Given five real numbers, print only the smallest. Do not assume that the numbers are listed in the data in any special order. You may assume that no two of the numbers are equal.

---

*The reader can refer to the preface on pages iii through iv for a discussion of how the seven rounds in this book should most effectively be used.

In Exercises 8 through 11 read rational numbers A, B, and C, which are the coefficients of a linear equation of the form $Ax + By = C$. (Assume that A and B are not both zero.)

8. Compute and print the slope of the graph of the equation. Remember that the slope may be undefined.

9. Print the *x*-intercept of the graph as an ordered pair.

10. Print the *y*-intercept of the graph as an ordered pair.

11. Input real numbers R and S. Decide whether the point (R, S) lies on the graph of $Ax + By = C$.

12. Input a real number x. Print x, its additive inverse, and (if it has one) its multiplicative inverse

13. Read real numbers A and B. Without computing $A + B$, decide whether the sum of A and B is positive, negative, or zero.

14. Given the number of a baseball team's wins and losses, compute its winning percentage. Assume that there are no ties.

15. Input the number of a team's wins, losses, and ties, and print its winning percentage. Assume that a tie game counts as a full game played and a half-game won.

16. Assume that a baby-sitter works for a rate of 50 cents per hour until 11 P.M. and 75 cents per hour thereafter. Given the time he or she begins and the time he or she ends, compute the fee for an evening's work. (Hint: Input the times using the twenty-four hour clock; e.g., for 7 P.M. input 1900.)

17. Arrange a set of three numbers in descending order. For example, for the data values 8, 11, −3, print   11 8 −3   . Two or three of the numbers may be equal.

18. Given a linear equation $Ax + B = C$ (A, B, C real numbers), solve for *x*. For example, if the equation is $7x + 5 = 19$, print $x = 2$.

19. Given an inequality $Ax + b > c$ (A, B, C real numbers), solve for *x*. For example, if the inequality is $7x + 5 > 19$, print $x > 2$.

GEOMETRY

20. Given the length of a side of a square, compute the perimeter.

21. Given the length of a side of a square, compute the area.

22. Given an angle measure greater than 0 and less than 180, classify the angle as ACUTE, RIGHT, or OBTUSE.

23. Given the lengths of any two sides of a right triangle, the Pythagorean Theorem enables you to compute the third side. Design a flowchart which finds the length of the missing side whether it is a leg or the hypotenuse. One way to accomplish this is to READ A, B, C but enter 0 for the unknown side. Then test if A = 0, B = 0, or C = 0 and branch to one of three assignment steps to compute the missing length and print it.

24. Input the radius of a sphere and compute its volume.

25. Input the radius of a sphere and compute its surface area.

26. Accept L, the length of one side of an equilateral triangle, and compute the perimeter.

27. Accept L as defined in Exercise 26 and compute the area.

28. Read the measure of the vertex angle of an isosceles triangle. Print the measure of a base angle of the triangle.

29. Read three positive numbers A, B, and C. Determine if these could be the lengths of the sides of a right triangle. (Note: You must first check that A, B, and C can be sides of *any* triangle.)

30. Input N, a positive integer denoting the number of sides of a polygon. Compute the sum of the interior angles of the polygon.

31. Input N as defined in Exercise 30. Assume that the N-gon is regular and print the measure of each interior angle.

Consider isosceles triangle *ABC* with *AB* = *AC*. Input the lengths of $\overline{BC}$ and $\overline{AB}$. Do Exercises 32 and 33.

32. Compute the perimeter of the triangle.

33. Compute the area of the triangle.

34. Find the slant height of a regular square pyramid, given the length of a side of the base and the length of a lateral edge.

35. Given the coordinates of three points in the *xy*-plane, determine if the points are collinear.

36. In Exercise 35, if the points are not collinear, decide whether the triangle formed by joining the three points is ISOSCELES, EQUILATERAL, or SCALENE.

37. In Exercise 35, if the points are not collinear, print the perimeter of the triangle formed by joining the three points.

38. Given the measures of two angles of a triangle, print the measure of the third angle.

Read the lengths of three sides of a triangle and the lengths of the three corresponding sides of a second triangle. Solve the following problems.

39. Are the triangles congruent?

40. Are the triangles similar?

41. Read the lengths of the four sides of a quadrilateral. Decide whether the quadrilateral is equilateral.

42. Read the lengths of the five sides of a pentagon. Decide whether the pentagon is equilateral.

43. Given the coordinates of four points in the xy-plane, determine if the quadrilateral formed by joining the points in order is a parallelogram.

44. Knowing the ratio of the measures of the angles of a triangle, determine the measure of each angle. For example, if the ratio of the angle measures is 2:3:4, input 2, 3, 4 as data.

A right triangle ABC is given with altitude $\overline{CD}$ drawn to the hypotenuse $\overline{AB}$. Let a, b, c, h, x, and y represent lengths as indicated in the figure at the right. Solve the following problems.

45. Given c and x, find a.

46. Given c and x, find h.

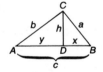

47. Given h and a, find b.

48. Given h and x, find b.

The coordinates of two points A and B in the coordinate plane are given for Exercises 49 and 50.

49. Compute AB, the length of the segment $\overline{AB}$.

50. Determine the coordinates of the midpoint of $\overline{AB}$.

51. Compute the perimeter of a triangle, given the lengths of its sides.

52. Compute the perimeter of a right triangle, given the lengths of the two legs.

53. Compute the perimeter of a right triangle, given the length of the hypotenuse and the length of one leg.

ALGEBRA TWO

54. A cubic polynomial function is defined by $y = \text{A}x^3 + \text{B}x^2 + \text{C}x + \text{D}$ (A, B, C, D rational). Read A, B, C, D, and N. Compute y for $x = \text{N}$ and print N and y.

55. Given the coordinates of two points in the *xy*-plane, print the equation of the line through the two points.

Read real numbers A, B, and C, which are the coefficients of a quadratic equation $Ax^2 + Bx + C = 0$. Do Exercises 56 through 59.

56. Determine if the equation has real roots. Print either REAL ROOTS or NO REAL ROOTS. Do not actually compute the roots.

57. Decide if the equation has zero, one, or two real roots. Do not actually compute the roots.

58. Determine the sum and product of the roots without actually computing the roots. (This applies whether the roots are real or not.)

59. If the equation has one or more real roots, compute and print the root(s).

For the system of linear equations $\begin{cases} Ax + By = C \\ Dx + Ey = F, \end{cases}$ input the coefficients. Do Exercises 60 through 65.

60. Determine whether the graphs of the equations are parallel. (Here "parallel to" means "having the same slope" so that parallel lines might coincide.)

61. Determine whether the graphs of the equations are perpendicular.

62. Determine whether the graphs intersect. If they do, do they intersect in one point or in infinitely many points?

63. Determine whether the solution set of the system is the null (empty) set, a one-element set, or an infinite set.

64. If the solution set has one element, print it as an ordered pair.

65. Determine whether the equations are consistent or inconsistent, and dependent or independent.

A parabola is defined by $y = Ax^2 + Bx + C$, $A \neq 0$. Read rational numbers A, B, and C. Do Exercises 66 through 70.

66. Print the coordinates of the vertex of the parabola.

67. Print whether the vertex is a maximum or minimum point.

68. Print the equation of the axis of symmetry.

69. Print the coordinates of the focus.

70. Print the equation of the directrix.

71. Input a real number x such that $1 < x < 10^9$. Print *X* and the characteristic of its common logarithm. For example, if $x = 73$, print 73 1 .

72. The equation of an ellipse with its center at the origin is $\frac{x^2}{A^2} + \frac{y^2}{B^2} = 1$.

    Read A and B (neither is zero) and print the coordinates of the foci of the ellipse. Remember that the foci sometimes are on the x-axis and sometimes are on the y-axis.

73. Solve absolute value equations of the form $|x - A| = B$ (A and B real).

74. Read a real number x. Print the cube root of x. Then, if x is nonnegative, print the principal fourth root of x. If x is negative, print NØ REAL FØURTH RØØT.

75. Given a quadratic equation $Ax^2 + Bx + C = 0$ and a proposed real root R. Determine by substitution if R is a root.

Given $f(x) = 3x + 4$ and $g(x) = x^2 - 7$, do Exercises 76 through 78.

76. Find $f(g(x))$ for x-values that you select.

77. Find $g(f(x))$ for x-values that you select.

78. Decide in each case if $f(g(x)) = g(f(x))$.

79. Accept two ordered pairs and print the equation of the perpendicular bisector of the line segment determined by these points.

ADVANCED MATHEMATICS

80. Compute and print the square roots of any real number including imaginary roots.

81. Test the addition of two-dimensional vectors to determine if it is commutative.

82. Test the addition of two-dimensional vectors to determine if it is associative.

83. Test the addition of three-dimensional vectors to determine if it is commutative.

84. Test the addition of three-dimensional vectors to determine if it is associative.

85. Input the lengths of the legs of a right triangle. Compute and print the values of the six trigonometric functions of either acute angle of the triangle.

86. An angle of rotation in standard position in the coordinate plane may have any measure, positive, negative, or zero. Read a measure M ($-360 \leq M \leq 360$); determine in which quadrant the terminal side of an angle with measure M lies or, if the terminal side lies on an axis, which part of which axis.

87. Compute and print the determinant of a 2×2 matrix $\begin{bmatrix} A & B \\ C & D \end{bmatrix}$.

88. To input a complex number $A + Bi$, read A and B, the "real" and "imaginary" parts respectively. ("I" has no special significance to a computer; it is just another real variable.) Compute and print the absolute value of $A + Bi$.

For an arithmetic progression, read A, the first term, D, the common difference, and N, a positive integer. Do Exercises 89 and 90.

89. Print the Nth term of the sequence.

90. Print the sum of the first N terms of the progression.

Input the components of two two-dimensional vectors. Do Exercises 91 and 92.

91. Decide if the vectors are perpendicular.

92. Decide if the vectors are parallel.

93. Given pure imaginary numbers Ai and Bi, read A and B and print the product of Ai and Bi.

94. Input real numbers X and Y ($X \neq Y$). Print three arithmetic means between X and Y.

95. Given sin x, compute and print (**a**) cos x, (**b**) tan x, (**c**) cot x, (**d**) sec x, and (**e**) csc x. Remember that tan, cot, sec, or csc may be undefined. Since SIN X may not be used as a variable in a flowchart, let s = sin x and READ S. Similarly use single letters for the other five functions.

96. Compute the distance between two points in a three-dimensional coordinate system.

For a geometric progression, input A, the first term, R, the common ratio ($R \neq 1$), and N, a positive integer. Do Exercises 97 and 98.

97. Print the Nth term of the sequence.

98. Print the sum of the first N terms of the sequence.

Read S and T, the components of a vector $\vec{v} = (S, T)$. Do Exercises 99 and 100.

99. Compute and print the norm of $\vec{v}$.

100. Input a scalar K and print the product $K\vec{v}$.

101. Given three consecutive terms of a sequence of real numbers, decide if the sequence is arithmetic, geometric, or neither.

2

ELEMENTARY PROGRAMS

Beginning with this chapter and continuing throughout the rest of the book, you will learn how to write programs in the BASIC language. The flowcharts of Chapter 1 were prepared with BASIC in mind, so you should find it easy to move from flowcharting to programming.

2-1 AN EXAMPLE

We begin by studying the BASIC program shown at the right.

Let's take a closer look at this same program, making comments along the way.

Program 2-1

```
10 READ L,W
20 LET P=2*L+2*W
30 PRINT "PERIMETER = " P
40 DATA 6.5,2.3
50 END
```

This is a statement number (a positive integer ≤ 99999).

Note this comma.

10 READ L, W ◄——*There is no punctuation at the end of a line.*

These blank spaces are not necessary but they make reading the program easier.

These are multiplication symbols, which must
20 LET P=2*L+2*W   *always be explicitly shown.*
These are optional blanks.

"Print" means "print on the teletype."

30 PRINT "PERIMETER = " P ◄— *P has a value from step 20 and that value (answer) is printed at this point.*

The computer will print everything between two quotation marks.

The first number will be read by the computer as the value of the first variable "L" in the READ *step.*

40 DATA 6.5,2.3◄——*This second number will be read as the value for the second variable "W" in the* READ *step.*

This step supplies the data needed in the READ *step.*

50 END◄——*This step informs the computer that the flow of steps has logically terminated.*

Here is the BASIC program alongside the corresponding flowchart.

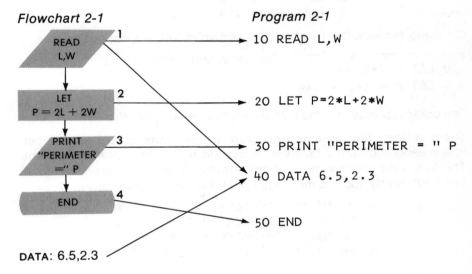

Flowchart 2-1

Program 2-1

10 READ L,W

20 LET P=2*L+2*W

30 PRINT "PERIMETER = " P

40 DATA 6.5,2.3

50 END

DATA: 6.5,2.3

The arrows show the linkages between the flowchart and the program. The READ box requires that there be both a READ statement and a DATA statement in the program.

There are many other correct ways of writing the above program. Here are some. Study each and notice how it differs from the first example.

```
10 DATA 6.5, 2.3           10 READ L, W
20 READ L,W                20 DATA 6.5, 2.3
30 LET P=2*L+2*W           30 LET P=2*L+2*W
40 PRINT "PERIMETER = " P  40 PRINT "PERIMETER="P
50 END                     50 END
```

```
10 READ L,W
20 LET P = 2*L + 2*W
30 DATA 6.5,2.3
40 PRINT "PERIMETER = " P
50 END
```

These alternate ways of writing the program emphasize these points.

1. The DATA step may appear anywhere in the program as long as it comes before the END statement.
2. After the statement number has been typed, blank spaces are ignored (with one exception mentioned below). The calculation step of Program 2-1 on page 34 could have been typed numerous ways.

```
20LETP=2*L+2*W
20 LET P=2*L+2*W
20 LET P=2*L + 2*W
20 LET P = 2*L + 2*W
20 LET P = 2 * L + 2 * W
20 L E T P = 2 * L + 2 * W
```

On some systems the two versions shown below are *not* acceptable.

```
20 LET P=2*L+2*W
2 0 LET P = 2*L + 2*W
```

Do not indent a line.

The computer may assume a zero here and hence read this as line "200."

There is one other area in a program where blank spaces are critical: in a message dictated between quotation marks in a PRINT statement. The following versions of the PRINT statement of the program would all print differently spaced messages (with the same value for P).

```
30 PRINT "PERIMETER=" P
30 PRINT "PERIMETER =" P
30 PRINT " PERIMETER = " P
30 PRINT "P E R I M E T E R = " P
```

EXERCISES 2-1

A   Each of these programs contains at least one error. Identify each error and correct it. (If necessary, rewrite the entire statement or, if a statement has been omitted, write it with the proper number.)

1.
```
10 READ X;Y
20 LET P = X*Y
30 PRINT "PRØDUCT IS" P
40 DATA 6,8
50 END
```

2.
```
10 LET R = 6
20 READ S
30 LET X = R+2*S
40 PRINT X
50 END
```

3.
```
10 READ S
20 LET T=S*S
30 PRINT SQUARE IS T
40DATA 6.8
50 END
```

4.
```
10 READ X,Y,Z
20 LET A=(X+Y+Z)/3
30 PRINT "AVERAGE =" A
40 DATA 821.3 287.6
50 END
```

5. READ M,N
   20 LET Q=MN+3
   30 PRINT Q
   40 DATA 78,61
   50 END

6. 10 R E A D R
   20 LET R*4=S
   30 PRINT S
   40 DATA 71
   50 END

7. 10 READ C,D
   20 LET X=C+D;
   30 PRINT"SUM IS X"
   40 DATA 37,6.2
   50 END

8. 10 READ X,Y,Z,
   20 LET R=X/Y + Z.
   30 PRINT "RESULT IS " R
   40 DATA 81.4,-16,70
   50 END

B Construct a flowchart that corresponds to each program.

9. 10 READ X
   20 PRINT "NUMBER IS " X
   30 LET Y = X*X
   40 PRINT "SQUARE IS " Y
   50 DATA -4
   60 END

10. 10 LET P = 3.14159
    20 READ D
    30 LET C = P * D
    40 PRINT C
    50 DATA 10
    60 END

11. Write a program for the flowchart shown below.

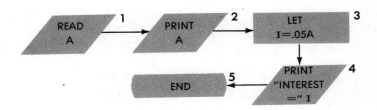

2-2 PROCESSING MORE THAN ONE SET OF DATA

Program 2-1 on page 34 processes just one set of data, that is, it computes the perimeter of only one rectangle. Suppose we have several rectangles for which we want perimeters. Adding one step to the program will allow us to process as many sets of length-width values as we wish.

Program 2-2

```
10 READ L,W
20 LET P=2*L+2*W
30 PRINT "PERIMETER = " P
40 GØ TØ 10
50 DATA 6.5,2.3,7.86,6.03,21,17
60 END
```

Comment:

In programming it is necessary to distinguish between the letter "O" and the digit "0" because these are two different keys on a card punch or on a teletype and are coded differently in the computer. Hence it is customary to put a slash through one of them to distinguish it from the other. In this book "Ø" will represent the letter and "0" the digit. On some teletypes, however, the reverse is true: "Ø" represents the digit and "O" the letter.

The output from Program 2-2 will be as follows.

```
PERIMETER = 17.6
PERIMETER = 27.78
PERIMETER = 76

ØUT ØF DATA LINE # 10
```

The flowchart for Program 2-2 is below, with the correspondence of boxes and statements shown by arrows.

Flowchart 2-2   *Program 2-2*

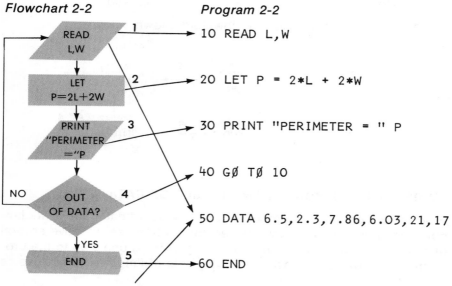

DATA: 6.5, 2.3, 7.86, 6.03, 21, 17

Each time the computer reaches the   GØ TØ 10   step, it returns to the READ statement and inputs the next two items from the data list. Since there are six numbers in line 50, the computer calculates and prints three perimeters. The fourth time it returns to the READ step, it finds that there are no more numbers in the data list. The computer branches to the END statement and prints   ØUT ØF DATA LINE # 10 and terminates execution of the program.

There are five errors to be avoided in DATA statements.

1. Putting semicolons in place of commas. This would make the DATA statement of Program 2-2 on page 37 look like this.

50 DATA 6.5,2.3; 7.86,6.03; 21,17

The temptation is to use the semicolon to group the pairs of length-width values. This may help the programmer organize his DATA but it will cause rejection of the program by the computer.   10 READ L,W will have the effect of grouping the data since the computer is thus instructed to read *two* data items at a time, calling the first L and the second W.

2. Grouping data with extra spacing. It would be erroneous to omit the commas in an attempt to group DATA.

50 DATA 6.5,2.3   7.86,6.03   21,17

3. Putting operation signs in DATA lists. The following DATA statement

50 DATA 6.5,2.3,3/4,6.03,21,17

should be written as follows.

50 DATA 6.5,2.3,.75,6.03,21,17

4. Putting variables in DATA lists.
5. Including in DATA lists special characters such as $ or %. However, decimal points and negative signs are allowed.

If the data list is so long that it cannot fit on one line, it may be broken into several lines, but each line must be numbered and the word DATA repeated each time. For example, if the data values are 6.5, 2.3, 7.86, 6.03, 21, 17, 0.01, 2.34, 81.7, 6.43, 9.13, 10.2, 1.87, 61, 90, .23, 11.4, 67.54, 89.07, 34.2, and 45.06, then they should be entered in the program like this.

50 DATA 6.5,2.3,7.86,6.03,21,17,0.01,2.34,81.7,6.43,9.13
51 DATA 10.2,1.87,61,90,.23,11.4,67.54,89.07,34.2,45.06

On many systems a comma at the end of line 50 would not cause any error.

"Amazing! It would take four thousand mathematicians four thousand years to make a mistake like that!"

Drawing by Alan Dunn, © 1968.
The New Yorker Magazine, Inc.

EXERCISES 2-2

A   Correct any errors in these DATA statements.
1. 60 6.5,2.3,7.86,6.03,21,17
2. 100 DATA 76,-81,2 .5,173
3. 41 DATA $8.01,7.63,9.12;$8.42,61.01,10.30
4. 80 DATA 12%,81%,14%, 18%,104%,61%,.5%
5. 90 DATA 4,16,25,40,3,55,10,60,40,6,8,-7,9,12,11,
   2,-5,1.1,5,1000,.03,20,10000,-5,1.1,5,1000,.03,
   20,10000,.05,40,1,.50,50,2.25,35,1.5
6. 20 DATA A,B,C

B   7. 1,834,614 is one of the items in a DATA list. It is entered like this: 60 DATA 1,834,614   . How will the computer interpret this line?

Write a program for each of these flowcharts.
8. DATA: 6, 4, −3, 7, 8, 8, 5, −2   9. DATA: 2, −3, 5, 0

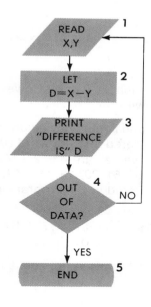

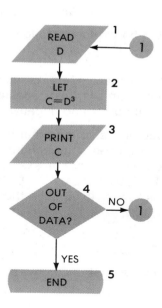

Flowchart each of these programs.

10. 10 READ S
    20 LET T = S*S-S+7
    30 PRINT T
    40 GØ TØ 10
    50 DATA 1,3,5
    60 END

11. 5 DATA 6,8,-4,4,10,20
    10 READ M,N
    20 LET A = (M+N)/2
    30 PRINT "AVERAGE = " A
    40 GØ TØ 10
    50 END

2-3 TRACING A PROGRAM

Just as a flowchart can be traced, so can a program be traced. The following trace illustrates the format to be used and the steps involved in tracing a program. The data listed in line 50 will be used.

Program 2-2

```
10 READ L,W
20 LET P=2*L+2*W
30 PRINT "PERIMETER = " P
40 GØ TØ 10
50 DATA 6.5,2.3,7.86,6.03,21,17
60 END
```

Table 2-1   Trace of Program 2-2

Step Number	State- ment Number	Values of Variables			Test	Yes or No?	Output
		L	W	P			
1	10	6.5	2.3				
2	20			17.6			
3	30						PERIMETER = 17.6
4	40				Out of Data?	No	
5	10	7.86	6.03				
6	20			27.78			
7	30						PERIMETER = 27.78
8	40				Out of Data?	No	
9	10	21	17				
10	20			76			
11	30						PERIMETER = 76
12	40				Out of Data?	Yes	
13	END						

The steps generally follow the procedure used for flowcharts, but a word of explanation is necessary for steps 4, 8, and 12 in the trace shown above. They correspond to line 40 of the program,   GØ TØ 10   . This is the only convenient point in the trace to show the OUT OF DATA?   test which is performed inside the computer as it attempts to execute   10 READ L,W   . A DATA statement never appears directly in the trace.

As in flowchart traces, when a value is entered in a column for a variable, it remains the value until a new numeral is entered in the column.

Now study a new program and its trace.

Program 2-3

```
10 LET P = 3.14159
20 READ R
30 DATA 5,7
40 LET C = 2*P*R
50 PRINT "CIRCUMFERENCE = " C
60 GØ TØ 20
70 END
```

Table 2-2   Trace of Program 2-3

Step Number	State-ment Number	Values of Variables			Test	Yes or No?	Output
		P	R	C			
1	10	3.14159					
2	20		5				
3	40			31.4159			
4	50						CIRCUMFERENCE = 31.4159
5	60				Out of Data?	No	
6	20		7				
7	40			43.98226			
8	50						CIRCUMFERENCE = 43.98226
9	60				Out of Data?	Yes	
10	END						

Given the radius, the program computes the circumference of a circle using the formula $c = 2\pi r$. The symbol "π" does not appear on the keyboard of standard card punches and teletypes. Hence a constant approximating pi must be entered into the program. 3.14159 is suggested here since most BASIC systems use six significant digits. (Some versions of BASIC allow the word "PI" for 3.14159 in a program.) Since 3.14159 is a constant, we can eliminate line 10 and revise line 40 as follows: 40 LET C = 2 * 3.14159 * R.

EXERCISES 2-3

A 1. In Program 2-2 on the previous page, replace line 50 with 50 DATA 4, 5, 10, 7.5, 11, 3   . Now prepare a table like the one on the previous page and trace the program.
   2. Draw a flowchart for Program 2-3 above.
   3. In Program 2-3 replace line 30 with   30 DATA 2, 10   . Prepare a table like the one above and trace the program.

Prepare tables like the ones on pages 41 and 42 and trace each program.

4.
```
10 READ X,Y
20 LET A = (X + Y)/2
30 PRINT "AVERAGE="A
40 GØ TØ 10
50 DATA 10,12,6,5,-4,8
60 END
```

5.
```
10 DATA 100,200,50
20 LET R = .05
30 READ P
40 LET I = P*R
50 PRINT "INTEREST = " I
60 GØ TØ 30
70 END
```

B 6. Prepare a flowchart for the program in Exercise 4.
   7. Prepare a flowchart for the program in Exercise 5.
   8. Trace the programs in Exercises 8 through 11 on page 40.

2-4 NUMBERING STATEMENTS

Program 2-2, shown again at the right, illustrates one reason for numbering the statements of a program: statements such as GØ TØ 10 refer to another line of the program and obviously line 10 must be identified for the computer.

Program 2-2

```
10 READ L,W
20 LET P=2*L+2*W
30 PRINT "PERIMETER = " P
40 GØ TØ 10
50 DATA 6.5,2.3,7.86,6.03,21,17
60 END
```

The second reason for numbering statements results from a convenient editing capability of BASIC. The following example illustrates the possibilities. Suppose a student types Program 2-2 as follows.

```
10 READ L,W
20 LET P=2*L+2*W
30 PRINT "PERIMETER = " P
50 DATA 6.5,2.3,7.86,6.03,21,17
60 END
```

He has forgotten line 40. However, this is no problem; just type it now, numbering it "40." The program will then look like this.

```
10 READ L,W
20 LET P=2*L+2*W
30 PRINT "PERIMETER = " P
50 DATA 6.5,2.3,7.86,6.03,21,17
60 END
40 GØ TØ 10
```

Before proceeding with this explanation, we stop to explain what a compiler is, because it is the compiler that allows us to add a statement at the end of the program as we have just done. Once entered into the computer system, a BASIC program is stored in memory where the BASIC compiler, part of the software of the system, "decodes" it. A *compiler* is a program that translates a program from a source language such as BASIC to machine language, which is the only language the central processor can actually "understand" and execute. The compiler finds any errors of form or syntax, and also sorts the statements into numerical order before translating into machine language for execution. This ability of the compiler makes possible the editing procedures being explained in this lesson.

Why, in the programs shown thus far, are the statements numbered with multiples of 10? Why not type the program in the following ways?

Program 2-2A

```
1 READ L,W
2 LET P=2*L+2*W
3 PRINT "PERIMETER = " P
4 GØ TØ 1
5 DATA 6.5,2.3,7.86,6.03,21,17
6 END
```

Program 2-2B

```
18 READ L,W
71 LET P=2*L+2*W
213 PRINT "PERIMETER = " P
476 GØ TØ 18
812 DATA 6.5,2.3,7.86,6.03,21,17
999 END
```

To the compiler there is nothing wrong with these numberings. To understand why multiples of 10 are preferred, consider Program 2-2A. Suppose that George types the program in the manner shown below.

```
1 READ L,W
2 LET P=2*L+2*W
3 GØ TØ 1
4 DATA 6.5,2.3,7.86,6.03,21,17
5 END
```

He realizes that he has forgotten the PRINT statement. To add the omitted line, he must now type the correct version of line 3 and then re-type the original lines 3, 4, and 5. His completed program is shown on the next page.

```
1 READ L,W
2 LET P=2*L+2*W
3 GØ TØ 1
4 DATA 6.5,2.3,7.86,6.03,21,17
5 END
3 PRINT "PERIMETER = " P
4 GØ TØ 1
5 DATA 6.5,2.3,7.86,6.03,21,17
6 END
```

There are now two steps numbered "3," two numbered "4," and two numbered "5." When a statement is retyped, the compiler automatically replaces the earlier version of that line in memory with the later version. Hence a statement can be retyped as many times as necessary until it is correct.

If the lines of program 2-2A on page 44 had been numbered with multiples of 10, adding the omitted PRINT statement would have been easy.

```
10 READ L,W
20 LET P=2*L+2*W
30 GØ TØ 10
40 DATA 6.5,2.3,7.86,6.03,21,17
50 END
25 PRINT "PERIMETER = " P
```

By proceeding in this way the student does not have to retype lines 30, 40, or 50.

There is another rather important editing capability in BASIC programming: deleting a step. Suppose that a student types the program shown at the left below. He realizes that since he has only one data value to process, he does not need line 40. He can delete this line simply by typing "40" and leaving the remainder of the line blank. The completed program would then look like the one at the right below.

```
10 READ X                        10 READ X
20 LET Y=8.6201*X*X              20 LET Y=8.6201*X*X
30 PRINT Y                       30 PRINT Y
40 GØ TØ 10                      40 GØ TØ 10
50 DATA 76.1                     50 DATA 76.1
60 END                           60 END
                                 40
```

REMEMBER: In memory the lines of a program are stored in statement number order. The sequence in which the lines are typed is not significant.

EXERCISES 2-4

A State whether or not each of the programs below is equivalent to the program at the right. ("Is equivalent to" means "produces the same output as.")

```
10 READ X
20 LET S=X*X
30 PRINT S
40 DATA 7.26,8.91,6.081
50 GØ TØ 10
60 END
```

1.
```
10 READ X
30 PRINT S
40 DATA 7.26,8.91,6.081
50 GØ TØ TEN
60 END
20 LET S=X*X
```

2.
```
1 READ X
2 LET S=X*X
3 PRINT S
4 DAA
4 DATA 7.26,8.91,6.081
5 GØ TØ 1
6 END
```

3.
```
5 READ X
30 END
10 LETS=X*X
20 PRINT S
15 GØ TØ 5
25 DATA 7.26,8.91,6.081
```

4.
```
10READ X
20 LET S=X*X
30 PRINT S
40 DATA 7.26,8.91,6.081
50 END
```

What would be the output from each program below?

5.
```
10 READ J,K
20 LET S=J+K-J*K
30 GØ TØ 10
40 PRINT S
50 DATA 2,3,8,10,-6,14
60 END
```

6.
```
10 READ X,Y
20 LET Z=X-3*Y
30 PRINT "ANSWER IS " Z
40 DATA 8,-3,0,16,-2.7
45 DATA -6,8
50 END
```

Suppose a student has written the program at the right. He types this program at the teletype but makes mistakes. He attempts to correct his errors. Which version(s) below, if any, is (are) equivalent to the program he wishes to run?

```
10 READ R
20 LET X=.5*R*R
30 PRINT X
40 DATA 86.1
50 END
```

7.
```
10 RA
10 READ R
20 LET X=.5*R
30 PRINT X
40DATA 86.1
50 END
20 LET X=.5*R*R
```

8.
```
1Ø READ R
10 READ R
20 LET X=.5*R*R
30 DATA 86.1
40 PRINT X
50 END
```

9.
```
10 READ R
20 PRINT X
30 LET X=.5*R*R
20
40 PRINT X
50 DATA 86.1
60 END
```

2-5 LEGAL VARIABLE NAMES AND SIGNS OF OPERATION

In all flowcharts and programs thus far, only single letters have been used for variables. Actually, there are also two other types of variables.

A variable may be denoted by:

1. a single letter such as A, B, C, D, . . . , X, Y, Z,
2. a single letter followed by a single digit, for example, A0, A1, A2, . . . , Z8, Z9, or
3. a subscripted variable such as X(I) or Y(J, K).

Each variable used in a program corresponds to a distinct memory location chosen by the compiler.

Several signs of operation have already been introduced. Here is a complete list.

Sign	Operation
$+$	addition
$-$	subtraction
$*$	multiplication
$/$	division
$\uparrow$	exponentiation (raising to a power)

Every formula used in a program must lie in a single line, with no superscripts, subscripts, or built-up fractions.

Examples:

Algebra	BASIC
$t = \dfrac{d}{r}$	`10 LET T = D/R`
$y = x^2 + 3x - 7$	`10 LET Y = X↑2 + 3*X - 7`
$M = \dfrac{y_2 - y_1}{x_2 - x_1}$	`10 LET M = (Y2-Y1)/(X2-X1)`

The last example shows the need for parentheses in a LET statement.

What would be the algebraic equivalent of this BASIC statement?

```
10 LET M = Y2 - Y1/X2 - X1
```

To answer this question we need an understanding of the *hierarchy of operations* followed by the computer. This "hierarchy" is the order of precedence given to the symbols of a formula. It is shown on the top of the next page.

1. Operations within parentheses are worked out, from the innermost parentheses outward, from left to right.

2. Exponentiations are performed, left to right.

3. Multiplications and divisions are performed in order from left to right.

   Multiplication and division are of equal standing. This rule does not mean that multiplications are worked out first, then divisions. It means that, after steps 1 and 2 have been completed, the compiler scans the formula from left to right, working out multiplications or divisions as it hits either one. Addition and subtraction (step 4) are also of equal rank and are handled in a similar fashion.

4. Additions and subtractions are performed in order from left to right.

Example:

Identify the order of operations in the statement below.

$$20 \text{ LET } S = (X - Y)/Z\uparrow3 + X*Y - Z$$

Here is the formula again with numerals indicating the order in which the computer will perform the operations.

$$20 \text{ LET } S = (X - Y)/Z\uparrow3 + X*Y - Z$$
$$\qquad\qquad\quad 1 \quad 3\ 2 \quad 5 \quad 4 \quad 6$$

Adding another pair of parentheses, like this:
20 LET S=((X−Y)/Z)↑3 + X*Y − Z changes the order to the following.

$$20 \text{ LET } S = ((X - Y)/Z)\uparrow3 + X*Y - 2$$
$$\qquad\qquad\quad 1 \quad 2 \ 3 \quad 5 \quad 4 \quad 6$$

(In BASIC neither brackets nor braces are used because they do not universally appear on teletype and card punch keyboards.)

Three "rules of thumb" will help the programmer in writing correct expressions.

1. Every expression must contain an *even* number of parentheses. The number of left parentheses must equal the number of right parentheses.

2. There is no way that two operation signs can appear next to each other. For example, A * −B is not a valid expression but A * (−B) is.

3. Multiplication signs are never understood.

ab	must be written	A*B.
$2(x+y)$	must be written	2*(x+Y).
$(7+a)(b-6)$	must be written	(7+A)*(B−6).

EXERCISES 2-5

A Write *Yes* or *No* to tell whether each of the following is a legal BASIC variable name.

  1. A   **2.** B   **3.** AB   **4.** SUM   **5.** (R)   **6.** AZ
  7. Z23   **8.** X1   **9.** L.   **10.** 1X2   **11.** K9   **12.** Z0
  13. TØ   **14.** 42G   **15.** 7B   **16.** E2   **17.** .Y   **18.** R+S

Shown below are a number of mathematical expressions and corresponding BASIC expressions. Each BASIC expression contains at least one error. Correct each error, rewriting the expression if necessary.

19. $\dfrac{x+2}{y+4}$; X + 2/Y + 4   **20.** $\dfrac{ab}{c+2}$; AB/(C + 2)

21. $\left(\dfrac{x+a}{2z}\right)^{2}$; (X + A)/(2*Z) ↑ 2   **22.** $\left(\dfrac{x}{y}\right)^{n-1}$; (X/Y) ↑ N−1

What is the order of evaluation in each of the following BASIC expressions? Put numerals beneath the signs as in the examples of the lesson.

23. B ↑ 2 − 4*A*C   **24.** A/B/C*D   **25.** −B/2*A
26. A/C*B/D   **27.** A ↑ B/3   **28.** A+(C−D*(X/3+Y/2) ↑ 2)+6

For each of the following expressions, write a single BASIC statement that will compute each quantity. Start each statement with 10 LET Z = ...

29. $3b - 2c$ **30.** $\dfrac{c-d}{3}$ **31.** $\dfrac{n-7}{6.5+m}$ **32.** $x + y^{3}$

33. $x^{\frac{1}{2}}$ **34.** $-a + \dfrac{b}{c+d}$ **35.** $\dfrac{7}{-ab}$

36. $\left(\dfrac{a+b}{c+d}\right)^{2} + x^{2}$ **37.** $\dfrac{xy}{3}$ **38.** $(c - d)(m + n)$

If A = 3, B = 5, and C = 2, what value is assigned to X by each of these LET statements?

39. 20 LET X = A + B * C   **40.** 30 LET X = A * B + C
41. 25 LET X = A + B/C   **42.** 60 LET X = (A + B)/C
43. 50 LET X = A + C↑2
44. 15 LET X = (A + C)↑2
45. 70 LET X = A/B + C
46. 80 LET X = A/B*C
47. 85 LET X = A/(B*C)
48. 90 LET X = A + B / C + 7
49. 60 LET X = A + B / C ↑ 2
50. 40 LET X = (A + B)↑2/(B - C)↑2

B **51.** Two resistors, with resistances R_1 and R_2, are connected in parallel. The equivalent resistance between the input point and the output point is given by the formula $R = \dfrac{R_1 R_2}{R_1 + R_2}$.

Write a LET statement containing this formula.

2-6 TAKING ROOTS

In programming there is no radical sign ($\sqrt{\ }$) because this symbol usually does not appear on the keyboard of a card punch or teletype. The corresponding fractional power must be used to compute a root. Common fractions may be used, but decimal fractions are preferred as the following examples illustrate.

$y = \sqrt{x}$	becomes	10 LET Y = X↑(1/2) or 10 LET Y = X↑.5
$y = \sqrt[3]{x}$	becomes	10 LET Y = X↑(1/3)
$y = \sqrt[4]{a + 7}$	becomes	10 LET Y = (A + 7)↑(1/4) or 10 LET Y = (A + 7)↑.25

In algebra, great care is taken to define when a radical expression may be legitimately used, that is, when it names a real number. For example, $\sqrt{x}$ names a real number if $x = 4$ but not if $x = -4$. Since computers deal only with real numbers, fractional powers may be computed only when the expression names a real number.

For example, if $x = -4$, the following expressions would *not* name real numbers and would cause some type of error message during execution of a program.

x ↑ .5   x ↑ .25   x ↑ (1/6)   x ↑ (3/4)   x ↑ (5/2)   etc.

Thus, no fractional powers may be computed if the numerator is odd, the denominator even, and the base negative.

For $x = -4$, the following expressions *would* yield real numbers and are acceptable.

x ↑ (1/3)   x ↑ (1/5)   x ↑ (3/7)   etc.

Thus, odd roots of negative numbers are real numbers and can be computed.

CAUTION: Computing powers is an area of BASIC where systems differ from one another. Consult the manual for your system and experiment with a variety of power expressions and values to see which ones are accepted and what results are printed each time. (See Ex. 24, p. 51.)

EXERCISES 2-6

A   Write each of these formulas in a LET statement.

1. $z = \sqrt[5]{x}$ **2.** $z = \sqrt{x^2 - y^2}$

3. $z = \sqrt{y + 2x}$ **4.** $z = \sqrt{2xy - 6}$

5. $z = \dfrac{\sqrt[3]{7}}{x}$ **6.** $z = \dfrac{4.5}{\sqrt{8.6}}$

7. $z = \dfrac{1}{1 + \sqrt{x}}$ **8.** $z = \sqrt[4]{\dfrac{x}{3}}$

9. $z = \dfrac{1 - 2\sqrt{x}}{3\sqrt{x} + 2}$ **10.** $z = \sqrt{\dfrac{x + 5}{4 - x}}$

11. Jane writes $y = \sqrt{x}$ in a BASIC statement like this.

$$10 \ \text{LET Y} = X\uparrow1/2$$

Will this statement actually assign to Y the principal square root of x? If not, what is computed by the right side of the assignment statement?

B   If $x = -8$, which of these LET statements would produce an error message because the right side would not yield a real number?

12. 20 LET Z = X↑.5   **13.** 30 LET Z = X↑(1/3)
14. 50 LET Z = (X↑2)↑.5   **15.** 60 LET Z = -X↑.5
16. 45 LET Z = (-X)↑.5   **17.** 90 LET Z = X↑(1/X)

State whether each BASIC expression below is defined for all values of x. If an expression is not always defined, state the value(s) of x for which it is not defined.

Example: x↑.5   **Answer:**   Undefined for $x < 0$

18. x ↑ (1/9)   **19.** x ↑ (2/3)
20. 0↑ (−x)   **21.** x ↑ (3/2)
22. x↑0   **23.** (−x) ↑ .5

C   **24.** Run the program below on your system and note what value or error message is printed for each set of data. Also notice whether an error terminates the run or whether the system processes the remaining data anyway. Also note if any mathematically incorrect answers are printed for Y.

```
10 READ N,X
20 LET Y = X ↑ (1/N)
30 PRINT N,X,Y
40 GØ TØ 10
50 DATA 2,4,2,-4,2,0,3,8,3,-8,3,0,0,6,6,0,-4,0
60 END
```

2-7 ERRORS IN LET STATEMENTS

This program contains an error associated with line 20.

```
10 READ X,Y
20 LET Q = X + Y - 2*Z
30 PRINT Q
40 DATA 61,-83
50 END
```

The variable z has not received a value. In some languages this would cause rejection of the program. In BASIC, however, most compilers automatically assign a value of zero to a variable that is otherwise undefined. What then would be the output of the above program?

Another common error is illustrated by the following program involving the Pythagorean Theorem.

```
10 READ A,B
20 LET C↑2 = A↑2 + B↑2
30 PRINT C↑2
40 DATA 6.3,8.9
50 END
```

The error lies in line 20: the expression to the left of $=$ in a LET statement may not contain an operation sign. A LET statement is called an *assignment* statement. Recall the explanation of the assignment box in chapter one. In the statement $20 \text{ LET } X = Y + 2 * Z$, the value of $Y + 2 * Z$ is being assigned to the variable x. The left expression in an assignment statement must be simply a variable name.

The program above should be written as follows.

```
10 READ A,B
20 LET C = (A↑2 + B↑2)↑.5
30 PRINT C
40 DATA 6.3,8.9
50 END
```

EXERCISES 2-7

A   State whether each of the following is a valid LET statement.

1. 20 LET Z1 = 7
2. 40 LET 9 = C
3. 80 LET Z = A + B
4. 90 LET A + B = Z
5. 100 LET X = Y = 0
6. 120 LET C/2 = A/2

Correct any errors in the following programs.

7. 10 READ S, T, U
20 LET R + S = T + U
30 PRINT R
40 DATA 76.891,-3.074
50 END

8. 5 READ A, B, C
10 LET P = A/B + C/D
20 PRINT P
30 DATA 17,41,53, 12,72,86, 81,23
999 END

C State whether each of the following is a valid LET statement.

9. 95 LET C = C + 1   **10.** 80 LET A = 2*A
11. 100 LET X = Y↑2 + X **12.** 20 LET N = N - 1

If, when line 50 is reached in the program, $I = 10$, what value is assigned to I by each of these statements?

13. 50 LET I = I + 1   **14.** 50 LET I = I -1
15. 50 LET I = I - 2   **16.** 50 LET I = I + 2
17. 50 LET I = 2*I   **18.** 50 LET I = I↑2

2-8 CALCULATIONS IN A PRINT STATEMENT

A feature of BASIC that we shall now discuss allows the alert programmer to save a step by putting a formula into a PRINT statement. This principle is applied to Program 2-1 (perimeter of a rectangle).

Program 2-1

Old Version

```
10 READ L,W
20 LET P = 2*L + 2*W
30 PRINT "PERIMETER = " P
40 DATA 6.5,2.3
50 END
```

New Version

```
10 READ L,W
20 PRINT "PERIMETER = " 2*L + 2*W
30 DATA 6.5,2.3
40 END
```

The variable P is not needed in the new version. In fact it would be *incorrect* to write a PRINT statement such as the following one:
20 PRINT P = 2 * L + 2 * W . However, the following statement *would* be acceptable: 20 PRINT "P = " 2 * L + 2 * W   . The quotation marks make   P =   a message to the computer and not a part of the formula.

This new technique is not recommended if the perimeter is needed in a later step of the program. In this case use the original method and store the perimeter in location P for further use. For example, suppose the perimeters of two rectangles must be computed and added. Then the following program could be used.

Program 2-4A

```
10 READ L1,W1
20 LET P1 = 2*L1 + 2*W1
30 PRINT "1ST PERIMETER = " P1
40 READ L2,W2
50 LET P2 = 2*L2 + 2*W2
60 PRINT "2ND PERIMETER = " P2
70 PRINT "SUM ØF PERIMETERS = " P1 + P2
80 DATA 6,4,10,9
90 END
```

The values for P1 and P2 are needed in line 70. Hence it is wise to use LET statements 20 and 50 to compute *and store* the two perimeters.

Compare version A of the program with version B.

Program 2-4B

```
10 READ L1,W1
30 PRINT "1ST PERIMETER = " 2*L1 + 2*W1
40 READ L2,W2
60 PRINT "2ND PERIMETER = " 2*L2 + 2*W2
70 PRINT "SUM ØF PERIMETERS = " 2*L1+2*W1 + 2*L2+2*W2
80 DATA 6,4,10,9
90 END
```

Notice in version B how a programmer must type the expressions 2 * L1 + 2 * W1 and 2 * L2 + 2 * W2 twice each. For expressions that are longer than these it becomes even more advisable to use a LET statement to compute and store a value in a location, such as P1 or P2. The programmer can then simply refer to the stored variable or variables, from that point on in the program.

It is legitimate to print a constant. See the examples below.

```
50 PRINT 1
60 PRINT "X = " 7
30 PRINT 0 " IS THE SØLUTIØN"
```

On many systems, if the programmer desires more (or fewer) than six significant digits in an answer, he can put a SET DIGITS statement at the beginning of his program. The program on the top of the next page illustrates this fact.

```
 5 SET DIGITS 11
10 READ L,W
20 LET P=2*L + 2*W
30 PRINT P
40 DATA 267.9132,84.637526
50 END
```

The value for P will now be printed with eleven significant figures. On most systems eleven is the maximum number available.

EXERCISES 2-8

A State whether each of the following is a valid PRINT statement.

1. 35 PRINT -4   **2.** 10 PRINT A↑2 + B↑2
3. 20 PRINT X = R + S   **4.** 97 PRINT "RØØT IS " O
5. 98 PRINT "RØØT IS O"
6. 99 PRINT "RØØT IS" ZERØ

If C = 8, D = 7, and E = 5, show what will be printed by each of the PRINT statements in Exercises 7 through 14.

Example: 90 PRINT "RESULT = " C + D - E
Answer: RESULT = 10

7. 110 PRINT C - 6   **8.** 15 PRINT C * D + E
9. 20 PRINT "X = " D/E   **10.** 90 PRINT D/E " = D/E"
11. 30 PRINT D "/" E " = " D/E
12. 40 PRINT 2 * C + E ↑ 2
13. 25 PRINT C " + " D
14. 50 PRINT C + D " = " C " + " D

Correct any errors in these two programs.

15. 20 SET DIGITS AT 11   **16.** 10 SET DIGIT 8
     30 READ X,Y   20 READ R,S
     40 PRINT X * Y   30 PRINT T = R↑2 + S↑2
     50 DATA 67,83   40 DATA 6.4,8.3,7.06
     60 END   50 GØ TØ LINE 10
                             60 END

B **17.** Let us now agree to allow in flowcharts the same shortcut as in BASIC: calculations in a PRINT statement (box). Hence for Program 2-4A on page 54, line 70 would correspond to the box at the right. With this agreement in mind, make a flowchart for Program 2-4A.

18. Trace Program 2-4A.

2-9 FUNCTIONS

Many calculations involve standard mathematical functions such as sine, cosine, log, etc. BASIC handles a number of functions, provided they are abbreviated correctly. Each function is designated by a three-letter code.

Function	Explanation
ABS(X)	absolute value of x
SQR(X)	square root of x ($x \geq 0$)
SIN(X)	sine x, x measured in radians
CØS(X)	cosine x, x measured in radians
TAN(X)	tangent x, x measured in radians
ATN(X)	arctangent x, answer in radians
CLG(X)	common logarithm (base ten) of x

(Note: The system you are working with may use different abbreviations for some of these functions and undoubtedly has others not listed here. Consult the manual that explains your system.)

In the list above, x is used as the "argument" of each function. Actually the argument may be any valid BASIC expression and may even itself contain a function. (Note: arguments such as "2*A", "P+Q", "TAN(X)", and even simply "x" are each more precisely referred to as a "rule for a function" but in this book they will usually be referred to as "functions." This is standard practice.)

Correct statements:
```
10 LET Y = SIN(2*A)
25 PRINT CØS(P+Q)
50 LET Z = SQR(TAN(X))
15 PRINT ABS(X) + CLG(Y↑2 - 6.1)
```

There is no way one of these functions could correctly appear to the left of the equal sign in a LET statement. Nor could a function occur in a READ statement.

Incorrect statements:
```
20 LET SIN(X) = SQR(1 - CØS(X) * CØS(X))
35 LET ABS(X) = (A - B)/2
15 LET CLG(Y*Z) = CLG(Y) + CLG(Z)
25 READ ABS(X)
```

In each of these incorrect statements, a legitimate variable, such as R or S, should be substituted for SIN(X), ABS(X), or CLG(Y*Z). The PRINT statement can be used to label R or S correctly as "SINE" or "ABSØLUTE VALUE" or "LØG".

EXERCISES 2-9

A   State whether each of the following is a valid BASIC statement.

   1. 20 LET ABS(X) = -X
   2. 30 LET Y = SQR Z
   3. 15 PRINT ABS VALUE (R - 1)
   4. 50 PRINT SQRT(M*N)
   5. 25 LET M = SQR(ABS(N+7)
   6. 60 PRINT "SQUARE RØØT = " SQR(Z)
   7. 5 READ X, SQR(X)
   8. 70 LET X2 = ABS(SQR(X) - 6*X)
   9. 35 LET DISC = SQR(B↑2 - 4*A*C)
   10. 255 PRINT "ABSØLUTE VALUE ØF" A " = "ABS(A)

   Write a LET statement for each of these formulas.

   11. $y = |x|$ **12.** $z = \sqrt{-x}$
   13. $t = |2r - 3|$ **14.** $x = \sqrt{7 + 6v}$
   15. $z = \sqrt{|e + g|}$ **16.** $c = \sqrt{a^2 + b^2}$
   17. $m = |x| - 7$ **18.** $v = |6x| - |x + 9|$

B   Correct any errors in these BASIC expressions.

   19. SINE(X) + CØS(3*Z↑2)
   20. TAN*SIN(Y) - 8.312*ATN(-1)
   21. ABS(SIN(X)↑2 - CØS(X)↑2
   22. SQR(TAN(P+Q) - CLG(16*Z)

   Write a LET statement for each of these formulas.

   23. $q = \dfrac{1 - \sin x}{1 + \sin x}$ **24.** $c = 2r \sin \frac{1}{2}\theta$

   25. $s = a \sin kw - b \cos kw$ **26.** $y = \dfrac{1}{1 + |\tan x|}$

   27. $f = \cos^2 x + 1$ **28.** $c = \log_{10}(x + \sqrt{x^2 + 1})$

   Check the accuracy of several of the BASIC functions on your system by writing and running the following programs.

   29. Calculate and print $\sin^2 x + \cos^2 x$ for x values between 0 and 1, inclusive.
   30. Calculate and print $(\sqrt{x})^2$ for positive x values. Do not choose just integers for x.

C   **31.** Design a BASIC program directing the computer to solve the equation

   $$\tan^2 x - 3 \tan x + 2 = 0 \text{ for } -\frac{\pi}{2} < x < \frac{\pi}{2}.$$

2-10 NUMBERS IN EXPONENTIAL FORM (Optional)

The computer may print a number in one of the three following forms:

1. As an integer, for example, 8, −71, 8341, 927683.
2. As a decimal, for example, 6.2, −.192308, .067.
3. In exponential form, for example, 1.36424E2, −6.92308E3, 1.92308E−3.

BASIC normally prints a maximum of *six* significant digits. Nonsignificant zeros are dropped. When the number of significant positions exceeds six, the answer is printed in exponential form. For example, an answer of .00192308 is printed as 1.92308E−3, which means 1.92308×10^{-3}. 93,000,000 is printed 9.3E7.

Data can be READ in exponential form as in this program.

```
10  READ L,W
20  LET P = 2*L + 2*W
30  PRINT P
40  DATA 2.67E4,  .81920E-2
50  END
```

EXERCISES 2-10

A   Write the number represented by each exponential form.

Example: $9.861E2 = 9.861 \times 10^2 = 986.1$

1. 6.07E2   **2.** 1.92308E3   **3.** 1.15385E−2
4. 1E6   **5.** 8.4615E−2   **6.** 3.63798E−12
7. 1.86E3   **8.** 6.6430E9

B   **9.** The amount of energy E (ergs) of a nuclear particle of mass M (grams) traveling at a speed v (centimeters per second) is given by the formula $E = \frac{1}{2}Mv^2$. For an alpha particle, $M = 6.6430 \times 10^{-24}$ g (grams). Write a BASIC program to compute the energy of an alpha particle traveling 2.2×10^9 cm/sec (centimeters per second). Write constants in exponential form in the program.

10. According to the theory of relativity, if the length of a space-craft at rest on the launching pad is L_0, then its length when it moves at a speed v will be $L = L_0\sqrt{1 - \frac{v^2}{c^2}}$, in which $c = 3 \times 10^8$ m/sec (meters per second) or 186,000 mi/sec (miles per second). Write a BASIC program to compute and print L for input values of L_0 and v.

11. The speed of light is 2.99776×10^8 m/sec. Write a BASIC program to compute the number of meters in one light year.

2-11 REM STATEMENTS

Consider the program below.

Program 2-5

```
1 REM FIND THE AREA ØF A CIRCLE, GIVEN ITS RADIUS.
10 READ R
20 LET A = 3.14159 * R * R
30 REM A SIX-DIGIT APPRØXIMATIØN IS USED FØR PI.
40 PRINT "AREA IS " A
50 DATA 10,20
60 GØ TØ 10
70 END
```

"REM" is short for "REMARK." A REM statement is ignored by the compiler and does not affect execution. It provides the programmer a means for explaining his procedure for other readers (such as the teacher or the boss) or for himself should he review the program at a future date.

A REM statement may appear anywhere in a program before END but must have a line number. If the remark takes more than one line, all lines of the remark must be numbered and start with the REM abbreviation (just as all DATA lines must have a statement number and the word DATA).

In Program 2-5 above notice that line 60 says   GØ TØ 10   and not GØ TØ 1   . On most systems   GØ TØ 1   would cause no error, but since a REM statement is a nonexecutable statement, it is logically better to return to the READ.

SUGGESTION: Use one or more REM statements at the beginning of each program you write to give your name, the round and number (or page and number) of the problem, and perhaps a brief description of the program.

Example:

```
10 REM    JØHN PERSØN
15 REM    RØUND TWØ  NØ. 120
20 REM    CØMPUTES THE PERIMETER ØF A RECTANGLE GIVEN
30 REM    THE LENGTH AND WIDTH.
40 READ L,W
50 PRINT "P = " 2*L + 2*W
60 GØ TØ 40
70 DATA 21,17,83,46
80 END
```

Since REM statements are not executable, they should not appear in a flowchart or trace.

The following are the steps that you should follow when assigned a program.

1. Write the program on paper (flowcharting the logic first if necessary).

2. Punch the program into paper tape.

3. Go on-line to the computer and feed the program tape.

4. If the program is compiled and executed correctly, the task is finished.

5. If there are errors in compilation or execution, the student must find and correct the errors (on-line if possible) and run the program again until correct output is obtained.

For the more detailed steps of punching the program into tape, correcting punching errors, and running the program, follow your teacher's directions.

EXERCISES 2-11

A   Correct any errors in these programs.

1.
```
1   DØN BAGERT    NØ. 84
10 READ X
20 PRINT "AREA = " X*X
30 GØ TØ 10
40 END
```

2.
```
100 REM   THIS PROGRAM CALCULATES THE CIRCUMFERENCE
101       ØF A CIRCLE GIVEN THE RADIUS R.
110 READ R
120 PRINT C = 3.14159 * 2R
130 DATA 10,20
140 GØ TØ 100
9999 END
```

3.
```
10 DATA 71.6,82.05
20 READ L,W
30 REM   L IS THE LENGTH ØF THE RECTANGLE.
         W IS THE WIDTH.
40 LET P = 2*(L + W)
50 PRINT "PERIMETER = P"
60 END
```

B   **4.** Flowchart Program 2-5 on page 59.

5. Trace Program 2-5.

CHAPTER REVIEW

Which of the following are not BASIC variables?
 1. X9   2. 2Z   3. 7   4. (Y1)
 5. NET   6. 6E−2   7. P − Q   8. GØ

Correct any errors in these BASIC statements.

 9. 1.5 READ (X,Y)   10. 30 READ Ø,A/B
11. 45 LET X + Y = R   12. 70 LET M = 2K - 7
13. 100 LET N = SQR X   14. 80 PRINT O
15. 91 SET DIGITS AS SIX   16. 1DATA 6,7;8,3
17. 86 PRINT "TIME IS " T (HØURS)
18. 80 LET S = X*2   REM   S IS THE STRESS.

Write BASIC statements to do each of the following.

19. Add the contents of locations designated by "A" and "B" and store the sum in a location called "s".
20. Multiply "A" and the sum of "B" and "C" and store the product in "X".
21. Assign the cube root of the number "X" to "C".
22. Print the contents of "A" followed by the words   IS THE AN-SWER   .

Write each of these expressions in a LET statement. Start each statement with   20 LET M = ...

23. $6s - t^2$ 24. $(6 + 2s)^4$

25. $\sqrt[4]{\dfrac{r}{2t}}$ 26. $\dfrac{a + b}{2c + d^2}$

27. $\sqrt{uv - 7z}$ 28. $|16 - t^{\frac{1}{3}}|$

29. $-7(c - 2f)$ 30. $(k + 9)(k - 1)$

31. $\left(\dfrac{x^2}{6}\right)^{n+1}$ 32. $\dfrac{xy}{z^3}$

If $X = 2$, what value is assigned to Z by each of these LET statements?

33. 10 LET Z = -X↑3   34. 20 LET Z = 2*X↑2
35. 30 LET Z = (-4*X)↑2   36. 40 LET Z = (X + 8)/X + X↑2

37. Write a BASIC program to compute the perimeter and the area of a square, given the length of a side. (See Ex. 20 and 21, p. 28.)

Put numerals beneath the operation signs in each expression to specify the order in which the operations will be performed.

38. $2 - 3 * z + 7$ 39. $(x + 5) * (x - 1) ↑ 2$
40. $5 - P ↑ 2 + 9$ 41. $(3 * (Y - 2))/4$
42. A * B / C * D   43. M ↑ 2 ↑ (X − 4)

ROUND TWO: *PROGRAMS FOR STUDENT ASSIGNMENT*

GENERAL INSTRUCTIONS:

1. In each exercise on pages 62 through 69, write a program that will do what is specified in the exercise.

2. Research may be necessary to learn the meaning of a word or to find the formula needed for a calculation.

3. Print results with an appropriate message, for example, "AREA =" or "SOLUTION IS", etc.

4. The program should be written to handle numerous DATA sets.

5. Include at least three sets of DATA. As a check, calculate the first answer yourself and have it ready to compare with the computer output.

6. If your teacher requires it, submit a flowchart.

ALGEBRA ONE

1. Find the arithmetic mean of two real numbers.

2. The "slugging percentage" of a baseball hitter is the ratio of his total bases to his at-bats. Given his number of singles, doubles, triples, home runs, and at-bats, print a player's slugging percentage. Note: Like batting average, slugging percentage is expressed as a three-place decimal. A slugging percentage over .500 is considered outstanding.

3. Calculate a man's gross weekly pay, given his rate per hour, overtime rate per hour, number of regular hours worked that week, and number of overtime hours that week.

4. Given a linear equation $Ax + B = C$ ($A \neq 0$), input A, B, and C and solve for x. For example, if the equation is $7x + 5 = 19$, print $x = 2$.

5. Read a positive integer N and print the product P of the four consecutive integers N, N + 1, N + 2, and N + 3. If the program runs correctly, P + 1 will be a perfect square each time.

6. A baseball pitcher's "earned-run average" is computed using the formula $\text{ERA} = \dfrac{R \cdot 9}{I}$ where R = number of earned runs allowed and I = innings pitched. Given R and I, compute and print a pitcher's ERA. Assume that a whole number of innings is pitched.

7. The withholding tax on a weekly salary (let us assume) is computed as follows: 14% of the difference between a man's gross pay and $13 times the number of dependents he claims. Read the values

for a man's gross pay and the number of dependents; print his with-holding tax.

8. Accept the coordinates of two points on the real number line. Sub-divide the line segment determined by these two points into four equal subsegments. Print the coordinates of the endpoints of each segment. (See Ex. 4, p. 27.)

   Example:

   Suppose the given points are 0 and 1. The endpoints of the subdivisions are 0, .25, .5, .75, and 1.

9. Given the number of a baseball team's wins and losses, compute its winning percentage. Assume there are no ties. (See Ex. 14, p. 28.)

10. Input the number of a team's wins, losses, and ties, and print its winning percentage. Assume that a tie game counts as a full game played and a half-game won. (See Ex. 15, p. 28.)

11. Compute a baseball player's "fielding percentage," given his put-outs, assists, and errors.

$$\text{fielding percentage} = \frac{\text{chances handled successfully}}{\text{total chances}} = \frac{P + A}{P + A + E}$$

12. Convert Centigrade (Celsius) temperatures to Fahrenheit.

13. Convert Centigrade temperatures to Kelvin.

14. Convert Fahrenheit temperatures to Centigrade.

15. Convert Fahrenheit temperatures to Kelvin.

16. Convert Kelvin temperatures to Centigrade.

17. Convert Kelvin temperatures to Fahrenheit.

The mileage records of four automobiles are given below. Do Exercises 18 and 19.

Car	Miles	Gallons Used
1	420	25.1
2	305	21.5
3	227	14.9
4	195	15.2

18. Compute each car's average mileage per gallon.

19. Compute the average miles/gallon of all four cars.

GEOMETRY

20. Find the sum of the interior angles of a polygon, given its number of sides. (See Ex. 30, p. 29.)

21. Find the measure of each angle of a regular polygon, given the number of sides. (See Ex. 31, p. 29.)

22. Find the number of sides of a polygon, given the sum of the measures of the interior angles.

23. Find the number of sides of a regular polygon, given the measure of each interior angle.

24. Find the geometric mean (mean proportional) of two positive real numbers.

25. Find the measure of an exterior angle of a triangle, given the measures of the two remote interior angles.

26. Input the radius of a sphere and compute its volume. (See Ex. 24, p. 29.)

27. Input the radius of a sphere and compute its surface area. (See Ex. 25, p. 29.)

Accept as given the length, width, and height of a rectangular prism. Do Exercises 28 through 30.

28. Compute the length of a diagonal of the prism.

29. Compute the total surface area of the prism.

30. Compute the volume of the prism.

31. Input the lengths of $\overline{BC}$ and $\overline{AB}$ of isosceles triangle ABC with $AB = AC$ and compute the perimeter and area of the triangle.

32. Given the measure of angle A of isosceles triangle ABC with $AB = AC$, find the measure of angle B.

In Exercises 33 through 35 suppose that two triangles ABC and XYZ are similar (have the same shape).

33. Given AB, XY, and BC, find YZ.

34. Given AB, XY, and the perimeter of $\triangle ABC$, find the perimeter of $\triangle XYZ$.

35. Given AB and XY, print the ratio of the areas of the two triangles.

36. Find the area of a triangle, given the lengths of the three sides. (See Ex. 28, p. 26.)

37. Convert an angle from degrees, minutes, and seconds to degrees with a decimal fraction.

For a regular square pyramid, given the length of a side of the base and the length of a lateral edge, solve the problems in Exercises 38–41.

38. Find the slant height of the pyramid. (See Ex. 34, p. 29.)

39. Find the lateral area of the pyramid.

40. Find the total surface area of the pyramid.

41. Find the volume of the pyramid.

42. Given the lengths of three segments formed by two intersecting chords in a circle, find the length of the fourth segment.

Compute the area of the figures described in Exercises 43 through 48.

43. a triangle, given the base and height

44. an equilateral triangle, given the length of a side (See Ex. 27, p. 29.)

45. a parallelogram, given the length and height

46. a rhombus, given the lengths of the diagonals

47. a trapezoid, given the height and the lengths of the bases

48. a regular polygon, given the number of sides and the measures of the apothem and one side

For a right circular cylinder, given the length of the altitude and the radius of the base, solve the problems in Exercises 49 through 51.

49. Find the lateral area of the cylinder.

50. Find the total surface area of the cylinder.

51. Find the volume of the cylinder.

52. Given that a segment of length L is divided into two segments whose ratio is L_1 to L_2, find the length of each segment.

53. Knowing the ratio of the measures of the angles of a triangle, determine the measure of each angle. For example, if the ratio of the angle measures is 2:3:4, input 2, 3, 4 as data. (See Ex. 44, p. 30.)

A right triangle ABC is given with altitude $\overline{CD}$ drawn to the hypotenuse $\overline{AB}$. Let a, b, c, h, x, and y represent lengths as indicated in the figure at the right. Solve the following problems. (See Ex. 45 through 48, p. 30.)

54. Given c and x, find a.

55. Given c and x, find h.

56. Given h and a, find b.

57. Given h and x, find b.

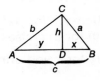

The coordinates of two points A and B in the coordinate plane are given for Exercises 58 and 59. (See Ex. 49 and 50, p. 30.)

58. Compute AB, the length of the segment $\overline{AB}$.

59. Determine the coordinates of the midpoint of $\overline{AB}$.

60. Compute the perimeter of a right triangle, given the lengths of the two legs. (See Ex. 52, p. 30.)

61. Compute the perimeter of a right triangle, given the length of the hypotenuse and the length of one leg. (See Ex. 53, p. 30.)

In Exercises 62 through 64 consider an isosceles right triangle.

62. Find the length of the hypotenuse, given the length of a leg.

63. Find the length of a leg, given the length of the hypotenuse.

64. Find the perimeter, given the length of a leg.

Input the number of degrees in an acute angle for Exercises 65 and 66.

65. Print the measure of its complement.

66. Print the measure of its supplement.

The altitude and the radius of the base of a right circular cone are given for Exercises 67 through 69.

67. Find the lateral area.

68. Find the total surface area.

69. Find the volume.

70. In parallelogram $ABCD$ at the right, $m\angle A = 45°$. Given x and b, find the area of $ABCD$.

71. In parallelogram $WXYZ$ at the right, $m\angle W = 30°$. Given l and w, find the area of $WXYZ$.

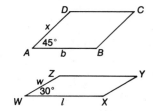

ALGEBRA TWO

72. A cubic polynomial is defined by $y = Ax^3 + Bx^2 + Cx + D$ (A, B, C, D rational). Read A, B, C, D, and N. Compute y for $x = N$ and print N and y. (See Ex. 54, p. 30.)

73. Given the height from which an object falls, determine the time it will take to fall. (See Ex. 14 and 15, p. 11.)

For the quadratic equation $Ax^2 + Bx + C = 0$, input A, B, and C (A, B, and C rational, A ≠ 0) for Exercises 74 through 76.

74. Read a value for x and print x and the value of $Ax^2 + Bx + C$.

75. Evaluate the discriminant of the equation.

76. Determine the sum and product of the roots without actually computing the roots. (This applies whether the roots are real or not.)

77. Given the height of an object, the object distance, the image distance, and the focal distance, determine the height of the image.

78. Input the slope of an oblique line *l* in the *xy*-plane. (An "oblique" line is neither horizontal nor vertical.) Print the slope of any line perpendicular to *l*.

A parabola is defined by $y = Ax^2 + Bx + C$, $A \neq 0$. Read rational numbers A, B, and C. Do Exercises 79 through 82.

79. Print the coordinates of the vertex of the parabola. (See Ex. 66, p. 31.)

80. Print the equation of the axis of symmetry. (See Ex. 68, p. 31.)

81. Print the coordinates of the focus. (See Ex. 69, p. 31.)

82. Print the equation of the directrix. (See Ex. 70, p. 31.)

83. The period T (in seconds) of a simple pendulum of length L (in meters) is given by $T = 2\pi\sqrt{\dfrac{L}{g}}$ where *g* is the gravity constant. Given L and *g*, compute T.

84. Convert pH values to the corresponding hydrogen ion concentration.

85. Given a function *f* defined by $y = 2x - 7$. The domain of *f* is {−5, −2, −1, 0, 3, 11}. For each member of the domain, print *x* and the corresponding *y*.

86. Given the atomic weight of an element, use the Einstein equation $E = mc^2$ to find the amount of energy produced when that element is converted to energy.

87. Given the candle power of a light source and its distance from a point, compute the illumination on an object placed at that point.

88. Find $f(g(x))$ where $f(x) = 3x + 4$ and $g(x) = x^2 - 7$ for *x*-values that you select. (See Ex. 76, p. 32.)

89. For the same functions *f* and *g* as defined in Exercise 88, find $g(f(x))$ for *x*-values that you select. (See Ex. 77, p. 32.)

Given a point $P(x, y)$, print the ordered pair of the point which is symmetric to *P* with respect to the following.

90. the *x*-axis   **91.** the *y*-axis

92. the origin   **93.** the line defined by $y = x$

ADVANCED MATHEMATICS

94. Given the radian measure of an angle, compute the degree measure.

95. Given the degree measure of an angle, compute the radian measure.

96. Given A and B (in radians), find cosine (A + B) without using "CØS(A + B)".

97. Given the lengths of the hypotenuse and one leg of a right triangle, find the sine, cosine, and tangent of either one of the acute angles of the triangle.

For an arithmetic progression, input A, the first term, D, the common difference, and N, a positive integer. Do Exercises 98 and 99. (See Ex. 89 and 90, p. 33.)

98. Print the Nth term of the sequence.

99. Print the sum of the first N terms of the sequence.

100. Compute and print the determinant of a 2 × 2 matrix $\begin{bmatrix} A & B \\ C & D \end{bmatrix}$. (See Ex. 87, p. 33.)

101. For the complex number A + Bi (A and B real), input A and B and print the absolute value of the complex number. (See Ex. 88, p. 33.)

102. A ball is dropped straight down from a tower 102 feet high and rebounds each time to 36% of its previous height. What is the total vertical distance traveled by the ball before it comes to rest? (Since this problem has built-in data, you may ignore General Instructions 4 and 5.)

103. Given the angle of refraction of a light ray, determine the angle of incidence for any given index of refraction.

The length of the hypotenuse and the measure of one acute angle of a right triangle is given for Exercises 104 through 107.

104. Compute the measure of the other acute angle.

105. Compute the length of each leg.

106. Compute the perimeter of the triangle.

107. Compute the area of the triangle.

108. Given pure imaginary numbers Ai and Bi, read A and B and print the product of Ai and Bi. (See Ex. 93, p. 33.)

109. Input real numbers X and Y (X $\neq$ Y). Print three arithmetic means between X and Y. (See Ex. 94, p. 33.)

110. Find the resultant of two forces which act simultaneously at the same point on a body, given the magnitude and direction angle of each force.

111. Compute the distance between two points in a three-dimensional coordinate system. (See Ex. 96, p. 33.)

For a geometric progression, input A, the first term, R, the common ratio (R $\neq$ 1), and N, a positive integer. Do Exercises 112 and 113. (See Ex. 97 and 98, p. 33.)

112. Print the Nth term of the sequence.

113. Print the sum of the first N terms of the sequence.

Read S and T, the components of a vector $\vec{V} =$ (S, T). Do Exercises 114 and 115. (See Ex. 99 and 100, p. 33.)

114. Compute and print the norm of $\vec{V}$.

115. Input a scalar K and print the product $K\vec{V}$.

Read S and T, the components of a vector $\vec{V} =$ (S, T), and X and Y, the components of vector $\vec{W}$. Do Exercises 116 and 117.

116. Print the sum of vectors $\vec{V}$ and $\vec{W}$.

117. Print the inner product (dot product) of $\vec{V}$ and $\vec{W}$.

118. Accept the components of two three-dimensional vectors $\vec{y}$ and $\vec{z}$. Print the cross-product of $\vec{y}$ and $\vec{z}$.

119. Compute the area of a triangle by taking one-half the product of two sides times the sine of the included angle.

3

CONTROLLING OUTPUT;
IF...THEN STATEMENTS

The output rules explained in the first five lessons of this chapter are intended to cover the majority of BASIC compilers. However, the explanations given here may sometimes differ from those that apply to the system that you are using. Consult the manual and experiment with your system to determine if the rules given here are followed exactly.

3-1 COMMAS

In many programs we want to print several numbers as output. Here is an example.

Example: Given a nonzero real number, print the number along with its additive inverse and its multiplicative inverse.

Program 3-1

```
10 READ X
20 PRINT X, -X, 1/X
30 GØ TØ 10
40 DATA 5,-100,4
50 END
```

In line 20 notice the commas separating the quantities to be printed. In addition to serving as separators, they tell the compiler how to space the numerals to be printed. Each execution of a PRINT statement normally produces one line of output.

The output from Program 3-1 on the previous page is shown below.

```
     5             -5              .2
  -100            100            -.01
     4             -4             .25
```

If we want the number, its additive inverse, and its multiplicative inverse on separate lines, we would write the program as shown below.

Program 3-2   Here is the output of Program 3-2.

```
10 READ X                          5
20 PRINT X                        -5
30 PRINT -X                       .2
40 PRINT 1/X                    -100
50 GØ TØ 10                      100
60 DATA 5,-100,4                -.01
70 END                            4
                                 -4
                                .25
```

We usually prefer the method of Program 3-1 on page 70 since it saves space and keeps associated values together on the same line.

We have still not explained exactly how commas govern the spacing of numerals printed. Most terminals can print a maximum of 75 characters across the page. These "print positions" are numbered 1 to 75 left-to-right. Let us look again at the output from Program 3-1, but this time with the print positions indicated.

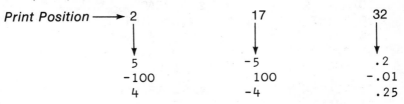

RULE:
When the output expressions are separated by commas in a PRINT statement, the compiler automatically assigns each quantity *fifteen* print positions.

When commas separate expressions in a PRINT statement, the output line is divided into five "zones": columns 1 through 15, 16 through 30, 31 through 45, 46 through 60, and 61 through 75. For numerical output the first position in each zone is reserved for a negative sign. For example, in the output of Program 3-1 above, the first 5 falls in column two rather than in column one. The first significant digit of each numeral is actually printed in column 2, 17, 32, 47, or 62.

What happens when we try to print six expressions separated by commas, as in this program?

Program 3-3

```
10 READ A,B
20 PRINT A+B,A-B,A*B,A/B,A↑B,B↑A
30 GØ TØ 10
40 DATA 5, 2, 2, 3
50 END
```

Since only the first five expressions of line 20 can fit on one line, the sixth (B ↑ A) is printed on the next line, like this.

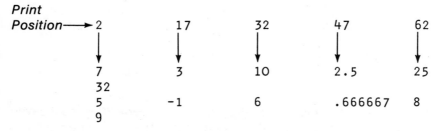

*Print
Position* ⟶ 2 .... 17 .... 32 .... 47 62

7	3	10	2.5	25
32				
5	-1	6	.666667	8
9				

EXERCISES 3-1

A As in the examples of this lesson, show the output from each of these programs, with the leftmost print position of each quantity numbered.

1.
```
10 READ R
20 PRINT R,R↑2,R↑3
40 DATA 2, 6
50 GØ TØ 10
60 END
```

2.
```
5 READ S, T
10 PRINT S,T,S*T,S/T,T/S
15 GØ TØ 5
20 DATA 12, 6, 3, 4
25 END
```

3.
```
20 READ X,Y,Z
21 PRINT X*Y,X*Z,Y*Z
22 PRINT X-Y,X-Z,Y-Z
23 DATA 4, 2, 3
24 END
```

4.
```
10 READ C, D
20 PRINT C,D,-C,-D,1/C,1/D
30 DATA 2,4,8,10
40 GØ TØ 10
50 END
```

5. Show the output from Program 3-2 on page 71 if it is revised as shown at the right (with line 45 added).

```
10 READ X
20 PRINT X
30 PRINT -X
40 PRINT 1/X
45 PRINT "END ØF DATA SET"
50 GØ TØ 10
60 DATA 5,-100,4
70 END
```

3-2 SEMICOLONS

The use of semicolons in a PRINT statement permits an alternate output format that packs together the numerals more closely than commas do. Let us rewrite Program 3-1 on page 70 to illustrate this fact.

Program 3-1A

```
10 READ X
20 PRINT X;-X;1/X
30 GØ TØ 10
40 DATA 5,-100,4
50 END
```

Putting semicolons in line 20 causes the output to look like the following.

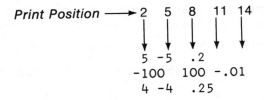

The semicolon in a PRINT statement causes the compiler to organize the output in a format according to the following rules.

1. It prints the first quantity, beginning in print position one if the quantity is negative, in print position two if it is positive or zero.

2. If the next quantity is negative, it skips one space, prints the negative sign and then the significant digits of the numeral.

3. If the next quantity is positive or zero, it skips two spaces and prints the next numeral.

There is nothing wrong with mixing semicolons and commas in PRINT statements, as the following examples show.

```
30 PRINT A;B,C
40 PRINT X+Y, X-Y; X↑Y; Y↑X, X/Y
```

In a PRINT statement such as

```
50 PRINT "PERIMETER = " P
```

most systems assume that there is an understood semicolon between the second quotation mark and the variable P. On some systems the semicolon must be explicitly shown, like this.

```
50 PRINT "PERIMETER = "; P
```

CAUTION: The rules just stated for semicolon output apply only to numerical output. For alphamerical output (*alpha*betical characters in combination with nu*merical*), such as messages, no spaces are skipped *before* an open quotation mark. Hence if P = 25, the statement

$$50 \quad PRINT \quad P \quad "= \quad PERIMETER"$$

would produce the line

$$25= \quad PERIMETER$$

with no space skipped between numeral (25) and the message (= PE-RIMETER). To space the message better, use

$$50 \quad PRINT \quad P \quad " \quad = \quad PERIMETER"$$

since the spaces inside the quotation marks will be honored by the compiler.

By understanding this rule, a programmer can avoid producing the awkward output of a statement such as this.

$$50 \quad PRINT \quad "L \quad = \quad " \quad L \quad "W \quad = \quad " \quad W \quad "P \quad = \quad " \quad 2*L+2*W$$

If L = 5 and w = 3, then line 50 would print the following.

$$L \quad = \quad 5W \quad = \quad 3P \quad = \quad 16$$

Notice that no space is skipped at either of these points.

Revise line 50 to the following.

$$50 \quad PRINT \quad "L \quad = \quad " \quad L \quad " \quad W \quad = \quad " \quad W \quad " \quad P \quad = \quad " \quad 2*L+2*W$$

Notice the spaces included at these points inside *quotation marks.*

The output would now look like this.

$$L \quad = \quad 5 \quad W \quad = \quad 3 \quad P \quad = \quad 16$$

EXERCISES 3-2

A Show each output, indicating the print positions as in earlier examples.

1.
```
10 READ S
20 LET Y = S↑2 - 7
30 PRINT S;Y
40 GØ TØ 10
50 DATA 2, -3
60 END
```

2.
```
10 READ N
20 PRINT N↑3, N↑4; -N
30 GØ TØ 10
40 DATA 1, -2, 3
50 END
```

If P = 30, show the line produced by each of these PRINT statements. Use an underline to indicate a blank space.

Example: 50 PRINT "PERIM =" P
 Answer: PERIM_=__30

3. 50 PRINT "P ="P   **4.** 50 PRINT "P = "P

5. 50 PRINT P "= P"   **6.** 50 PRINT P " = PERIMETER"

B   If L = 4 and W = 3, show the output from each of these PRINT statements. Use an underline to indicate a blank space.

7. 60 PRINT "L =" L " W =" W " P =" 2*L+2*W

8. 60 PRINT L "= L" W "= W" 2*L+2*W "= P"

9. 60 PRINT "LENGTH" L " WIDTH" W " PERIMETER" 2*L+2*W

3-3 SKIPPING LINES

Returning to Program 3-1 on page 70, let us assume that the programmer would like the output double-spaced, like this.

5	-5	.2
-100	100	-.01
4	-4	.25

This can be accomplished by using a "dummy" PRINT statement (line 30 below).

Program 3-1B

```
10 READ X
20 PRINT X, -X, 1/X
30 PRINT
40 GØ TØ 10
50 DATA 5,-100,4
60 END
```

The "dummy" PRINT is equivalent to a line like this.

30 PRINT "   "

where the "message" being printed is just a line of blanks.

EXERCISES 3-3

A   **1.** What would be the output if Program 3-1B on the previous page were written in the following manner?

```
 5 PRINT
10 READ X
20 PRINT X, -X, 1/X
30 GØ TØ 5
40 DATA 5, -100, 4
50 END
```

Show the output of each of these programs.

2.
```
10 READ R
20 PRINT R↑2, R↑3
30 PRINT
40 DATA 2, 6
50 GØ TØ 10
60 END
```

3.
```
10 PRINT
20 READ S
30 LET T = 4*S↑2
40 PRINT S; T
50 PRINT
60 GØ TØ 10
70 DATA 2, 3, 4
80 END
```

3-4 COLUMNS AND COLUMN HEADINGS

Programmers often print output in tabular form with columns of figures, each column identified with a heading. As a simple example, suppose we want the output from Program 3-1 on page 70 to look like this.

X	-X	1/X
5	-5	.2
-100	100	-.01
4	-4	.25

The program would have to be tailored as follows.

Program 3-1C

```
 5 PRINT " X"," -X"," 1/X"
10 READ X
20 PRINT X, -X, 1/X
30 GØ TØ 10
40 DATA 5, -100, 4
50 END
```

Comment:

In statement 5, note the space at the beginning of each message. This space shifts the heading so that it begins over the first significant digit (or decimal point) of each numeral since the first column of each print zone is reserved for a negative sign.

Before any READ or calculation is performed, the headings are printed. Note that line 5 is executed only once, at the beginning of the program. Line 30 returns control to line 10 for the second set of data so that the headings will not be repeated.

An extension of this technique is to skip a line before and after printing the headings so that the output looks like this.

X	-X	1/X
5	-5	.2
-100	100	-.01
4	-4	.25

EXERCISES 3-4

A   Show the output of each of these programs.

1.
```
10 PRINT "REAL NØ.","SQRT"
20 READ A
30 PRINT A, SQR(A)
40 GØ TØ 20
50 DATA 4, 16, 25
60 END
```

2.
```
5 PRINT
6 PRINT "DISTANCE","RATE","TIME"
7 PRINT
10 READ R,T
20 PRINT R*T,R,T
30 GØ TØ 10
40 DATA 40,3,55,10,60,40
50 END
```

3.
```
5 PRINT "X";"X*X"
10 READ X
20 PRINT X;X*X
30 GØ TØ 10
40 DATA 2,-5,1.1
50 END
```

Identify and correct any error(s) in each program.

4.
```
10 PRINT "YEARS,""PRINCIPAL,""RATE,""INTEREST"
20 READ Y,P,R
30 LET I=P*R*Y
40 PRINT Y,P,R,I
50 GØ TØ 10
60 DATA 5,1000,.03,20,10000,.05
70 END
```

5.
```
5 PRINT "HØURS, RATE, PAY"
10 READ H,R
20LET P=H*R
30 PRINT H,R,P
40 DATA 40,1.50,50,2.25,35,1 1/2
50 GØ TØ 10
60 END
```

3-5 SUPPRESSING LINE FEED

In all programs written thus far each answer has been printed on a separate line. This procedure wastes space and, unless there are special requirements, can be avoided by putting either a comma or a semicolon at the end of the PRINT statement, as in the examples below.

The comma at the end of the PRINT line causes the compiler to allot each value fifteen spaces, as explained earlier. The semicolon makes the computer print the values closer together.

```
50 PRINT S,
50 PRINT S;
50 PRINT X+Y;
50 PRINT 2*A-4*B,
50 PRINT X,Y,
50 PRINT "NØS. ARE:";
```

EXERCISES 3-5

A   State whether each of the following is a valid PRINT statement.

1. 20 PRINT

2. 20 PRINT "   "

3. 20 PRINT "   ";

4. 20 PRINT "THE LIST IS",

5. 20 PRINT P = "PERIMETER"

6. 20 PRINT X1,X2;" AND " Y

Show the output from each of these programs.

7.
```
10 READ L,W
20 PRINT 2*L+2*W;
30 GØ TØ 10
40 DATA 2,3,5,6
50 END
```

8.
```
10 READ L,W
20 PRINT 2*L+2*W,
30 GØ TØ 10
40 DATA 2,3,5,6
50 END
```

B   **9.** Let's indulge in some computer "art." A program is shown at the left below for printing a geometric pattern.

```
10 PRINT "*        *"
20 PRINT "**      **"
30 PRINT "***    ***"
40 PRINT "********"
50 PRINT "********"
60 PRINT "***    ***"
70 PRINT "**      **"
80 PRINT "*        *"
90 END
```

```
NN        N
N N       N
N  N      N
N   N     N
N    N N
N       NN
```

Write programs to create your own patterns. For example, print your name or your initials. One interesting technique is to use the letter whose shape is being printed to form the shape as shown at the right above.

3-6 DECISIONS: IF . . . THEN STATEMENTS

We now return to the problem of Flowchart 1-3 on page 7.

Example:

Read a real number x. If x is nonnegative, give the square root. If x is negative, print   NØ REAL SQUARE RØØT

We now write the program and trace the program.

Program 3-4

```
10  READ X
20  IF X >= O THEN 50
30  PRINT "NØ REAL SQUARE RØØT"
40  GØ TØ 10
50  PRINT X↑.5
60  GØ TØ 10
70  DATA 81,-2,0
80  END
```

Comment:

Unlike Flowchart 1-3, Program 3-4 has been written to process several values of x.

Table 3-1   Trace of Program 3-4

Step Number	Statement Number	Value of Variable x	Test	Yes or No?	Output
1	10	81			
2	20		81 >= 0?	Yes	
3	50				9
4	60		OUT OF DATA?	No	
5	10	-2			
6	20		-2 >= 0?	No	
7	30				NØ REAL SQUARE RØØT
8	40		OUT OF DATA?	No	
9	10	0			
10	20		0 >= 0?	Yes	
11	50				0
12	60		OUT OF DATA?	Yes	
13	END				

The decision of the program is made in line 20, an IF . . . THEN statement. Such statements must be written in the following form.

IF (equation or inequality) THEN (statement number)

Note that, while it might be grammatically correct to use a comma before the word THEN, none is inserted. The statement number may be the number of a statement earlier in the program or of one that comes later. That is, the IF . . . THEN statement may branch the computer forward or backward.

Here are examples of valid IF . . . THEN statements.

```
15 IF Y = Z THEN 40
20 IF A + B < B - 16 THEN 100
40 IF R >= 71 THEN 10
60 IF X/Y < Z↑3 THEN 40
50 IF A <> B THEN 80
```

Refer to Table 3-2 below to interpret the inequality symbols used in the examples. Many systems allow alternate forms: >< as well as <>, =< instead of <= and => for >=. Some systems use # for ≠.

Table 3-2   Relation symbols

Algebra	BASIC
=	=
<	<
>	>
≠	< >
≤	< =
≥	> =

Unlike LET statements, IF . . . THEN statements may have operation signs on either or both sides of the equation or inequality in the IF clause.

IF . . . THEN statements are handled by the computer as follows.

The machine tests the condition stated in the IF clause.

1. If this condition holds true, the computer branches to the statement whose number appears after the word THEN.

2. If the condition is false, the computer ignores the THEN clause and continues to the next line of the program in regular sequence.

On the top of the next page is another program involving decisions. Recall Flowchart 1-4 on page 8.

Example:

Read a real number; print whether it is positive, negative, or zero.

Program 3-5

```
10  READ X
20  IF X > 0 THEN 60
30  IF X < 0 THEN 80
40  PRINT "ZERØ"
50  GØ TØ 10
60  PRINT "PØSITIVE"
70  GØ TØ 10
80  PRINT "NEGATIVE"
90  GØ TØ 10
100 DATA 8,-16,0,73,-124
110 END
```

Notice in both Program 3-4 on page 79 and Program 3-5 above the repetition of the   GØ TØ 10   statement. In Program 3-4 both GØ TØ statements are needed. If you are puzzled as to why, study Program 3-4 without the first   GØ TØ 10

```
10  READ X
20  IF X >= 0 THEN 50
30  PRINT "NØ REAL SQUARE RØØT"
50  PRINT X↑.5
60  GØ TØ 10
70  DATA 81,-2,0
80  END
```

Trace the program until you find the error that develops. It will occur when $x = -2$.

A common mistake is to write an IF . . . THEN statement which is no decision at all, as in this program segment.

```
            . . .
30  IF X = Y THEN 40
40  LET Z = X + 7
            . . .
```

If $x = y$, the THEN clause directs the computer to go to line 40. If $x \neq y$, the machine goes to the next statement, which is 40. In either case it goes to 40; there is no decision, no breaking into two branches.

RULE:

In an IF . . . THEN statement, the statement number after THEN should not be the number of the statement immediately following the IF . . . THEN statement.

Consider the version below of Program 3-5 on page 81, with line 50 and line 70 changed.

```
10 READ X
20 IF X > 0 THEN 60
30 IF X < 0 THEN 80
40 PRINT "ZERØ"
50 GØ TØ 90
60 PRINT "PØSITIVE"
70 GØ TØ 90
80 PRINT "NEGATIVE"
90 GØ TØ 10
100 DATA 8,-16,0,73,-124
110 END
```

While not wrong, this version does send the computer on a "run-around," since lines 50 and 70 send it to 90, which then sends it to 10. In general, one GØ TØ statement should never send the computer to another GØ TØ.

EXERCISES 3-6

A State whether each of the following is a valid IF . . . THEN statement.

1. 20 IF A + B > 6 THEN -30
2. 20 IF M - N <> 0 THEN 75
3. 30 IF X↑2 + Y↑2 = R↑2 THEN 210
4. 20 IF A = B = C THEN 63
5. 20 IF (K+1)*(K+1) > M THEN GØ TØ 90
6. 20 IF D = 0, THEN 80
7. 20 IF X*Y = Y*Z THEN 20

8. Is this program equivalent to Program 3-4 on page 79? Trace until you can decide if the output will be the same.

```
10 READ X
20 IF X < 0 THEN 50
30 PRINT X↑.5
40 GØ TØ 10
50 PRINT "NØ REAL SQUARE RØØT"
60 GØ TØ 10
70 DATA 81,-2,0
80 END
```

Write BASIC statements that implement the flowchart decision section shown.

Example:

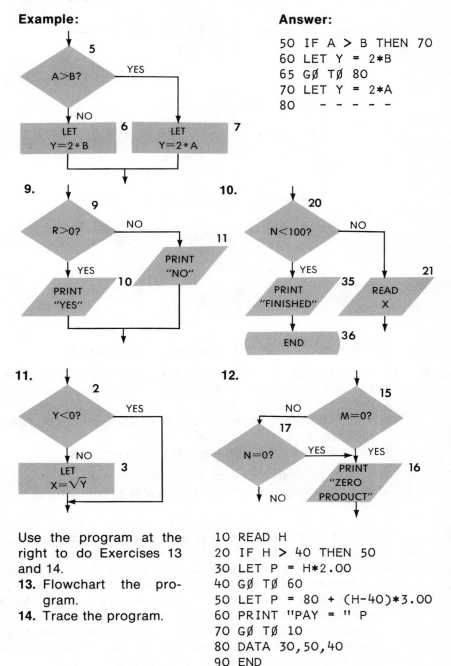

Answer:

```
50 IF A > B THEN 70
60 LET Y = 2*B
65 GØ TØ 80
70 LET Y = 2*A
80  - - - - -
```

9.

10.

11.

12.

Use the program at the right to do Exercises 13 and 14.

13. Flowchart the program.

14. Trace the program.

```
10 READ H
20 IF H > 40 THEN 50
30 LET P = H*2.00
40 GØ TØ 60
50 LET P = 80 + (H-40)*3.00
60 PRINT "PAY = " P
70 GØ TØ 10
80 DATA 30,50,40
90 END
```

15. Write a program for the flowchart below. Input DATA: 0, 2, −3

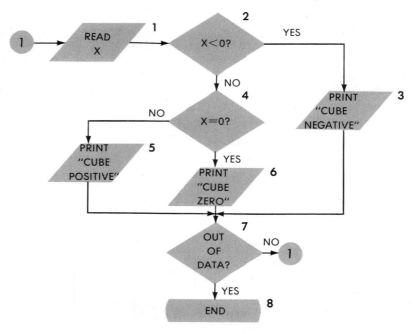

16. Trace the program that you wrote for Exercise 15.

B **17.** Write a program that is equivalent to Program 3-5 on page 81 but with a different inequality for at least one IF clause of a decision.

18. Trace your program for Exercise 17 using the DATA listed in Program 3-5.

19. Trace Program 3-5 with lines 50 and 70 removed.

Write BASIC programs for each of these problems.

20. Read two unequal real numbers X and Y. Print either "X > Y" or "Y > X".

21. Given a quadratic equation of the form $AX^2 + BX + C = 0$, determine if the equation has real roots without actually computing the roots. (See Ex. 56, p. 31.)

22. Given a real number, print the number and its absolute value without using the ABS function of BASIC. (See Ex. 1, p. 27.)

23. Assume that the cost, not including tax, for sending a telegram from Minneapolis to San Francisco is $1.95 for the first fifteen words or less, plus $0.10 for each additional word over fifteen. Write a program which, given the number of words in a telegram, computes the cost. (See Ex. 6, p. 27.)

3-7 MATHEMATICAL APPLICATIONS REQUIRING SPECIAL PRINT FORMATS

Suppose the output from a program is a set of points in the *xy*-plane. We usually list the coordinates of the points between parentheses and separated by commas, like this: (2, 7); (−3, 8); (0, −9); (−1.5, −6). If, as usual, x and y represent the first and second coordinates respectively, then a PRINT statement to produce the desired output would be the following one.

$$40 \text{ PRINT } "(" \text{ X } "," \text{ Y } ")"$$

Printing complex numbers is another application requiring a special format. A complex number is of the form A + B*i*, where *"i"* is the imaginary unit such that $i^2 = -1$. However, I is just another real variable in programming and has no special significance. When a complex number is to be printed, the "real part" (A) and the "imaginary part" (B) must be computed separately. "I" must be dictated between quotes in the PRINT statement; the "+" must also be inserted by means of quotes, as in the following example.

$$60 \text{ PRINT A } " + " \text{ B } " \text{ I}"$$

This type of PRINT statement, however, produces a difficulty if B is negative. For example, if B = −4 the output would look like this,   6 +−4I, which is awkward. In order to avoid such situations, any program that prints complex numbers must include two PRINT statements with a decision based on the value of B. This is shown below.

```
        . . .
60 IF B < 0 THEN 90
70 PRINT A " + " B " I"
80 GØ TØ 10
90 PRINT A; B " I"
100 GØ TØ 10
        . . .
```

If B is negative, no "+" sign is dictated (line 90).

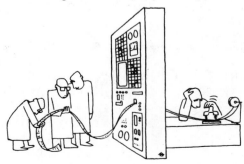

A similar approach is needed when the programmer must print a poly-nomial. Suppose the output will be a quadratic polynomial of the form $ax^2 + bx + c$. Decisions must be included to handle negative values for either b or c or both. The following sequence of steps would be one way of handling the problem.

. . .

```
 60 IF B < O THEN 100
 70 IF C < O THEN 130
 80 PRINT A "X↑2 + " B " X + " C
 90 GØ TØ 10
100 IF C < O THEN 150
110 PRINT A "X↑2 " B " X + " C
120 GØ TØ 10
130 PRINT A "X↑2 + " B " X " C
140 GØ TØ 10
150 PRINT A "X↑2 " B " X " C
160 GØ TØ 10
```

. . .

In this example it was assumed that the output would always be quad-ratic polynomials. Handling polynomials of varying degrees involves subscripted variables and will be explained in chapter 5.

The program could be made more complicated and handle zero coeffi-cients and one coefficients so that a polynomial such as $x^2 - 7$ would be printed simply as   x ↑ 2 − 7   and not as   1 x ↑ 2 + 0 x − 7   .

EXERCISES 3-7

A   Show the output of each of these programs.

1.
```
10 READ X,Y
20 PRINT "("X","Y")"
30 GØ TØ 10
40 DATA 2,3,-4,17,0,-2
50 END
```

2.
```
10 READ X,Y
20 PRINT "("X","Y")";
30 GØ TØ 10
40 DATA 2,3,-4,17,0,-2
50 END
```

3.
```
10 DATA 7,4,8,-6,-2,0
20 READ A,B
30 PRINT A " + " B " I"
40 GØ TØ 20
50 END
```

4.
```
10 READ A,B
20 DATA 7,4,8,-6,-2,0
30 IF B < O THEN 60
40 PRINT A " + " B " I"
50 GØ TØ 10
60 PRINT A; B " I"
70 GØ TØ 10
80 END
```

5. 20 READ A,B,C
    40 PRINT A "X↑2 + " B " X + " C
    60 GØ TØ 20
    80 DATA 7,4,3,8,-2,10,-1,4,-8,6,-7,0
    100 END

6. 10 READ A,B,C
    20 IF B < 0 THEN 60
    30 IF C < 0 THEN 90
    40 PRINT A "X↑2 + " B " X + " C
    50 GØ TØ 10
    60 IF C < 0 THEN 110
    70 PRINT A "X↑2 " B " X + " C
    80 GØ TØ 10
    90 PRINT A "X↑2 + " B " X " C
    100 GØ TØ 10
    110 PRINT A "X↑2" B " X " C
    120 GØ TØ 10
    130 DATA 7,4,3,8,-2,10,-1,4,-8,6,-7,0
    140 END

Correct any error(s) in each of these programs.

7. 10 READ A,B
    20 LET Z = A + B*I
    30 PRINT "THE COMPLEX NØ. IS" Z
    40 GØ TØ 10
    50 DATA 7,4,3,-2,-1,10
    60 END

8. 10 READ A,B,C
    20 LET P = A*X↑2 + B*X + C
    30 PRINT "THE QUADRATIC IS " P
    40 DATA 7,-10,8,4,2,-7
    50 END

9. 10 READ X,Y
    20 PRINT (X, Y) "IS THE VERTEX"
    30 GØ TØ 10
    40 DATA 7,-2,4,0,-8,10
    END
    50 END

10. 1 READ X,Y
    2 PRINT "("X,Y")"
    3 GØ TØ 1
    4 DATA 7,-2,4,0,-8,10
    5 END

Correct any error(s) in each of the following programs.

11. 10 READ X,Y
20 PRINT "("X","Y")
30 GØ TØ 10
40 DATA 7,-2,4,0,-8,10
50 END

12. 10 READ A,B
20 IF B < 0 THEN 40
30 PRINT A " + " B " I"
40 PRINT A; B " I"
50 GØ TØ 10
60 DATA 7,4,-2,-8,0,-7
70 END

B **13.** Rewrite the program segment that was given on page 86 for printing polynomials so that it also eliminates the printing of zero coefficients and one coefficients.

3-8 DIFFICULTY OF DETERMINING EXACT EQUALITY (Optional)

Consider the following statement.

40 IF SQR(D) = X/Y THEN 100

Its meaning is clear; if the square root of D equals the quotient of X divided by Y, branch to statement 100. Otherwise continue to the next statement in numerical sequence.

This seems straightforward, but there is a problem and it lies with the meaning of "=". The computer will branch to line 100 only if SQR(D) *exactly equals* X/Y. When a programmer traces his program using pencil and paper, he does the calculations himself. For example, if $D = 4$, $X = 8$, and $Y = 4$, then $SQR(4) = 8/4$ and the programmer expects the computer to branch to line 100. However, he should not be surprised if it does not, for reasons we will now explain.

Computers do not perform calculations the same way humans do. For one thing the computer represents numbers in the binary system. For integers this causes no inaccuracy but for fractions a finite decimal in base ten often converts to an infinite decimal in base two. Here is an example.

$$.3_{ten} = .010011001 \ldots_{two}$$

No computer can store this entire infinite repeating decimal. It must be "chopped off" after a certain number of digits.

Secondly, computers can only add. All other operations must be reduced to an addition process or a process of finding a tabular value. Thus the square root of 4, when calculated in base two by a complicated process and reconverted to base ten, may not turn out to be *exactly* two. Then the test in the IF clause of line 40 will yield "NO", the computer will not branch to line 100, and the program will go on to produce erroneous results.

What can be done to avoid this error?

The square root of 4 may not be calculated as precisely   2   but it will be close, say, 1.99999999. It will lie within a certain *tolerance* or margin of error of the true result. Instead of demanding exact equality, the programmer should test to see if the two quantities, SQR(D) and X/Y in the example above, lie within a specified tolerance of each other. Line 40 can be rewritten as the following.

40 IF ABS(SQR(D) - X/Y) < .00001 THEN 100

The tolerance is .00001. The test now is whether SQR(D) and X/Y are within .00001 of each other. The assumption is that if they are that close, the difference is probably due to roundoff or conversion to and from the binary system.

In algebraic notation the test is written as follows.

$$|\sqrt{D} - X/Y| < .00001 \ ?$$

The absolute value sign is needed because it is not known whether $\sqrt{D}$ will be slightly larger or slightly smaller than X/Y. If it is slightly larger, $\sqrt{D} - X/Y$ is positive; if it is smaller, $\sqrt{D} - X/Y$ is negative. But in either case as long as $\sqrt{D}$ lies within .00001 of X/Y, we want to assume equality and branch to 100.

Not all decisions of equality need be complicated by considerations of tolerance. For example, if a program begins like this,

10 READ X
20 IF X = 0 THEN 100
. . .

there is no need to revise line 20. X is being read from DATA and is not the result of a computation. Testing X for exact equality to 0 should cause no problem and the program should operate as expected.

Similarly, if all values are integers and only the four operations of addition, subtraction, multiplication, and division are used, the program should proceed as in a pencil-and-paper trace. For example, if A and B are integers, a decision such as   20 IF A − B = B THEN 100   should cause no problem, and no tolerance is needed. But
20 IF A ↑ (1/3) = B THEN 100   probably requires a tolerance.

The size of the tolerance is determined by several factors and no general rule can be given. The tolerance depends on the number of digits and method of computation used by the computer in question. If a program is not executing as planned because expected equality is not occurring, you should experiment with different tolerances until desired results are obtained.

EXERCISES 3-8

A   Rewrite each statement to introduce the tolerance specified.

Example 1: 50 IF X = Y/3 THEN 80   ;   .0005
Answer: 50 IF ABS(X - Y/3) < .0005 THEN 80

Example 2: 20 IF M <> SQR(K + 1) THEN 50   ;   .001
Answer: 20 IF ABS(M - SQR(K + 1)) >= .001 THEN 50

   1. 12 IF C/D = .5 THEN 90   ;   .0001
   2. 35 IF (2*N)↑(1/5) = P THEN 10   ;   .00001
   3. 25 IF R - S <> L/2 THEN 75   ;   .005
   4. 67 IF A↑2 + B↑2 = C↑2 THEN 110   ;   .00005

Write an IF . . . THEN statement that corresponds to each algebraic decision.
   5. If $|x - a| < .1$, then 100.
   6. If $|2r - s^2| > .01$, go to 80.
   7. If $|z| < .0005$, then go to 75.
   8. If $|x^2 - 2x + 1| < .005$, then go to 79.
   9. If $|m - \sqrt{p}| \leq .00001$, then 47.

Write BASIC statements that implement the flowchart portions shown below.

10.

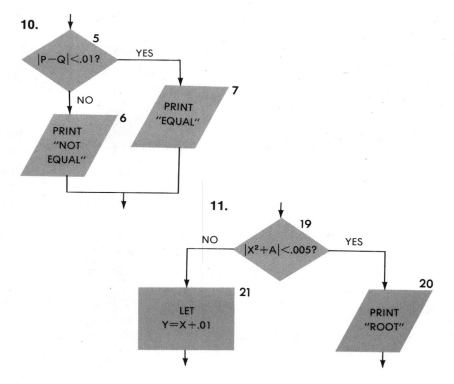

11.

CHAPTER REVIEW

Show the output from each program. Number the key print positions.

1.
```
10 READ X
20 IF X < O THEN 10
30 PRINT X,-X
40 GØ TØ 10
50 DATA 5,-2,0,.5
60 END
```

2.
```
5 READ R,S
10 PRINT R*S;R/S
15 GØ TØ 5
20 DATA 3,2,-8,4,0,6
25 END
```

3.
```
10 PRINT "PERIMETERS = ";
20 READ L,W
30 PRINT 2*L+2*W;
40 GØ TØ 20
50 DATA 4,3,10,5
60 END
```

4.
```
10 READ L,W
20 PRINT "P="2*L+2*W
25 PRINT
30 GØ TØ 10
40 DATA 4,3,10,5
50 END
```

Correct any errors in these programs.

5.
```
10 READ A,B
20 IF A > B THEN 50
30 IF A = B THEN 60
40 IF A < B THEN 70
50 PRINT A "GREATER"
60 PRINT "EQUAL"
70 PRINT B "GREATER"
80 GØ TØ 10
90 DATA 6,4,5,5,2,11
100 END
```

6.
```
5 PRINT "ØRDERED PAIR IS":
10 READ (X,Y)
20 IF X > Y THEN 50
30 PRINT "CLØSER TØ Y-AXIS"
40 GØ TØ 60
50 PRINT "CLØSER TØ X-AXIS"
60 GØ TØ 10
70 DATA 11,3,-4,-1,0,9
80 END
```

Which of the following are valid IF . . . THEN statements?

7. `10 IF X = Y ØR X = Z THEN 50`
8. `20 IF X = 9 THEN LET Q = 4`
9. `50 IF A/B >= C - 2 THEN 10`
10. `15 IF R*7 < S THEN GØ TØ 60`

11. Trace and flowchart the following program.

```
10 READ M
20 IF M↑2 > 50 THEN 50
30 PRINT "SQUARE <= 50"
40 GØ TØ 10
50 PRINT "SQUARE > 50"
60 GØ TØ 10
70 DATA 5,10,7
80 END
```

12. Write a BASIC program to read real numbers A and B. If B ≠ 0, print A/B. If B = 0, print "QUØTIENT UNDEFINED."

ROUND THREE: *PROGRAMS FOR STUDENT ASSIGNMENT*

GENERAL INSTRUCTIONS:

1. In each exercise on pages 92 through 99, write a program that will do what is specified in the exercise.

2. If the program has several possible outcomes, the DATA must produce each outcome at least once.

3. Regardless of the possible outcomes, the program must process at least three sets of DATA.

4. Label output with appropriate messages or headings.

5. If your teacher requires it, submit a flowchart.

ALGEBRA ONE

1. Read nonzero real numbers A, B, C, and D. Are these numbers proportional in the order given? That is, does $\frac{A}{B} = \frac{C}{D}$?

2. Find the slope of the line through two given points in the coordinate plane. Include the possibility that the slope may be undefined. (See Ex. 2, p. 27.)

3. Input two real numbers. Without actually multiplying the numbers, determine whether their product is positive, negative, or zero. (See Ex. 3, p. 27.)

4. Given a positive real number, compute its square root by using the SQR function, the .5 power, and the 1/2 power. Print the output in four labeled columns.

    NUMBER   SQR   .5 PØWER   1/2 PØWER

5. Read the coordinates of a point in the *xy*-plane. Decide the number of the quadrant in which the point lies or, if it lies on an axis, decide whether it lies on the *x*-axis, on the *y*-axis, or on both. (See Ex. 5, p. 27.)

Use a variety of values for A and B to test the truth of the following.

6. $|A + B| = |A| + |B|$ **7.** $|A \cdot B| = |A| \cdot |B|$ **8.** $|A - B| = |B - A|$

In Exercises 9 through 12 read rational numbers A, B, and C, which are the coefficients of a linear equation of the form AX + BY = C. (Assume that A and B are not both zero.) (See Ex. 8 through 11, p. 28.)

9. Compute and print the slope of the graph of the equation. Remember that the slope may be undefined.

10. Print the x-intercept of the graph as an ordered pair.

11. Print the y-intercept of the graph as an ordered pair.

12. Input real numbers R and S. Decide whether the point (R, S) lies on the graph of Ax + By = C.

13. Input a real number x. Print x, its additive inverse, and (if it has one) its multiplicative inverse. (See Ex. 12, p. 28.)

14. Read real numbers A and B. Without computing A + B, decide whether the sum of A and B is positive, negative, or zero. (See Ex. 13, p. 28.)

15. Four dice are rolled. Accept the four numbers which appear on the top faces of the dice and decide whether 0, 2, 3, or 4 of the dice show the same value, or whether two show one value and the other pair show another value.

16. Given five real numbers, print only the smallest. Do not assume that the numbers are listed in the DATA in any special order. You may assume that no two of the numbers are equal. (See Ex. 7, p. 27.)

17. Assume that a baby-sitter works for a rate of 50 cents per hour until 11 P.M. and 75 cents per hour thereafter. Given the time he or she begins and the time he or she ends, compute the fee for an evening's work. (Hint: Input the times using the twenty-four hour clock; e.g., for 7 P.M. input 1900.) (See Ex. 16, p. 28.)

18. Arrange a set of three numbers in descending order. For example, for the data values 8, 11, −3, print 11 8 −3 . Two or three of the numbers may be equal. (See Ex. 17, p. 28.)

19. Given a linear equation Ax + B = C, solve for x. For example, if the equation is $7x + 5 = 19$, print $x = 2$. A, B, and C are real numbers. Do *not* assume that A ≠ 0. (See Ex. 18, p. 28.)

20. Given an inequality Ax + B > C (A, B, C real numbers), solve for x. For example, if the inequality is $7x + 5 > 19$, print $x > 2$. (See Ex. 19, p. 28.)

21. Input the sales and expenses of the Acme Trucking Company for the past year. Calculate the profit as sales minus expenses. Then compute the tax by the following rule.

If 0 < profit ≤ $20,000, the tax is 30% of the profit;

if profit > $20,000, the tax is 30% of the $20,000 plus 50% of the profit above $20,000;

if profit ≤ 0, the tax is zero.

Print the profit, net tax, and the ratio of the tax to the profit.

GEOMETRY

22. Read three positive numbers. Determine whether these could represent the lengths of the sides of a triangle. (See Ex. 19, p. 11.)

23. Given an angle measure greater than 0 and less than 180, classify the angle as ACUTE, RIGHT, or OBTUSE. (See Ex. 22, p. 28.)

24. Given the lengths of any two sides of a right triangle, the Pythagorean Theorem enables you to compute the third side. Design a program which finds the length of the missing side whether it is a leg or the hypotenuse. One way to accomplish this is to READ A, B, C but enter 0 for the unknown side. Then test if $A = 0$, $B = 0$, or $C = 0$ and branch to one of three assignment steps to compute the missing length and print it. (See Ex. 23, p. 29.)

25. Given the radius of a circle, compute the area by using $3\frac{1}{7}$ for pi and 3.1416 for pi. Find the difference each time. Print the output in three labeled columns.

26. Determine the number of points of intersection of a circle with center at (x_1, y_1) and radius r_1 with the circle with center (x_2, y_2) and radius r_2. Assume that neither circle lies in the interior of the other.

27. Given the coordinates of four points in the xy-plane, determine whether the quadrilateral formed by joining the points in order is equilateral.

28. Read three positive numbers A, B, and C. Determine whether these could be the lengths of the sides of a right triangle. (Note: You must first check that A, B, and C can be sides of *any* triangle.) (See Ex. 29, p. 29.)

29. Given the lengths of the sides of a triangle, determine whether the triangle is EQUILATERAL, ISOSCELES, or SCALENE. (See Ex. 20, p. 11.)

30. Given the coordinates of four points in the xy-plane, determine whether the quadrilateral formed by joining the points in order is a parallelogram. (See Ex. 43, p. 30.)

Read the lengths of three sides of a triangle and the lengths of the three corresponding sides of a second triangle. Solve the following problems. (See Ex. 39 and 40, p. 30.)

31. Are the triangles congruent?

32. Are the triangles similar?

33. Read the lengths of the four sides of a quadrilateral. Decide whether the quadrilateral is equilateral. (See Ex. 41, p. 30.)

34. Read the lengths of the five sides of a pentagon. Decide whether the pentagon is equilateral. (See Ex. 42, p. 30.)

35. Given the coordinates of three points in the *xy*-plane, determine whether the points are collinear. (See Ex. 35, p. 29.)

36. In Exercise 35, if the points are not collinear, decide whether the triangle formed by joining them is ISOSCELES, EQUILATERAL, or SCALENE. (See Ex. 36, p. 29.)

37. In Exercise 35, if the points are not collinear, print the perimeter of the triangle formed by joining them. (See Ex. 37, p. 29.)

38. In Exercise 35, if the points are not collinear, compute the area of the triangle formed by joining them. (See Ex. 28, p. 26).

39. Determine if a given point (x_1, y_1) lies within, on, or outside a circle with center (x_2, y_2) and radius r. (If you have not done so already, read Lesson 3-8: "Difficulty of Determining Exact Equality" on pages 88 through 90.)

40. Given two positive real numbers X and Y, print X, Y, their arithmetic mean, their geometric mean, and which of the two means is larger. Run the program for at least ten X-Y pairs.

41. Given the coordinates of the vertices of quadrilateral ABCD in the *xy*-plane, what kind of quadrilateral is formed when the midpoints of the sides of ABCD are joined?

ALGEBRA TWO

42. Given the coordinates of the center and the length of its radius, print the equation of a circle.

43. Given the coordinates of two points in the *xy*-plane, print the equation of the line through the two points. (See Ex. 55, p. 31.)

44. Given the coordinates of two points in the *xy*-plane, print the equation of the perpendicular bisector of the segment determined by the two points.

In Exercises 45 through 47 read real numbers A, B, and C, which are the coefficients of a quadratic equation $Ax^2 + Bx + C = 0$.

45. Decide whether the equation has zero, one, or two real roots. Do not actually compute the roots. (See Ex. 57, p. 31.)

46. If the equation has one or more real roots, compute and print the root(s). (See Ex. 59, p. 31.)

47. Input a proposed real root R and determine by substitution whether it is a root. (See Lesson 3-8 on pages 88 through 90.)

For the system of linear equations $\begin{cases} Ax + By = C \\ Dx + Ey = F, \end{cases}$ input the coefficients. Do Exercises 48 through 54. (See Ex. 60 through 65, p. 31.)

48. Determine whether the graphs of the equations are parallel. (Here "parallel to" means "having the same slope as" so that parallel lines might coincide.)

49. Determine whether the graphs of the equations are perpendicular.

50. Determine whether the graphs intersect. If they do, do they intersect in one point or in infinitely many points?

51. Determine whether the solution set of the system is the null (empty) set, a one-element set, or an infinite set.

52. If the solution set has one element, print it as an ordered pair.

53. Determine whether the equations are consistent or inconsistent.

54. Determine whether the equations are dependent or independent.

55. A quadratic polynomial can be written as $Ax^2 + Bx + C$ or as $A(x - K)^2 + H$. Given the first form, derive the second.

56. For the parabola defined by $y = Ax^2 + Bx + C$, read rational numbers A, B, and C and then print the coordinates of the vertex and whether the vertex is a MAXIMUM or MINIMUM point. (See Ex. 67, p. 31.)

57. Given the coordinates of a point in the xy-plane, decide whether the point lies in the solution set of the following system of inequalities.

$$2x - y < 3$$
$$x \le 3 - 3y$$
$$x > 0$$
$$y > 0$$

58. The equation of an ellipse with its center at the origin is $\dfrac{x^2}{A^2} + \dfrac{y^2}{B^2} = 1$.

Read A and B (neither is zero) and print the coordinates of the foci of the ellipse. Remember that the foci sometimes are on the x-axis and sometimes are on the y-axis. (See Ex. 72, p. 32.)

59. Solve absolute value equations of the form $|x - A| = B$ (A and B real). (See Ex. 73, p. 32.)

60. Read a real number x. Print the cube root of x. Then, if x is non-negative, print the principal fourth root of x. If x is negative, print NØ REAL FØURTH RØØT   . (See Ex. 74, p. 32.)

61. Given two integers which are the roots of a quadratic equation, print the equation in the form $Ax^2 + Bx + C = 0$.

62. Let a function f be defined by $f(x) = 3x + 4$ and let g be defined by $g(x) = x^2 - 7$. Use a variety of values for x and decide in each case whether $f(g(x)) = g(f(x))$. (See Ex. 78, p. 32.)

Accept the ordered pairs of three noncollinear points in the xy-plane. For the triangle formed by joining these points, solve the following problems.

63. Print the equations of the lines that contain the three medians.

64. Print the equations of the lines that contain the altitudes.

65. Print the equations of the lines that contain the perpendicular-bisectors of the sides.

66. Compute the coordinates of the center of the circumscribed circle.

67. Compute the length of the radius of the circumscribed circle.

ADVANCED MATHEMATICS

In Exercises 68 through 71 consider a complex number $A + Bi$ and input A and B.

68. Print the conjugate of $A + Bi$.

69. Print the reciprocal of $A + Bi$.

70. Print the square roots of $A + Bi$.

71. Print the polar form of $A + Bi$.

72. Given the coordinates of a point in the xy-plane, compute the trigonometric functions of the angle in standard position having that point on its terminal side. Assume that the point is not the origin but allow the possibility that the point may lie on an axis.

73. Given a 2×2 matrix, print its multiplicative inverse (if it has one).

74. Input the coefficients of a quadratic equation $Ax^2 + Bx + C = 0$ (A, B, and C rational with $A \neq 0$) and a proposed root $D + Ei$. Check by substitution whether $D + Ei$ is a root.

Given complex numbers $A + Bi$ and $C + Di$, print the following in standard form.

75. their sum

76. their product

77. the quotient (if it exists) of $A + Bi$ divided by $C + Di$

78. Given the coordinates of a point in the Cartesian plane, convert to polar coordinates.

79. Given the polar coordinates of a point, convert to Cartesian coordinates.

80. Given the Cartesian coordinates of a point in three-dimensional space, print the spherical coordinates of the point.

81. Given the equation $Ax^2 + Bxy + Cy^2 + Dx + Ey + F = 0$ (all coefficients rational), determine whether the graph of the equation is a circle, parabola, ellipse, hyperbola, two lines, one line, a point, or the empty set.

82. Use the Euclidean Algorithm to find the greatest common divisor of two positive integers.

The components of two two-dimensional vectors $\vec{u}$ and $\vec{v}$ are given. Solve the following problems.

83. Determine whether $\vec{u}$ and $\vec{v}$ are perpendicular. (See Ex. 91, p. 33.)

84. Determine whether they are parallel. (See Ex. 92, p. 33.)

85. Decide whether they satisfy the Triangle Inequality $|\vec{u} + \vec{v}| \le |\vec{u}| + |\vec{v}|$, where $|\vec{u}|$ represents the norm of vector $\vec{u}$.

86. Given a linear equation $Ax + By = C$ (A, B, and C rational), convert it to polar form.

87. Given a real number (positive, negative, or zero), print its square roots (that is, include imaginary roots). (See Ex. 80, p. 32.)

88. Given sin x, compute and print: (**a**) cos x; (**b**) tan x; (**c**) cot x; (**d**) sec x; (**e**) csc x. Remember that tan, cot, sec, or csc may be undefined. Do not use any of the BASIC trigonometric functions available on your system. (See Ex. 95, p. 33.)

Solve for the remaining parts of a right triangle, given the following combinations of data.

89. HL (hypotenuse-leg)   **90.** HA (hypotenuse-acute angle)

91. LA (leg-acute angle)   **92.** LL (leg-leg)

Input the components of two three-dimensional vectors $\vec{v}$ and $\vec{w}$. Do Exercises 93 through 96.

93. Decide whether the vectors are perpendicular.

94. Decide whether the vectors are parallel.

95. If neither of the vectors is the zero vector, compute the cosine of the angle between vectors using this formula: $\cos A = \dfrac{\vec{v} \cdot \vec{w}}{|\vec{v}| \cdot |\vec{w}|}$

where $0 \leq A \leq \pi$, $|\vec{v}|$ represents the norm of vector $\vec{v}$, and $\vec{v} \cdot \vec{w}$ represents the inner product ("dot" product) of $\vec{v}$ and $\vec{w}$.

96. Compute the direction cosines of $\vec{v}$ and of $\vec{w}$.

97. Given a complex number in polar form, convert it to standard form.

For a nonright triangle, given the right combination of three of the parts of the triangle, it is possible to "solve" the triangle, that is, to find the remaining three parts (side and angles). Solve nonright triangles, given the following combinations of data.

98. ASA **99.** SAA **100.** SSS **101.** SAS

102. SSA (This is the so-called "ambiguous case.")

103. Solve cubic equations using a formula similar to the Quadratic Formula.

104. Given the degree measure of an angle and its sine and the degree measure of another angle and its sine, interpolate to find the sine of a desired angle between the first two.

105. Given three consecutive terms of a sequence of real numbers, decide whether the sequence is arithmetic, geometric, or neither. (See Ex. 101, p. 33.)

106. Compute square roots of positive integers using Newton's Method, which consists of an alternation of dividing and averaging. Stop when the estimate squared is within .001 of the given number.

Given a scalar R and the components of two-dimensional vectors $\vec{v}$ and $\vec{t}$, decide for each set of data whether the following properties of scalar multiplication hold.

107. Commutative Property: $R\vec{v} = \vec{v}R$

108. Distributive Properties: $R(\vec{v} + \vec{t}) = R\vec{v} + R\vec{t}$ and $(\vec{v} + \vec{t})R = \vec{v}R + \vec{t}R$

109. Norm property: $|R\vec{v}| = |R| \cdot |\vec{v}|$

110. Find the roots of *any* quadratic equation with rational coefficients. Solve over C, the field of complex numbers.

LOOPS

4-1 COUNTING

How can we program a computer to count? Accomplishing this task will open the door to numerous programs in widespread use. To start with a simple example, suppose we want the computer to count from one to ten, that is, to print 1, 2, 3, 4, 5, 6, 7, 8, 9, 10.

In an earlier chapter we used the word *algorithm*. An **algorithm** is a set of steps for performing a task, usually a repetitive task. You have learned many algorithms. Every time you perform long division you use an algorithm. You have developed your own algorithm for traveling to school each morning. BASIC, like FORTRAN, is called an "algorithmic" programming language because it was created with problem-solving in mind.

When confronted with a problem, the programmer's first job is to create an algorithm to accomplish the task. To guide his thinking he may want to state the steps in words. For example, our count-to-ten problem could be handled by this algorithm.

1. Start I at zero.
2. Add one to I.
3. Print I.
4. Is I < 10? If it is, go back to step 2.
   If it is not, go to step 5.
5. End.

Flowchart 4-1

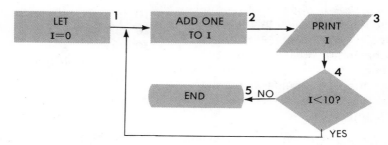

The flowchart shows that this algorithm contains a three-step *loop*, that is, a set of steps that is performed many times (ten in this case).

The only step of the program that involves a new idea is step 2: "Add one to I." We will need a LET statement to accomplish this. We add one to I by writing this statement.

$$20 \ \text{LET} \ I = I + 1$$

This is not an algebraic equation. If it were, it would have no solution. It is a LET statement in a BASIC program and it must be interpreted the way the computer will interpret it.

In handling a LET statement

1. The machine starts with the expression to the *right* of the equal sign.
2. Using the current values of any variables in this expression, it evaluates the formula according to the rules discussed in Lesson 2-5 on page 48. The right side is thus reduced to a single value.
3. The computer now examines the left side of the equality to find what name (that is, what memory location) the programmer wishes to assign to the value computed from the right-hand formula.

Let us apply this procedure to our key line   20 LET I = I + 1

1. The computer starts with "I + 1."
2. It adds the current value of I (which has been set to zero by step 1) to 1, getting 1 as the answer.
3. It stores this 1 as the *new* value of I.

Thus the effect of line 20 was to change location I from 0 to 1. The next time the statement is executed, I changes from 1 to 2, then from 2 to 3, and so on. The program is working because the location "I" in memory is serving as a *counter*. Because of the statement "I = I + 1," the computer is counting. The program itself can now be written.

In Program 4-1 at the right, line 10 is not needed. Most BASIC compilers start all variables at zero automatically. Also, the semicolon is optional in line 30. It saves space by printing 1 to 10 on a single line rather than one numeral per line.

Program 4-1

```
10 LET I = O
20 LET I = I + 1
30 PRINT I;
40 IF I < 10 THEN 20
50 END
```

EXERCISES 4-1

A   Write *Yes* or *No* to show whether each of the following is a valid LET statement.

1. 20 LET S = 2*S
3. 50 LET S = S + K

2. 10 LET I + 2 = I
4. 90 LET K = K + 4*(T-2)

If, entering line 20, I = 5, what value is assigned to I by each LET statement?

5. 20 LET I = I + 5
7. 20 LET I = I - 1

6. 20 LET I = 3*I
8. 20 LET I = I * I

Write programs for Exercises 9 through 12. In each exercise have your program resemble Program 4-1 except in one line.
  9. Count by 2's from 2 to 10.   **10.** Count from 1 to 20.
11. Count from 1 to 10, printing each numeral on a separate line.
12. Count from 4 to 10.

13. Write a BASIC program to count backwards from 10 to 1.
14. A costly error has been made in the following program. What will be the output (if any)?

```
20 LET I = O
30 LET I = I + 1
40 PRINT I;
50 IF I < 10 THEN 20
60 END
```

(In connection with this exercise, it is appropriate to point out that on many time-sharing systems, striking the 'ESC' (escape) key or the 's' key pulls the computer out of a program that is giving erroneous results.)

B   For each program: **(a)** trace; **(b)** flowchart.

15.
```
10 LET N = 6
20 PRINT N;
30 LET N = N - 1
40 IF N >= 1 THEN 20
50 END
```

16. 10 LET N = 6
     20 IF N < 1 THEN 99
     30 PRINT N;
     40 LET N = N - 1
     50 GØ TØ 20
     99 END

For each flowchart: (**a**) trace; (**b**) write a program.

17. DATA: none needed

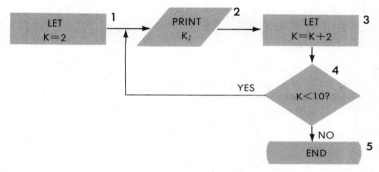

18. DATA: 3, 10, 8, 5

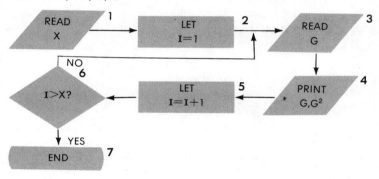

C   19. DATA: none needed

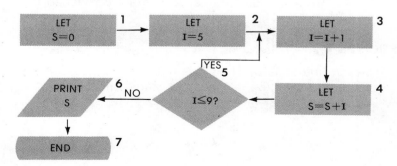

4-2 SUMMATIONS

Example:

A triangular brick wall is to be built with one brick on the top row, two bricks on the second row, three on the third, etc., for 100 rows. How many bricks are needed?

A mathematical model for this problem is: Add the whole numbers from 1 to 100. The algorithm builds on the work of the last lesson. We must count 1 to 100, adding these numbers as we go. Our algorithm can be stated this way.

> **1.** Start I at 0.   *(I will count from 1 to 100.)*
> **2.** Start s at 0.   *(s will accumulate the sum.)*
> **3.** Add one to I.
> **4.** Add I to s.
> **5.** Has I reached 100? If not, go to 3. If it has, go to 6.
> **6.** Print s.
> **7.** End.

Recalling that BASIC handles steps 1 and 2 for us, we write the following program. (We will continue to state steps 1 and 2 in the algorithm because they are a logical part of the solution and some compilers do not handle these steps.)

Program 4-2

```
10 LET I = I + 1
20 LET S = S + I
30 IF I < 100 THEN 10
40 PRINT S
50 END
```

Notice that in this program, unlike the counting program of the previous lesson, the PRINT statement is outside the loop. We do not print s until the total sum has accumulated, that is, until I has reached 100.

EXERCISES 4-2

A   If, when line 30 is reached in a program, $s = 10$ and $I = 4$, what value is assigned to s by each LET statement?

> **1.** 30 LET S = S - I
> **2.** 30 LET S = I↑2 + S
> **3.** 30 LET S = S + .05*S
> **4.** 30 LET S = S + I * S

Write programs for Exercises 5 through 8. In each exercise write your program so that it resembles Program 4-2.
5. Add the even whole numbers 2 to 100.
6. Add the whole numbers from 1 to 200.
7. Add the whole numbers from 4 to 10.
8. Add the whole numbers from 1 to 100, printing each sum (1, 3, 6, 10, 15, etc.).

B Discuss the output of each program below.

9.
```
10 LET I = I + 1
20 LET S = S + I
30 IF I < 100 THEN 20
40 PRINT S
50 END
```

10.
```
10 LET I = I + 1
20 LET S = S + 1
30 IF I < 100 THEN 10
40 PRINT S
50 END
```

11.
```
10 LET I = 1
20 LET S = S + I
30 LET I = I + 1
40 IF I <= 100 THEN 20
50 PRINT S
60 END
```

12.
```
10 LET I = 1
20 LET S = S + I
30 LET I = I + 1
40 IF I <= 100 THEN 10
50 PRINT S
60 END
```

13. Prepare a flowchart for Program 4-2 on page 104.
14. Trace and flowchart the program at the right.
```
10 LET I = 0
20 READ L,W
30 LET A = L * W
40 PRINT A
50 LET I = I + 1
60 IF I < 4 THEN 20
70 DATA 1,2,8,10,6,4,5,5
80 END
```

Discuss the result of replacing line 30 in Program 4-2 with each of these steps.
15. 30 IF I <= 100 THEN 10
16. 30 IF I <= 99 THEN 10
17. 30 IF I < 101 THEN 10
18. 30 IF I < 99 THEN 10

For the flowchart: (a) trace; (b) write a program.
19. DATA: none needed

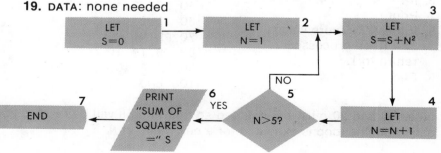

For the flowchart: (**a**) trace; (**b**) write a program.

20. DATA: 5

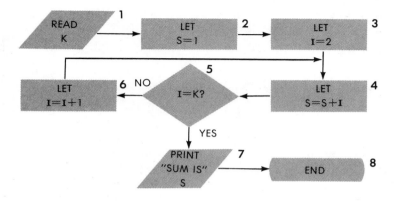

4-3 VARIABLE LOOPS

Thus far in the lessons and exercises we have written one program to add from 1 to 100, another to add from 1 to 200, another to add 4 to 10, and so on. Is it possible to write one flexible program that will handle all such problems? Yes, it is, and in this lesson we develop such a program in stages. At the left below is an algorithm for adding from 1 to N, where N is read from a DATA statement each time we execute the program. The program appears at the right below.

1. Start I at 0.
2. Start s at 0.
3. Read N.
4. Add 1 to I.
5. Add I to s.
6. If $I < N$, go to 4.
7. Print s.
8. If there are more values of N to be processed, return to 1.
9. End.

Program 4-3

```
10 LET I = O
20 LET S = O
30 READ N
40 LET I = I + 1
50 LET S = S + I
60 IF I < N THEN 40
70 PRINT S
80 GØ TØ 10
90 DATA 100,200,50
100 END
```

Lines 10 and 20 must be included so that I and s will be reset to zero each time the loop is executed for a new value of N.

The next logical extension of the algorithm is to vary the initial value of the summation, that is, to add the whole numbers from J to N, where J and N are made explicit in a DATA statement. See Program 4-4 at the right.

The final stage of generalizing the program is to vary the step between values. For example, add the *even* whole numbers 2 to 100. See Exercise 4 below.

Program 4-4

```
10 READ J,N
20 LET I = J
30 LET S = J
40 LET I = I + 1
50 LET S = S + I
60 IF I < N THEN 40
70 PRINT S
80 GØ TØ 10
90 DATA 1,100,1,200,50,150
100 END
```

EXERCISES 4-3

A Discuss the output of the following programs. Change each program so that correct output can be obtained.

1.
```
10 READ N
20 LET I = I + 1
30 LET S = S + I
40 IF I < N THEN 20
50 PRINT S
60 GØ TØ 10
70 DATA 100,50
80 END
```

2.
```
10 READ J,N
20 LET I = J
30 LET S = 0
40 LET I = I + 1
50 LET S = S + I
60 IF I < N THEN 30
70 PRINT S
80 GØ TØ 10
90 DATA 1, 100, 50, 150
100 END
```

3. Is the program at the right equivalent to Program 4-4? Trace until you can decide if the output is the same.

```
10 READ J,N
20 LET I = J
30 LET S = 0
40 LET S = S + I
50 LET I = I + 1
60 IF I <= N THEN 40
70 PRINT S
80 GØ TØ 10
90 DATA 1,100,1,200,50,150
100 END
```

B **4.** Write a program to add the whole numbers from a variable initial value to a variable final value, with a variable step between numbers.

5. Prepare a flowchart for Program 4-3.

6. Write the algorithm and prepare a flowchart for Program 4-4.

4-4 ANATOMY OF A LOOP (Optional)

Figure 4-1:
Components of
a Loop

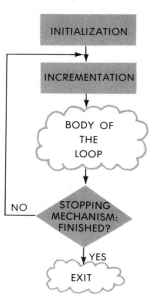

Loops are the heart of programming and deserve careful study. The diagram at the right illustrates the essential components of any loop.

While these components may occur in a different order from the one shown, they must all be present in a loop. Initialization is always first but the other phases can occur in any order.

Here is an explanation of each component.

INITIALIZATION: One or more statements that assign to one or more variables their starting values entering the loop. Initialization can be accomplished by READ or LET statements.

Examples:

```
10 READ A,B     5 LET I = 0     20 LET J = K
   50 LET L = K + 1     35 LET D = SQR(N)
```

INCREMENTATION: One or more LET statements that increase or decrease the values of one or more variables involved in the loop.

Examples:

```
20 LET I = I + 1     40 LET J = J - 5     80 LET K = 2*K
```

BODY OF THE LOOP: The statement or set of statements that accomplishes the objective(s) of the loop; for example finding the average of a set of numbers, finding the largest value, or computing the weekly pay of each employee of a company. A typical loop may include READ, LET, and PRINT statements.

STOPPING MECHANISM: A decision step that determines whether the loop is finished or should continue at least one more time.

Examples:

```
50 IF J = 10 THEN 60      40 IF I < 100 THEN 10
50 IF K > L THEN 20       35 IF M <> 50 THEN 100
```

EXIT: EXIT does not necessarily mean END. When a loop is completed, the computer exits to the first step after the loop that can be executed. This may or may not be the END statement. Often a large segment of the program follows a loop.

To make sense out of the diagram on page 108 and the explanation, let us identify these components as they occur in Programs 4-1 and 4-3.

Program 4-1

```
10 LET I = 0 ←——————————————— INITIALIZATION
20 LET I = I + 1 ←————————————— INCREMENTATION
30 PRINT I; ←—————————————————— BODY OF THE LOOP
40 IF I < 10 THEN 20 ←————————— STOPPING MECHANISM
50 END ←——————————————————————— EXIT
```

Program 4-3

```
10 LET I = 0 ⎤
20 LET S = 0 ⎬ ←——————————————— INITIALIZATION
30 READ N    ⎦
40 LET I = I + 1 ←————————————— INCREMENTATION
50 LET S = S + I ←————————————— BODY OF THE LOOP
60 IF I < N THEN 40 ←—————————— STOPPING MECHANISM
70 PRINT S ←——————————————————— EXIT
80 GØ TØ 10 ←————————— This statement creates a simple "outer
90 DATA 100, 200, 50        loop" that restarts the program for a new
100 END                     value of N; the stopping mechanism for
                            this outer loop is BASIC's built-in ØUT ØF
                            DATA? test.
```

In both these programs the components occur in the order shown in Figure 4-1 on page 108, and the body of the loop consists of just one statement. To illustrate a different configuration of the stages and a larger body of the loop, consider the following program.

Program 4-5 (See Ex. 14, p. 105.)

```
10 LET I = 0 ◄─────────────────── INITIALIZATION
20 READ L,W ⎫
30 LET A = L * W ⎬ ◄──────────── BODY OF THE LOOP
40 PRINT A ⎭
50 LET I = I + 1 ◄─────────────── INCREMENTATION
60 IF I < 4 THEN 20 ◄──────────── STOPPING MECHANISM
70 DATA 1,2,8,10,6,4,5,5
80 END ◄───────────────────────── EXIT
```

The body of the loop, three statements, comes before incrementation. The loop of the program serves merely to process a predetermined number of DATA sets, four in this case.

Strange as it may seem the stopping mechanism could even come before the body of the loop. Consider this revised version of Program 4-1.

Program 4-1A

```
10 LET I = 0 ◄─────────────────── INITIALIZATION
20 LET I = I + 1 ◄─────────────── INCREMENTATION
30 IF I > 10 THEN 60 ◄─────────── STOPPING MECHANISM
40 PRINT I; ⎫
50 GØ TØ 20 ⎭ ◄────────────────── BODY OF THE LOOP
60 END ◄───────────────────────── EXIT
```

Trace Program 4-1A until you are convinced that it executes in the same manner as Program 4-1 on page 102. It has an additional statement but the point is that a loop in a particular configuration can be recast into a different one.

Loops occur so frequently in algorithm design that it is convenient to introduce a new flowchart symbol, the *iteration box*. ("Iteration" means "repetition.")

Example: Count from 5 to 8.   *Flowchart 4-2*

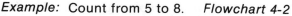

Note: to save space "LET" is omitted from compartments Ⓐ and Ⓒ.

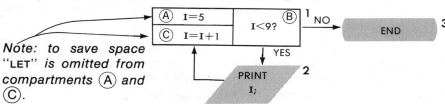

The iteration box is understood to have its own inner flow from compartment to compartment.

Figure 4-2: Flow within the iteration box
Enter here to start the loop

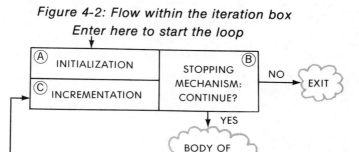

Begin the loop by entering compartment (A) and initializing the variable (I in Flowchart 4-2 on page 110) which is called the *index* of the loop. Compartment (A) will be entered only once during execution of the loop. Now jump to compartment (B) and apply the test. At this point the YES outlet will undoubtedly be followed and the body of the loop executed. Return to compartment (C) and increment the index. Then move to (B) and apply the stopping mechanism. Continue this procedure until the test yields a NO result and the loop is satisfied.

A diagram of the sequence looks like this.

Figure 4-3: Order of steps in execution of the Iteration Box

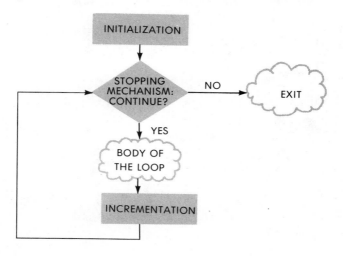

A trace of Flowchart 4-2 on page 110 is now shown.

Table 4-1 Trace of Flowchart 4-2

Step Number	Box Number	Value of Variable I	Test	Yes or No?	Output
1	1A	5			
2	1B		5 < 9?	Yes	
3	2				5
4	1C	6			
5	1B		6 < 9?	Yes	
6	2				6
7	1C	7			
8	1B		7 < 9?	Yes	
9	2				7
10	1C	8			
11	1B		8 < 9?	Yes	
12	2				8
13	1C	9			
14	1B		9 < 9?	No	
15	**END**				

In the second column of the trace, A, B, and C are used to distinguish which compartment of box 1 is entered at each step.

The iteration box is equivalent to two assignment boxes and one decision box. The following diagram of Flowchart 4-2 both with and without an iteration box illustrates this fact.

Flowchart 4-2   *Flowchart 4-2 without Iteration Box*

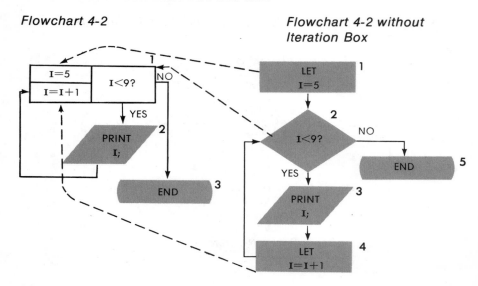

EXERCISES 4-4

A   **1.** In all possible configurations of a loop, what phase always comes first?

For each program of Exercises 2 through 5, (**a**) identify the components of each loop and name the index, (**b**) trace the program, (**c**) prepare a flowchart without using the iteration box, (**d**) prepare a flowchart using the iteration box, and (**e**) explain what the program does.

2.
```
10 LET I = 10
20 LET I = I + 10
30 PRINT I;
40 IF I < 50 THEN 20
50 END
```

3.
```
10 LET K = 10
20 IF K < 0 THEN 60
30 PRINT K;
40 LET K = K - 2
50 GØ TØ 20
60 END
```

4.
```
10 READ N
20 LET L = 1
30 PRINT L;
40 LET L = L + 1
50 IF L <= N THEN 30
60 GØ TØ 10
70 DATA 3,5
80 END
```

5.
```
5 LET S = 0
10 LET I = 1
20 READ L,W
30 LET P = 2*(L + W)
40 LET S = S + P
50 LET I = I + 1
60 IF I < 5 THEN 20
70 PRINT "SUM ØF P =" S
80 DATA 2,3,5,5,10,4,8,2
90 END
```

B   For each flowchart, (**a**) trace, and (**b**) write a BASIC program.

6. DATA: none needed

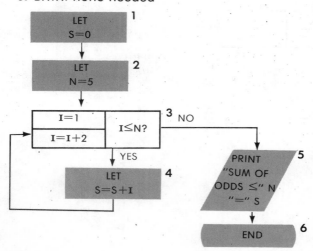

For each flowchart, (a) trace, and (b) write a BASIC program.

7. DATA: none needed

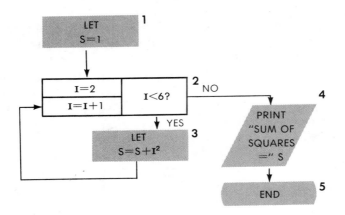

8. DATA: 0, 4, 11, 21

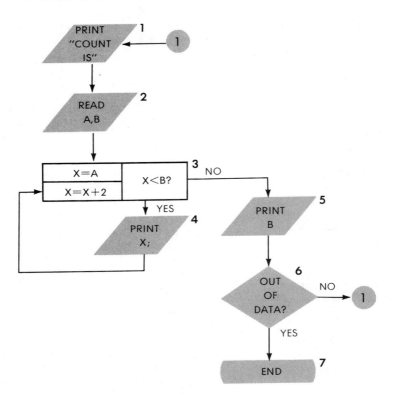

9. DATA: 4, 18, 15, 63, 12

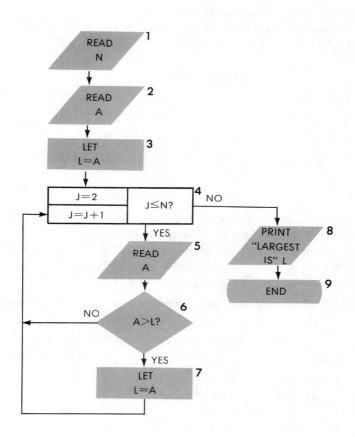

C **10.** DATA: none needed

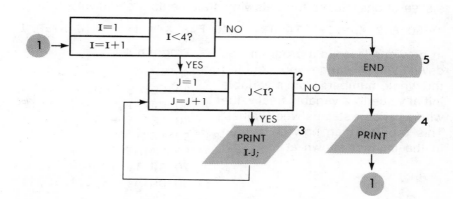

4-5 FØR-NEXT LOOPS

BASIC (like all algorithmic languages) provides an easy method for constructing loops: the FOR and NEXT statements. The two programs below are equivalent. (They each add the whole numbers from 4 to 200.)

Program 4-6

Version A	*Version B*
10 LET I = 4	10 FØR I = 4 TØ 200
20 LET S = S + I	20 LET S = S + I
30 LET I = I + 1	30 NEXT I
40 IF I < 200 THEN 20	40 PRINT S
50 PRINT S	50 END
60 END	

In version B, lines 10, 20, and 30 constitute a "FØR-NEXT loop." Such a loop may contain more than three statements but it must begin with a FØR statement and end with a NEXT statement. Furthermore the variable after the word FOR (I in Program 4-6) must match the variable after the word NEXT. The general form of the FØR statement is shown below.

FOR (variable) = (expression) TO (expression) STEP (expression)

INDEX   INITIAL VALUE of   FINAL VALUE of   INCREMENT (optional
        the index   the index   if the step is one)

Examples: 1. 25 FØR I = 0 TØ 100 STEP 2
            2. 80 FØR X = I+1 TØ J
            3. 90 FØR K1 = X/Y TØ Z↑2 STEP L+1
            4. 60 FØR J = 100 TØ 1 STEP -1

Example 1 would cause I to take on the successive values 0, 2, 4, 6, . . . , 96, 98, 100. If no STEP is listed, as in Example 2, the compiler assumes a STEP of one. Hence the following statements are equivalent.

     80 FØR X = I+1 TØ J   80 FØR X = I+1 TØ J STEP 1

In previous lessons a program was developed in which you counted the whole numbers from a variable initial value to a variable final value with a variable step between values. This program can now be written in the manner shown at the right.

Program 4-7

```
10 READ J,N,D
20 LET S = 0
30 FØR I = J TØ N STEP D
40 LET S = S + I
50 NEXT I
60 PRINT S
70 GØ TØ 10
80 DATA 1,5,1,1,10,2
90 END
```

The FØR-NEXT combination brackets the body of the loop and provides the initialization, incrementation, and stopping mechanism. In Program 4-6B, repeated at the left below, the index I is initialized at 4. Since $4 \leq 200$, the loop is executed. When NEXT I is encountered, I is incremented by the understood step of one. Since $5 \leq 200$, the loop is executed again. This sequence is repeated until I = 201. Since 201 > 200, this last value of I is discarded and the computer branches to the first statement after NEXT I that can be executed, that is, to 40 PRINT S

Program 4-6B

```
10 FØR I = 4 TØ 200
20 LET S = S + I
30 NEXT I
40 PRINT S
50 END
```

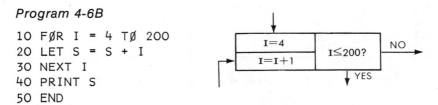

This sequence follows the order of events built into the iteration box shown at the right above. This is no fluke since the iteration box was designed in anticipation of FØR-NEXT loops of BASIC. However, there is no flowchart box corresponding to the FØR statement nor a box for NEXT. Instead the iteration box is used, as in this flowchart for Program 4-7 on page 116.

Flowchart 4-3

Program 4-7

```
10 READ J,N,D

20 LET S = 0

30 FØR I = J TØ N STEP D

40 LET S = S + I

50 NEXT I

60 PRINT S

70 GØ TØ 10

80 DATA 1,5,1,1,10,2

90 END
```

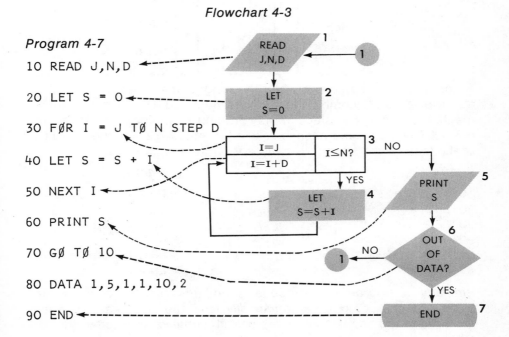

FØR-NEXT statements affect traces as is shown below.

Table 4-2 Portion of the trace of Program 4-7 for the first set of DATA (1,5,1)

Step Number	Statement Number	J	N	D	S	I	Test	Yes or No?	Output
1	10	1	5	1					
2	20				0				
3	30					1	1 ≤ 5?	Yes	
4	40					1			
5	50					2			
6	30						2 ≤ 5?	Yes	
7	40					3			

The first time FØR is executed, initialize I and test whether I ≤ N.

When NEXT I is reached, increment I.

Then on each succeeding FØR, test whether I ≤ N.

When the loop is satisfied, most compilers restore the index (I) to the last value that was actually used in the loop (5 here).

16	40				15				
17	50					6			
18	30						6 ≤ 5?	No	
19	60					5			15
20	70						OUT OF DATA?	No	

A common mistake occurs when the programmer does not realize all that the FØR-NEXT combination does for him and writes his own incrementation or decision steps in the FØR-NEXT loop. For example, in Program 4-8 line 30 is not needed and in fact interferes with the operation of the loop.   40 NEXT I   causes the I to be incremented.

Program 4-8

```
10 FØR I = 1 TØ 10
20 LET S = S + I
30 LET I = I + 1
40 NEXT I
50 PRINT "SUM = " S
60 END
```

NOT NEEDED!

Program 4-9

```
10 FØR I = 1 TØ 10
20 LET S = S + I
30 IF I > 10 THEN 50
40 NEXT I
50 PRINT "SUM = " S
60 END
```

Similarly in Program 4-9 line 30 is redundant. When executing a FØR-NEXT loop, the computer *automatically* tests the index each time it is incremented to see if it has gone past the final value listed in the FØR statement.

At the right is shown a revised version of Program 4-5 on page 110 using a FØR-NEXT loop. This program shows that the index need not even enter the calculations within the loop. I serves merely as a counter, clicking off the four times the programmer wants the loop executed.

Program 4-5A

```
10 FØR I = 1 TØ 4
20 READ L,W
30 LET A = L*W
40 PRINT A
50 NEXT I
60 DATA 1,2,8,10,6,4,5,5
70 END
```

Here are some miscellaneous points concerning FØR-NEXT loops.

1. If the STEP is negative, then the stopping mechanism is slightly different from the one discussed earlier. For example, the statement

$$10 \text{ FØR } I = 10 \text{ TØ } 0 \text{ STEP } -2$$

is equivalent to the iteration box shown at the right. The decision is $I \geq 0$. Compare this to loops with positive STEPs in which cases the decision is of the form $I \leq N$ (N the final value).

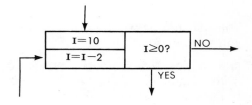

2. A good compiler tests the initial value of the index immediately to see if it is already outside the range of values intended for the loop. Some loops might be over before they start. For example, if $N = 3$, a loop beginning   20 FØR I = 2 TØ SQR(N)   should not be executed even once since $2 > \sqrt{3}$.

To test if your compiler follows this rule, run this program.

Test Program 1

```
10 READ N
20 FØR I = 2 TØ SQR(N)
30 PRINT I
40 NEXT I
50 PRINT "LØØP FINISHED FØR N = " N
60 GØ TØ 10
70 DATA 1,2,3,4
80 END
```

If the compiler operates as expected, the loop should not be executed at all for $N = 1$, 2, or 3 and should be executed once when $N = 4$.

If the compiler does not automatically test the initial value but rather blindly executes the loop once before applying the stopping mechanism, you may have to write steps to get around this defect.

3. As indicated in Table 4-2 on page 118 (step 19), good compilers re-turn the index to the last value for which the loop was actually executed when control transfers out of the loop to the first executable statement after NEXT. For example, if a loop begins   50 FØR J = 0 TØ 10 STEP 2 then the last time the loop is executed, J = 10. When J is incremented to 12, the loop is satisfied, since 12 > 10. Before continuing the pro-gram, most compilers restore the value 10 to J. To test how your com-piler operates, run this program.

Test Program 2

```
10 FØR I = 1 TØ 5
20 PRINT I;
30 NEXT I
40 PRINT
50 PRINT "ØUT ØF LØØP NØW; I = " I
60 END
```

The question is whether line 50 will print I = 5 or I = 6. In either case you have learned for later programs a useful fact about your compiler.

4. The index of the loop may not be changed in the body of the loop. If, for example, a loop begins   50 FØR I = 1 TO 10   , then each of the following statements is illegal in the body of the loop.

```
60 READ I               55 LET I = J + 1
70 READ A, B, I         95 LET I = I - 1
```

Each of these statements assigns a new value to I, thus contradicting the use of I as the index of the loop. I may be used on the right-side of "=" in an assignment statement or in a PRINT or IF . . . THEN statement because none of these uses changes its value. The index can legiti-mately be changed only when NEXT I is reached.

5. Do not use the index to the right of "=" in the FØR statement. Avoid statements such as the following.

```
15 FØR I = I TØ 10          30 FØR J = O TØ J
25 FØR D = 10 TØ 30 STEP D  50 FØR K = K/2 TØ 7
10 FØR M = 1 TØ 5*M         93 FØR A = 2 TØ 40 STEP A+1
```

Different compilers would react differently to these statements. Some would reject them immediately. Others would run the program but bog down during execution. For example, the problem with the statement 10 FØR M = 1 TO 5*M   is that the index, M, is constantly changing in value. Yet the stopping mechanism hinges on M. This loop would never end because as M increases (1,2,3,4, . . .), 5*M increases also (5,10,15, 20, . . .) and the test   M ≤ 5*M?   never yields a NO answer. The other statements listed above would cause similar problems.

EXERCISES 4-5

A   Give the NEXT statement that must appear in a program with each of these FØR statements. Choose any appropriate number for the NEXT statement.

   1. 50 FØR D = X TØ Z
   2. 20 FØR I = 15 TØ 50 STEP 5
   3. 110 FØR K = 1E6 TØ 1E7 STEP 1E2
   4. 35 FØR M1 = L1 TØ R*S STEP D

Correct any errors in the following programs.

   5. 10 IF I = 1 TØ 10
       20 LET Y = I↑2 + 3*I - 7
       30 PRINT Y
       40 NEXT Y
       50 END

   6. 10 READ M,N
       20 FØR J = M,N STEP 5
       30 LET S = S + J
       40 NEXT J
       50 PRINT S
       60 GØ TØ 10
       70 END

   7. 10 FØR I = 1 TØ 10
       20 LET Y = 4*I + 6
       30 PRINT Y;
       40 LET I = I + 1
       50 NEXT I
       60 END

   8. 10 READ N
       15 LET S = 0
       20 FØR I = 1 TØ N
       30 LET S = S + I
       40 IF I < N THEN 20
       50 NEXT I
       60 PRINT "SUM IS " S
       70 DATA 10,100,75
       80 END

Rewrite the program at the right using a FØR-NEXT loop so that the output is as follows.

   9. Vertical.   **10.** Horizontal.
     3   3 6 9 12 . . .
     6
     9
     .
     .

   10 LET N = 1
   20 IF N > 20 THEN 60
   30 PRINT 3*N
   40 LET N = N + 1
   50 GØ TØ 20
   60 END

Use a FØR-NEXT loop in rewriting each of these programs.

  11. 10 LET I = 0
       20 LET I = I + 1
       30 IF I > 5 THEN 60
       40 LET S = S + I
       50 GØ TØ 20
       60 PRINT "SUM IS " S
       70 END

  12. 10 LET J = 1
       20 PRINT J, J↑2, J↑3
       30 LET J = J + 1
       40 IF J <= 5 THEN 20
       50 END

B   **13.** For each revised program in Exercises 11 and 12, using a FØR-NEXT loop, flowchart the program and trace it.

For each iteration box, write a FØR statement and its NEXT companion.

Example: **Answer:** 10 FØR I = O TØ 10 STEP 2

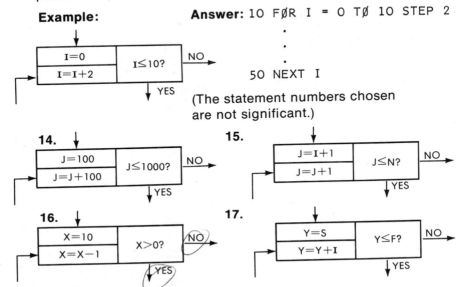

50 NEXT I

(The statement numbers chosen are not significant.)

Draw an iteration box corresponding to each FØR-NEXT combination.

18. 100 FØR L = 1 TØ 50   **19.** 50 FØR R = K TØ 1 STEP −2
     . . .   . . .

     200 NEXT L   80 NEXT R

20. 30 FØR D = 3 TØ SQR(P) STEP 2
     . . .

     100 NEXT D

21. 20 FØR J = X/Y TØ Z↑2 STEP D+2
     . . .

     80 NEXT J

Use a FØR-NEXT loop in writing these programs.

22. Add the odd whole numbers from 1 to 99.
23. Print the whole numbers from 1 to 1000.
24. Compute Y as a function of X according to the formula
     $Y = 16.7x + 9.2x^2 - 1.02x^3$ for x values from 1.0 to 2.0 in increments of .1. Print the output in two labeled columns.

Use an iteration box in flowcharting each of these programs.

25.
```
 5 PRINT "EVEN NUMBERS ARE:";
10 FØR J = 2 TØ 50 STEP 2
20 PRINT J;
30 NEXT J
40 END
```

26.
```
 5 LET S = 1000
10 READ N
20 FØR M = 1 TØ N
30 LET S = S + .05*S
40 NEXT M
50 PRINT "TØTAL AMØUNT AFTER"M" MØNTHS=" S
60 GØ TØ 5
70 DATA 12,24,36
80 END
```

Use a FØR-NEXT loop in programming each flowchart.

27.

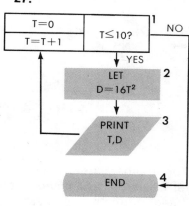

28.

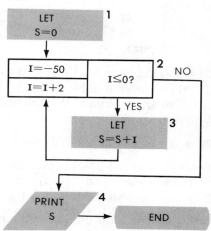

4-6 LOOPS CONTAINING DECISIONS

Example: Add all integers that are multiples of 3 from 1 to 50.

From previous lessons we realize that this program involves a loop. However, within the loop there must be a decision: Is the integer a multiple of 3? The algorithm can be written as at the right.

1. Start I at 0.
2. Start s at 0.
3. Add one to I.
4. Is I a multiple of 3?
   If it is not, go to step 6.
5. Add I to s.
6. I < 50? If so, go to step 3.
7. Print s.
8. End.

The flowchart of the algorithm on page 123 is shown at the right.

Steps 1 and 2 will be handled by the BASIC compiler. Steps 3 through 6 will form a loop.

Flowchart 4-4

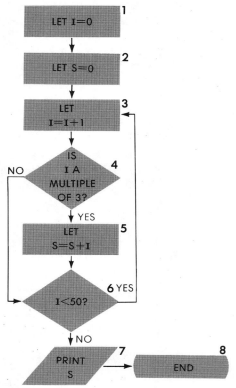

```
10 FØR I = 1 TØ 50
          ⋮
40 NEXT I
```

Adding I to S will be accomplished by the statement `30 LET S = S + I` . "PRINT S" and "END" pose no problems. So the program looks like this now.

```
10 FØR I = 1 TØ 50
20
30 LET S = S + I
40 NEXT I
50 PRINT S
60 END
```

Only the decision "Is I a multiple of 3?" (line 20) cannot be written from what we know already. We will need a statement of this form:

`20 IF (I not a multiple of 3) THEN 40.`

I is a multiple of 3 if it is *divisible* by 3 or, in other words, if 3 is a *factor* of I. To understand how the computer can be programmed to check this, we must stop and study the INT (integer) function of BASIC.

INT(X) means "the greatest integer less than or equal to X." In mathematics books this expression is usually written $[x]$. Here are examples.

INT(1.2) = 1	INT(0) = 0	INT(3.14159) = 3
INT(71) = 71	INT(−3.4) = −4	INT(−83) = −83

Applying this concept to the program at hand, we note that if I is a multiple of 3, then I/3 is an integer and hence INT(I/3) = I/3. Test this last statement for particular values of I.

12 is a multiple of 3.
INT(12/3) = 4 and 12/3 = 4.
Hence INT(I/3) = I/3.

31 is not a multiple of 3.
INT(31/3) = 10 but 31/3 = 10.33 . . .
Hence INT(I/3) ≠ I/3.

So asking if I is a multiple of 3 is the same as asking if INT(I/3) = I/3.

Our program can now be completed as follows.

Program 4-10

```
10 FØR I = 1 TØ 50
20 IF INT(I/3) <> I/3 THEN 40
30 LET S = S + I
40 NEXT I
50 PRINT S
60 END
```

Line 20 had to end "THEN 40" and not "THEN 10". Branching back to line 10 would start the loop over with $I = 1$; I would never reach 50 and the program would never end.

The following example illustrates an error to be avoided in programs involving loops.

```
10 FØR I = 1 TØ 10
20 READ X
30 IF X > 100 THEN 70
40 PRINT "LESS THAN ØNE HUNDRED"
50 NEXT I
60 GØ TØ 100
70 PRINT "GREATER THAN ØNE HUNDRED"
80 GØ TØ 50
90 DATA 84,113,97,101,105,33,12,99,134,82
100 END
```

The mistake lies in branching out of the loop when x is greater than 100 (line 30) and then attempting to reenter the loop by returning to "NEXT I" (line 80). Changing line 80 to "GØ TØ 10" would also be erroneous because returning to line 10 directly without passing through   50 NEXT I causes the loop to be restarted with $I = 1$ again.

Here is the correct version of the program.

Program 4-11

```
10 FØR I = 1 TØ 10
20 READ X
30 IF X > 100 THEN 60
40 PRINT "LESS THAN ØNE HUNDRED"
50 GØ TØ 70
60 PRINT "GREATER THAN ØNE HUNDRED"
70 NEXT I
80 DATA 84,113,97,101,105,33,12,99,134,82
90 END
```

The correct and incorrect "jumps" or branches in and out of loops are illustrated by the diagrams below. A bracket ⌈ is used to represent a loop. The top of the bracket is anchored on the FØR statement and the bottom on the NEXT statement.

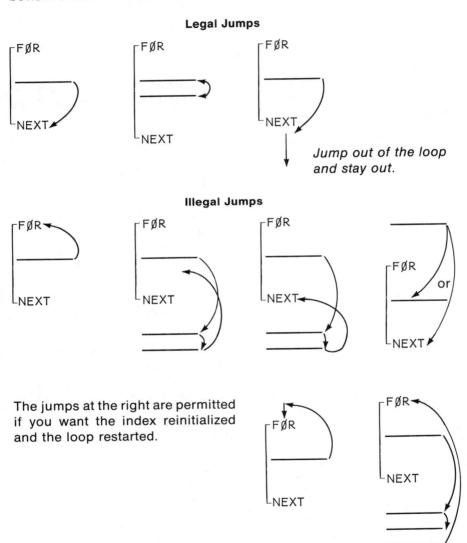

Legal Jumps

Jump out of the loop and stay out.

Illegal Jumps

The jumps at the right are permitted if you want the index reinitialized and the loop restarted.

SUMMARY: A program may not branch out of the body of a loop and then return to the body of the loop again. Once the program branches out of the loop, the loop may be reentered only through the FØR statement and the index will be reset to its starting value.

EXERCISES 4-6

A   Fill the following blanks.
1. INT(6.7) = __?__   2. INT(3/5) = __?__
3. INT(−4.5) = __?__   4. INT(43) = __?__
5. INT(−67) = __?__   6. INT(SQR(15)) = __?__

Write IF . . . THEN statements for each of these decisions.

7. If X is a multiple of 4, then go to line 30.
8. If I is even, then go to 45.
9. If Y is not a multiple of 7, then 60.
10. If Z is not divisible by 4, then 81.

11. Write a program to read integers X and Y and determine whether X is a factor of Y.

Correct any errors in the following programs.

12. 10 FØR J = 1 TØ 100
    20 LET S1 = S1 + J
    30 IF J/6 = INT(J/6) THEN 10
    40 LET S2 = S2 + J
    50 NEXT J
    60 PRINT "SUM ØF INTEGERS 1 TØ 100 IS S1"
    70 PRINT "SUM ØF MULTIPLES ØF SIX FRØM 1 TØ 100
       IS S2"
    80 END

13. 10 READ N
    20 FØR I = 1 TØ N
    30 READ X,Y
    40 IF X*Y < O THEN 90
    50 PRINT "PRØDUCT NØN-NEGATIVE"
    60 LET S = S + X*Y
    70 NEXT I
    80 PRINT "SUM ØF PRØDUCTS = " S
    85 GØ TØ 120
    90 PRINT "PRØDUCT NEGATIVE"
    100 GØ TØ 60
    110 DATA 4,8,5,−2,4,0,6,6,3
    120 END

B   Use the INT function to write an assignment statement that will *round* the variable Z to each nearest digit indicated below.

14. integer   15. tenth   16. hundredth   17. ten

18. Write a program to find all positive integers n less than 20 such that $2^n + 1$ is divisible by 3.

4-7 NESTED LOOPS

Mr. Williams plans to invest a sum of money at $5\frac{1}{2}$% interest. He must decide the amount to invest and the number of years. A computer can guide his decision by calculating the interest he would receive for various amounts and various time periods. The formula is $I = P * T * .055$ where I = interest, P = principal or amount, and T = time, in years.

Let us suppose Mr. Williams is considering investing $1000, $2000, $3000, or $4000 for 1, 2, 3, 4, or 5 years. Then the calculations can be accomplished by the program below.

Program 4-12

```
 5 PRINT " P"," T"," I"
10 FØR P = 1000 TØ 4000 STEP 1000
20 FØR T = 1 TØ 5
30 LET I = P*T*.055
40 PRINT P,T,I
50 NEXT T
60 NEXT P
70 END
```

outer loop → (10–60)
inner loop (20–50)

This program contains a "loop-within-a-loop" or a "nested loop." The output will look like this.

P	T	I
1000	1	55
1000	2	110
1000	3	165
1000	4	220
1000	5	275
2000	1	110
2000	2	220
. . .	. . .	. . .
4000	4	880
4000	5	1100

T (the inner loop index) varies more rapidly than P (the outer loop index). P is fixed at its first value (1000) and T is run through its cycle of values from 1 to 5. Then P is stepped to 2000 and T starts its cycle again. This procedure continues until P has reached 4000 and T completes 1 to 5 a last time.

For a nested loop the index in the *first* FØR statement must match the index in the *last* NEXT statement. Similarly the indices must match in the *second* FØR and the *second-to-last* NEXT.

Two, three, four, or more loops may be nested. Here is an example.

Program 4-13

```
10 READ X,Y,Z
20 FØR I = 1 TØ X
30 FØR J = 1 TØ Y
40 FØR K = 1 TØ Z
50 LET S = I↑3 + J↑2 - K
60 PRINT I,J,K,S
70 NEXT K
75 PRINT "K-LØØP FINISHED"
80 NEXT J
85 PRINT "J-LØØP FINISHED"
90 NEXT I
95 PRINT "I-LØØP FINISHED"
100 DATA 3,2,2
110 END
```

As illustrated at the right, the index
of an inner loop may key onto the
value of an outer loop.

```
30 FØR I = 1 TØ N-1
40 FØR J = I+1 TØ N
```

The following diagrams show legal and illegal ways of nesting loops.

Legal nesting

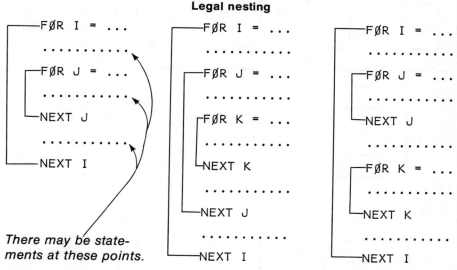

*There may be state-
ments at these points.*

The above diagrams show the nesting of two loops and three loops.
Similar nestings exist for four or more loops but will not be shown (see
Exercise 14 on page 131).

Illegal nesting

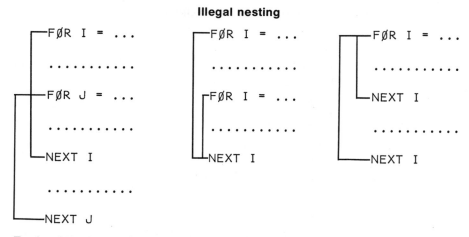

Each of these configurations would produce an error message such as the one shown below.

NEXT NØT MATCHED WITH FØR LINE #---

The following diagrams illustrate some legal and illegal ways of jumping within nested loops.

Legal Jumps

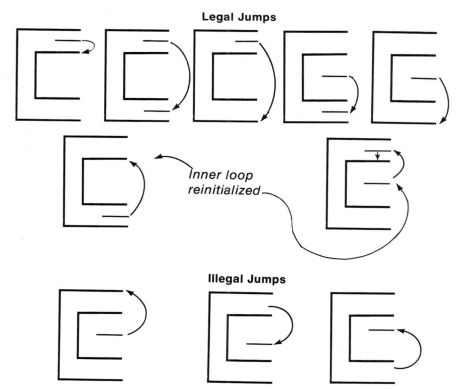

Inner loop reinitialized

Illegal Jumps

EXERCISES 4-7

A   In Program 4-12 how many times is each of these lines executed?

    1. 5   **2.** 30   **3.** 40

Correct any errors in each of the following programs.

4.
```
10  READ X
20  FØR J = 1 TØ X
30  READ M
40  IF M < 0 THEN 70
50  LET P = P + 1
60  NEXT J
70  LET N = N + 1
80  NEXT J
90  PRINT "SUM ØF PØSITIVES =" P
100 PRINT "SUM ØF NEGATIVES = " N
110 DATA 6,2,-3,5,-4,17
120 END
```

5.
```
10  READ R,S
20  FØR I = 1 TØ R
30  FØR J = 1 TØ S
40  IF I < J THEN 30
50  PRINT I, J, I+J
60  NEXT I
70  NEXT J
80  END
```

Consider the program at the right.

6. Show the first five lines of output.

7. Show the last five lines of output.

```
10 PRINT "LENGTH","WIDTH","AREA"
20 FØR L = 1 TØ 2 STEP .1
30 FØR W = 1 TØ 2 STEP .1
40 PRINT L,W,L*W
50 NEXT W
60 NEXT L
70 END
```

Consider the revised version of Program 4-12 that is shown at the right.

8. Show the first ten lines of output.

9. Show the last ten lines of output.

```
1  PRINT
5  PRINT " P"," T"," I"
6  PRINT
10 FØR P = 1000 TØ 4000 STEP 1000
20 FØR T = 1 TØ 5
30 LET I = P*T*.055
40 PRINT P,T,I
50 NEXT T
55 PRINT
60 NEXT P
70 END
```

B   **10.** Prepare a flowchart for Program 4-13 on page 129.

        11. Prepare a flowchart for the program for Exercises 6 and 7.

        12. Write a program to number twelve lines on the paper in three sets of four (1234 1234 1234).

        13. Write a program to print the sum $x + y$ for all integer pairs (x, y) such that $-5 \leq x \leq 5$ and $0 \leq y \leq 10$.

        14. Draw bracket-diagrams to illustrate all the ways that three loops may be nested inside a fourth loop.

CHAPTER REVIEW

Write *Yes* or *No* to show whether each of the following is a valid BASIC statement.

1. 35 LET I - 1 = I

2. 60 FØR J = 1,10

3. 50 LET K2 = K2 + 2

4. 100 NEXT I + 1

5. 85 FØR M = X + 7 TØ W*Z STEP K

6. 70 IF INT(X/Y = X/Y) THEN 91

7. 150 FØR L = L TØ L + 10 STEP L

8. Write a program to find the sum of the odd integers from −21 to 99 inclusive.

Consider the program at the right.

9. Trace the program.

10. Prepare a flowchart.

11. Rewrite the program using a FØR-NEXT loop.

```
10 LET K = 2
20 LET K = K + 1
30 PRINT K;
40 IF K < 8 THEN 20
50 END
```

If, entering statement 50, I = 10 and J = 3, what value is assigned to I by each of these statements?

12. 50 LET I = INT(I/J)

13. 50 LET I = I + J

14. 50 LET I = INT(SQR(J))

15. 50 LET I = INT(J/I)

Correct all errors in the programs of Exercises 16 and 17.

16.
```
13 FØR M = O TØ 6 STEP 1
17 READ K
22 IF K < O THEN 39
24 LET P = P + K
28 LET M = M + 1
31 NEXT M
34 GØ TØ 47
39 LET N = N + K
41 GØ TØ 28
47 PRINT P,N
86 DATA 83,-11,-17,42,91,13
99 END
```

17.
```
5 READ N
10 LET J = 1 TØ N
20 READ X
30 LET Y = X * 7 - 12
35 PRINT X, Y
40 IF J > N THEN 70
50 NEXT J
60 DATA 4,-2,8,-16,0
70 END
```

Write an IF . . . THEN statement for each decision.

18. If X is an integer, then 20.

19. If Y is a multiple of 5, branch to 100.

20. If M + N is not divisible by 6, then go to 90.

21. If Z divides I, jump to 40.

22. If Q is an odd integer, go to 25.

23. Write a program which, given a positive integer, prints whether the integer is EVEN or ØDD.

ROUND FOUR: *PROGRAMS FOR STUDENT ASSIGNMENT*

GENERAL INSTRUCTIONS:

1. In each exercise on pages 133 through 145, write a program that will do what is specified in the exercise.

2. If the program has several possible outcomes, the DATA must produce each outcome at least once.

3. Regardless of the possible outcomes, every program must process at least three sets of DATA.

4. Each program must use at least one FØR-NEXT loop.

ALGEBRA ONE

1. Given an integer A and a positive integer N, compute A^N without using ↑.

2. Extend Exercise 1 to handle any integer N. (Caution: Zero to a nonpositive power is undefined.)

3. Read ten values of x and ten values of Y (the x and Y-values alternate in the DATA). Compute the sum of the x-values, the sum of the Y-values, and the sum of the products XY.

4. Given a two-digit whole number, print its reversal. For example, given 89, print 98. Do not input the two digits of the integer separately; thus, for 89, do not put DATA 8,9 but instead use DATA 89.

5. Given a three-digit whole number, print its reversal.

6. Given a four-digit whole number, print its reversal.

7. Extend the program of Exercise 4 to handle five-digit whole numbers.

8. There are only two whole numbers less than 10,000 that are multiples of their reversals (where the reversal does not equal the original number). Both these integers are greater than 8700. Find both numbers.

9. There are only two more integers less than 100,000 that are multiples of their reversals (again excluding the trivial case where the reversal equals the original number; see Exercise 8). These two integers lie between 87900 and 99000. Find them.

Given fractions A/B and C/D (A, B, C, and D integers, B and D not zero), print the following in the lowest terms.

10. their sum

11. their product

12. the quotient of A/B divided by C/D (Test first whether $c = 0$.)

13. Find the abscissa values of the points resulting from the division of the segment from (1, 0) to (2, 0) on the x-axis into eight equal parts.

14. Input a set of twenty numbers. Print the number of positive values and the number of negative values in the set.

15. The number 153 has an interesting property. It equals the sum of the cubes of its digits, that is, $153 = 1^3 + 5^3 + 3^3$. There are no two-digit or four-digit whole numbers with this property and only four three-digit numbers (including 153). Find these four whole numbers. A check on the program is that the first integer found should be 153. Do not list the digits separately in the DATA.

16. Find every two-digit whole number that equals the sum of the squares of its digits.

17. Find every four-digit whole number that equals the sum of the fourth powers of its digits. To save computer time, start the search with 1600.

18. Decide whether a positive integer N (N $\le$ 100) is a perfect square.

19. Given a trinomial Ax^2 + Bx + C (A, B, and C integers with A $\le$ 100 and C $\le$ 100), input A, B, and C and determine whether the trinomial is a perfect square over the integers.

20. Extend the program for Exercise 19 so that for a trinomial that is a perfect square, the program prints the square root. For example, for $4x^2 - 12x + 9$, print   (2x − 3)

21. Given a three-digit whole number, compute the product of the digits. For example, for 423, print 24 (that is, $4 \times 2 \times 3$). Do not list the digits separately in the DATA. For example, do not use DATA 4, 2, 3 but rather put DATA 423.

22. Find all three-digit whole numbers that are divisible by the product of their digits. There are twenty such numbers. Note: Any number with a zero digit must be excluded to avoid a zero divisor. (This problem can be modified to find, for example, all the two-digit numbers divisible by the product of their digits.)

23. Find the forty four-digit whole numbers that are divisible by the product of their digits. (Again exclude any number with a zero digit to avoid division by zero.)

24. Convert a given improper fraction to a mixed number. For example, change $\frac{11}{8}$ to $1\frac{3}{8}$. Input the $\frac{11}{8}$ with   DATA 11, 8
Be sure that the fraction part of the mixed number is in lowest terms. For example, for $\frac{12}{8}$ output $1\frac{1}{2}$ and not $1\frac{4}{8}$.

25. Convert a mixed number to an improper fraction in lowest terms. Use three items of DATA to input the mixed number. For example, for $1\frac{3}{8}$ put   DATA 1, 3, 8

26. There are times when illegal cancellation produces correct results. For example, $\frac{16}{64} = \frac{1\cancel{6}}{\cancel{6}4} = \frac{1}{4}$. Cases like this have been humorously called "mathematical misteaks." Assuming that the numerator is less than the denominator, there are three other fractions with two-digit numerator and two-digit denominator where this illegal cancellation gives a correct result. Find the four fractions (including $\frac{16}{64}$).

27. Input a four-digit integer and determine whether all its digits are even. Do not feed the digits of the integer separately. For example, for 8675 use   DATA 8675

28. Given a four-digit number which represents a year, decide whether it is a leap year. (Note: The algorithm for determining whether a year is a leap year is more complicated than simply dividing by four.)

29. Read two four-digit numbers A and B, which stand for years. Print all leap years that occur between A and B. Include in the DATA the pair A = 1898, B = 2001.

30. Given a year, determine the next year in which January 1 will fall on the same day of the week.

GEOMETRY

31. Find the number of distinct triangles with sides of integral length no greater than ten. If the lengths of the sides are A, B, and C, the program can be made more efficient by assuming A $\leq$ B $\leq$ C. Then these statements can be used to generate the integer combinations to be tested.

```
50 FØR A = 1 TØ 10
60 FØR B = A TØ 10
70 FØR C = B TØ 10
```

32. Using the conditions of Exercise 31, count and print those combinations where A, B, and C are relatively prime (that is, one is their only common factor).

33. Bill has contracted for 36 meters (36 m) of fencing for a rectangular pigpen. Many rectangles have 36 meter perimeters, for example 10 × 8, 12 × 6, 17.5 × .5, and 9 × 9. Which of the possible rectangles has the largest area for the pigs? Answer by printing the length, width, and area of the rectangles with lengths from 9 m to 17.5 m in increments of 0.5 m.

34. Reverse Exercise 33. Fix the area of the rectangle at 36 square meters (36 m²). Decide which rectangle has the largest perimeter by letting the length range from 6 m to 36 m in increments of 1 m.

In 1650 the English mathematician John Wallis discovered the formula shown below. Use the formula to do Exercises 35 and 36.

$$\frac{\pi}{2} = \frac{2}{1} \cdot \frac{2}{3} \cdot \frac{4}{3} \cdot \frac{4}{5} \cdot \frac{6}{5} \cdot \frac{6}{7} \cdot \frac{8}{7} \cdots$$

35. Approximate π by doubling the product of the first twenty factors in Wallis' formula.

36. As more factors in the formula are multiplied, a better and better approximation of π is obtained. Continue multiplying until the difference between successive products is less than .00005.

37. Approximate π by finding the perimeters of regular n-gons inscribed in a circle of diameter one for $n = 4, 8, 16, 32, 64, 128, 256$.

A *Pythagorean Triple* is a set of three positive integers a, b, and c such that $a^2 + b^2 = c^2$. Use this information for Exercises 38 through 42.

38. Find all Pythagorean Triples whose components are all less than or equal to fifty. Computer time can be saved by assuming $a < b < c$. (Note that if $a = b$, c cannot be an integer.) Then the integers to be tested can be generated by the following statements.

```
10 FØR A = 1 TØ 48
20 FØR B = A + 1 TØ 49
30 FØR C = B + 1 TØ 50
```

39. Eliminate the c-loop of Exercise 38 by generating A and B and testing whether $\sqrt{A^2 + B^2}$ is an integer less than or equal to fifty.

40. Print only the *primitive* Pythagorean Triples whose components are all less than or equal to fifty. That is, print only those triples where a, b, and c are relatively prime. (See Ex. 32, p. 135.)

41. Verify that the product of a Pythagorean Triple is always divisible by sixty.

42. Find and test a relationship between the areas of primitive Pythagorean triangles (see Exercise 40) and the number six.

In addition to the equation $a^2 + b^2 = c^2$, other formulas have been discovered for generating Pythagorean Triples (see Exercises 38 through 42). In Exercises 43 through 45 use the given formulas to print Triples. (In all cases, m and n are positive integers and $m > 1$.)

43. $\left(m, \dfrac{m^2 - 1}{2}, \dfrac{m^2 + 1}{2}\right)$ m is odd. This method is attributed to Pythagoras himself (540 B.C.).

44. $(2m, m^2 - 1, m^2 + 1)$ This is Plato's formula (400 B.C.).

45. $(m^2 - n^2, 2mn, m^2 + n^2)$ $m > n$ Euclid's formula (320 B.C.)

In 1674 Leibniz found the following formula. Use this formula to do Exercises 46 and 47.

$$\frac{\pi}{4} = 1 - \frac{1}{3} + \frac{1}{5} - \frac{1}{7} + \frac{1}{9} - \cdots$$

46. Approximate π by taking the sum of the first twenty terms in Leibniz's formula and multiplying by four.

47. As more terms of the formula are added, a better approximation of π is obtained. Continue adding terms until two successive sums differ by less than .00005. Print four times the last sum as the approximation of π.

By the Pythagorean Theorem, if squares are constructed on the sides of a right triangle, the area of the square on the hypotenuse (III) equals the sum of the areas of the squares on the legs (I and II). Do Exercises 48 and 49.

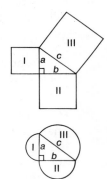

48. Suppose that instead of constructing squares on the sides of the triangle, we construct semicircles. Does the sum of the areas of semicircles I and II equal the area of semicircle III? Generate Pythagorean Triples and test the conjecture.

49. Construct equilateral triangles on the sides of right triangles and test whether the sum of the areas of the triangles on the legs equals the area of the triangle on the hypotenuse.

ALGEBRA TWO

50. Print a $\frac{3}{2}$ power table for $x = 1, 2, 3, \ldots, 10$, i.e., $1^{\frac{3}{2}}, 2^{\frac{3}{2}}, \ldots 10^{\frac{3}{2}}$.

51. Calculate logarithms to the base eight for $n = 1, 2, 3, \ldots, 20$. Print the output in two columns: n and $\log_8 n$.

52. Input a real number x such that $.0001 < x < 10^9$. Print x and the characteristic of its common logarithm. Do not use the INT or CLG functions (or the equivalent on your system).

53. Solve $x^x = 2$ for a value of x correct to the nearest hundredth. Use a trial-and-error method with a tolerance. (See Lesson 3-8 on p. 88.)

54. Given positive integers A and B, use the INT function to print the quotient and the remainder when A is divided by B. Do not assume that A > B.

55. Do Exercise 54 on page 137 without using the INT function.

56. Print a table of cube and fourth roots of x, $x = 1, 2, 3, \ldots, 10$.

57. Determine whether the equation $x^n + y^n = z^n$ has a solution for positive integers $x, y, z < 10$ and $3 \le n < 10$. (For $n = 2$, the equation is the Pythagorean formula.)

58. Given a positive integer $x > 1$, evaluate $\sqrt{x + \sqrt{x + \sqrt{x + \sqrt{x + \sqrt{x}}}}}$.

59. Extend the pattern of the expression in Exercise 58 to include ten x's. Then evaluate the expression.

60. Evaluate the expression in Exercise 58 with all the radicals changed to cube roots.

61. Miss Johnson, mathematics teacher at Regional High, uses the following grading scale on her tests.

94–100 = A, 85–93 = B, 77–84 = C, 70–76 = D, 69–below = F

First read N, which represents the number of students in a class. Then read the exam grade of each student and count the number of A's, B's, C's, D's, and F's in the class.

62. Many cash registers in use today automatically return the correct change. Write a program to simulate this procedure. Assume that the cost of the purchase is less than one dollar. The program will accept as input the cost of the purchase (in cents) and will output the coins that will be returned if a dollar bill were given to the cashier. The number of coins returned should be kept to a minimum. Thus you do not want to return nothing but pennies. For example, if the purchase price were 29 cents, the coins returned would be two quarters, two dimes, and one penny. Assume that half-dollars are not used.

63. Find the sum of the squares of the first ten consecutive positive integers.

The rational numbers form a *countable* set; that is, they can be lined up in an order and counted (though the counting does not end). The irrational numbers (and therefore the reals) are not countable.

64. Print the rational numbers between zero and one which are of the form A/B where A and B are integers from 1 to 10, inclusive. The list will look like this.

```
1/2  1/3  1/4  1/5  1/6  1/7  1/8  1/9  1/10
2/3  2/4  2/5  2/6  2/7  2/8  2/9  2/10
. . .          . . .          . . .
8/9  8/10
9/10
```

65. In the list of Exercise 64 the same number occurs several times. For example, $1/2 = 2/4 = 3/6 = 4/8 = 5/10$. Avoid this repetition by printing only the fractions A/B that are in lowest terms.

ADVANCED MATHEMATICS

66. Compute N! for N $= 1$ to 10. Print the output in two labeled columns, N and N-FACTØRIAL.

67. Compute the sum of the series $1 + \frac{1}{2} + \frac{1}{3} + \frac{1}{4} + \ldots + \frac{1}{100}$.

68. Find n such that $1 + \frac{1}{2} + \frac{1}{3} + \frac{1}{4} + \ldots + \frac{1}{n}$ exceeds five.

69. The function sin x is increasing at $x = 0$. Find experimentally the positive value of x (to the nearest hundredth) at which the function starts decreasing. Trigonometry specifies this value as $\frac{\pi}{2}$.

70. In the complex number system any number has two square roots, three cube roots, four fourth roots, . . . , n nth roots. Use De-Moivre's Theorem to calculate the nth roots (in standard form) of a complex number.

71. Evaluate the number of permutations of n things taken r at a time. n and r are nonnegative integers. Be sure to handle the case where $n < r$.

72. Compute the number of combinations of n things taken r at a time.

73. Compute the number of permutations of n things taken n at a time, where s of the objects are of the same type (s a non-negative integer).

74. Assume that in performing n experiments, the probability of an experiment being successful is p. Compute the probability of i successes using the following formula.

$$\frac{n!}{i!(n-i)!} (1-p)^{n-i}p^i$$

75. Find i^n for any natural number n (where i is the imaginary unit such that $i = \sqrt{-1}$).

76. Extend Exercise 75 to all integers n.

77. In trigonometry any angle whose degree measure is greater than 90 or less than zero has a "reference angle" between 0 and 90, inclusive. Given the degree measure of an angle between -720 and 720, inclusive, print the measure of its reference angle.

78. Given two real numbers x and y and a positive integer n, compute n arithmetic means between x and y.

79. Given two real numbers x and y and a positive integer n, compute (if possible) n geometric means between x and y. Sometimes there may be more than one set of means. For example, if $x = 1$, $y = 16$, and $n = 3$, one set of means is 2, 4, 8 and another is -2, 4, -8.

In Exercises 80 and 81 given the complex roots of a quadratic equation, print the equation.

80. Assume that the quadratic polynomial has real coefficients. (This implies something about the roots.)

81. Do not assume that the equation has real coefficients.

82. Given polar coordinates (r, θ) and (s, α) such that $-720° < \theta < 720°$ and $-720° < \alpha < 720°$. Decide whether the two sets of polar coordinates designate the same point.

83. Determine the limit of $\dfrac{\sin x}{x}$ as x approaches zero by printing x and $\dfrac{\sin x}{x}$ for $x = 1, .5, .25, .125, \ldots$ until the difference between successive values of the ratio is less than .00005.

Descartes' Rule of Signs establishes a connection between the number of sign changes between consecutive terms of a polynomial P and the number of possible real roots of the equation P = 0. Read the integral coefficients of a cubic polynomial $Ax^3 + Bx^2 + Cx + D = 0$ and do Exercises 84 and 85. (Hint for both exercises: if two real numbers have opposite signs, what is true of their product?)

84. Count the number of sign changes and print the maximum number of positive real roots the equation may have.

85. Decide the maximum number of negative real roots the equation may have.

BUSINESS

Many of the programs below involve *compound interest*, which is not the same as *simple* interest. An example will show the contrast.

Suppose a principal of $100 is invested at 6% simple interest. After one year the investment earns .06 × $100 or $6.00 interest. The $6 interest is *not* added to the principal. Thus the second year again yields $6 interest and the principal remains $100.

If the $100 is invested at 6% compound interest, the $6 interest after the first year is added to the $100 and for the second year the principal is $106. Hence the second year's interest is .06 × $106 or $6.36. The principal for the third year is then $112.36.

In all exercises the interest rates are *annual* rates unless explicitly stated otherwise.

86. Manhattan Island was purchased in 1626 for $24. If those early buyers had invested the same amount at 6% interest, compounded annually, how much would their investment be worth today?

87. Alice Snerdley plans to borrow $100 and wants to compare various loan plans. Suppose that Company A will lend her the money at compound interest at 1% monthly, and Company B will lend her the money at simple interest at $1\frac{1}{8}$% per month. Compare how much Alice would have to pay under each plan after 12, 24, or 36 months.

88. An employee of the Colonel Motors Company receives life insurance in an amount equal to three times his or her yearly salary to the next highest $100. For example, if an employee earns $7950 per year, he receives 3 × $8000 or $24,000 worth of insurance. Determine the amount of policy for an employee whose *weekly* salary is given. (An employee at CMC is paid for fifty-two weeks of the year, including vacation.)

89. $100 is invested at 5% compounded quarterly. Print the value of the account each year for ten years. Note: "Compounded quarterly" means that the interest is compounded four times a year (every three months). Remember, though, that the 5% is an *annual* interest rate. Use the quarterly rate ($1\frac{1}{4}$%).

90. Assume that Social Security payment is withheld from a worker's salary at the rate of 5.85% of the first $13,200 earned in a calendar year. First read N, the number of employees, and then for each employee input the number of hours worked this week, the hourly pay rate, and the year-to-date earnings prior to this week. Compute and write (**a**) the salary this week, (**b**) the social security withheld for the week, (**c**) the net pay, and (**d**) the new year-to-date. For the withheld tax the following cases are possible.
(i) If the year-to-date exceeds $13,200, the withholding for that week (and all subsequent weeks of that year) is zero, (ii) if the year-to-date is less than $13,200, the entire week's earnings are taxed, (iii) if this week's wages puts the year-to-date over $13,200, only that part up to $13,200 is taxed.

91. Job A lasts thirty days and pays $10 per day; job B lasts thirty days and pays as follows: $1 first day, $2 second day, $3 third day, and so forth. Which job pays more?

92. An individual has an account with a principal of $10,000. He withdraws $100 at the beginning of each month. Assuming that the bank adds interest at $5\frac{1}{4}$% on the minimum balance during the previous month, print the monthly balance for one year.

93. Suppose that you purchase the Newtown Spears, a minor league baseball team, for $48,000. The league tells you that the profit (in $1,000 units) of the franchise can be projected for the next eight years by using the following formula.

$$P = T^3 - 5T^2 + 10T - C$$

where P = profit, T = time in years, C = cost in thousands (48). Calculate and print your profit or loss for each of the next eight years and your net profit (or loss) at the end of eight years.

94. Assume that in 1960 the population figures for the United States and Mexico were 180,000,000 and 85,000,000 respectively and that the annual rate of growth of the U.S. is 1.23% and of Mexico, 2.23%. If these growth rates remain constant, in what year will the population of Mexico equal or exceed that of the United States?

95. Suppose that the world population is 3.7 billion. Each year it increases by 1.9%. Calculate the number of years from now in which world population will be double its present level and the number of years from now in which it will be triple its present level (assuming that the present growth rate remains constant).

NUMBER THEORY

96. Given a positive integer, print its positive integral factors.

97. Given an integer N and an integer M > 1, find the congruence class to which N belongs modulo M.

98. Accept integers J and N and decide whether they are congruent modulo M (M is an integer and is greater than 1).

99. Print a multiplication table modulo M for the integers 0, 1, 2, . . . , M − 1.

100. Find the LCM (least common multiple) of two integers.

101. Find the LCM of three integers.

102. Find the GCF (greatest common factor) of two integers.

103. Find the GCF of three integers.

104. Decide whether two given integers are relatively prime.

105. Decide whether three given integers are relatively prime.

106. A positive integer N is *prime* if and only if N $\neq$ 1 and N has no positive factors except itself and one. A positive integer greater than one is *composite* if and only if it is not prime. Every even integer is composite except two. One is the only positive integer that is neither prime nor composite. We develop the following algorithm for determining whether a given positive integer is prime, composite, or neither.

(a) Read N (a positive integer).
(b) If N $=$ 1, print NEITHER and go to **g**.
(c) If N $=$ 2, print PRIME and go to **g**.
(d) Test whether N is divisible by 2. If it is, print CØMPØSITE and go to **g**.
(e) Decide whether N is divisible by any *odd* integer from 3 to $\sqrt{N}$. If it is, print CØMPØSITE and go to **g**.
(f) If steps **d** and **e** result in no divisor, print PRIME.
(g) Out of data? If no, go to **a**. If yes, END.

Read a positive integer. Is it prime, composite, or neither?

107. Given a positive integer, print its prime factors. For example, for 315 output the list   3   5   7   .

108. For a positive integer print its prime factorization, showing by exponents the number of times each prime is used as a factor. For example, for 315 output $3\uparrow2 * 5 * 7$.

109. "Twin primes" are two consecutive primes that differ by two. For example, 5 and 7, 11 and 13, 41 and 43 are twin primes. Find the number of twin primes in each of the intervals 3–100, 101–200, 201–300, . . . , 901–1000. Print the results in tabular form. (Will the number of twins in each interval decrease as you reach larger and larger integers?)

110. A "palindromic prime" is a prime that is also a prime when its digits are reversed. 11, 13, and 17 are such primes. Find ten others.

111. Let $f(n) = n^2 - n + 41$. Test that $f(n)$ is prime for $n = 1, 2, 3, \ldots, 40$ but not prime for $n = 41$. Print the output in columns: $n, f(n)$, prime or composite.

112. Many formulas have been tried to see whether they always produce primes. (None has thus far been found. See Exercise 111.) Test each of the formulas below and verify that they produce primes for the values indicated but do not produce a prime for the next value in succession:

$$
\begin{array}{ll}
n^2 + n + 17 & \text{for } n = 0, 1, 2, \ldots, 15 \\
n^3 - 31n^2 + 320n - 1117 & \text{for } n = 0, 1, 2, \ldots, 24 \\
2n^2 + 29 & \text{for } n = 0, 1, 2, \ldots, 28 \\
3n^2 - 3n + 23 & \text{for } n = 0, 1, 2, \ldots, 22
\end{array}
$$

113. Three sailors, shipwrecked with a monkey on a desert island, have gathered a pile of coconuts that are to be divided early the next day. During the night one sailor arises, divides the pile into three equal parts, and finds one coconut left over, which he gives to the monkey. He then hides his share. Later during the night, each of the other two sailors arises separately and repeats the performance of the first sailor. In the morning all three sailors arise, divide the pile into three equal shares, and find one left over, which they give to the monkey. By trial-and-error compute the smallest integer that could represent the number of coconuts in the original pile.

114. All primes congruent to one (modulo 4) can be expressed as a unique sum of two integral squares (Fermat's "Two Square" Theorem). For example, $5 = 1^2 + 2^2$, $29 = 2^2 + 5^2$, and so forth. For the ten smallest primes that satisfy the conditions of Fermat's Theorem, print the number as the sum of two squares.

115. Find twelve consecutive composite integers. Do not use a trial-and-error method. (Hint: Find an algorithm that involves a factorial.)

116. Multiply pairs of positive base-ten integers by repeated addition. Execution time will be saved if the larger integer is used as the multiplicand and the smaller as the multiplier. For example, it is quicker to multiply 82×13 by adding 82 thirteen times than to add 13 eighty-two times.

117. Extend Exercise 116 to allow the multiplicand to have a decimal part. For example, 82.43×13.

118. Print the largest proper factor (any factor less than the number itself) for each odd integer from 1001 to 1019, inclusive.

119. A "perfect number" is a whole number that equals the sum of its proper factors. (See Ex. 118.) Find and print all perfect numbers that are less than 100.

120. A whole number n is "abundant" if the sum of its proper factors exceeds n, and "deficient" if the sum is less than n. Given a positive integer, classify it as perfect, abundant, or deficient.

121. Convert the binary representation of a whole number to its decimal form. Arrange the DATA in the following way: the number of digits in the binary numeral, followed by the digits separately. For example, for 1101_{two}, use DATA 4,1,1,0,1. (Note that the digits are listed left-to-right and not right-to-left.) For 1101, the program should print 13.

122. The British mathematician G. H. Hardy once casually mentioned to the brilliant young Indian mathematician Ramanujan that he, Hardy, had just ridden in a taxi with an "uninteresting" identification number. Upon being told the number, Ramanujan promptly replied that the number was quite interesting because it was the smallest integer that could be written as the sum of two cubes in two different ways. Find the number of Hardy's taxi. Warning: This program takes a large amount of computer time!

123. The integers 12 and 13 have the following characteristic: $12 \times 12 = 144$, $21 \times 21 = 441$; and $13 \times 13 = 169$; $31 \times 31 = 961$. Find a three-digit integer (if one exists) for which this same kind of relationship holds.

124. Goldbach's Conjecture, which has never been proved or disproved, claims that every even number greater than four is the sum of two odd primes. For example, $44 = 13 + 31$. (This pair is not unique: $44 = 41 + 3$, $44 = 37 + 7$.) Test the Conjecture for the even integers up to fifty. Print the result for each integer as an equation such as $44 = 3 + 41$. (Any one pair of odd primes is sufficient for each integer.) If the program gives faulty results, read Lesson 3-8 on pages 88 through 90.

125. Find all two-digit whole numbers that have the property that if the final digit of the numeral is deleted, the original number is divisible by the new number. For example, 2<u>4</u> is divisible by 2 but 2<u>5</u> is not divisible by 2.

126. 220 and 284 are called "friendly" or "amicable" numbers because the sum of the proper factors of each equals the other. Find another pair of amicable whole numbers.
Warning: This program can take a large amount of computer time!

127. In his *Laws*, Book 5, Plato recommends that a city be divided into plots of land so that the number of plots has as many proper divisors as possible (thus insuring the maximum flexibility for further subdivisions). He suggested 5,040 because it has 59 proper divisors, a very large number. However, computer research reveals that the largest number of proper divisors that a number less than 10,000 can have is 63, which tops Plato's number by four divisors. There are just two such 63-divisor numbers. One is 9,240. Find the other.

5

SUBSCRIPTED VARIABLES

5-1 COMPUTING THE AVERAGE OF A SET OF NUMBERS

Example:

Read a list of ten numbers and compute the average of the set.

A natural approach to programming this problem might be to start with either of the following statements.

```
        10 READ A,B,C,D,E,F,G,H,I,J
   or   10 READ AO,A1,A2,A3,A4,A5,A6,A7,A8,A9
```

Then the average could be computed with either of these statements.

```
        20 LET X = (A+B+C+D+E+F+G+H+I+J)/10
   or   20 LET X = (AO+A1+A2+A3+A4+A5+A6+A7+A8+A9)/10
```

These statements would work; they would compute the average of ten numbers. But suppose you must average one hundred numbers. Your READ and LET statements would grow so long as to become unwieldy.

The program does not require ten variable names (that is, ten storage locations) for the input numbers. Only one is needed since the numbers can be read and summed one at a time, as in this program.

Program 5-1

```
10 FØR I = 1 TØ 10        I serves as a counter.
20 READ A
30 LET S = S + A
40 NEXT I
50 PRINT "AVERAGE = " S/10              10 could be changed
60 DATA 71,67,73,84,52,58,64,80,68,71   to I, since the last
70 END                                  value for I is 10.
```

Let us take the program a step further.

Example:

Read a list of ten numbers and compute the average of the set; print the list of numbers followed by their average.

Program 5-1 used one memory location (A) over and over to hold the input numbers one at a time. Will this one variable suffice for the restated problem? Yes, because each number can be printed as soon as it is read.

Program 5-2

```
10 FØR I = 1 TØ 10
20 READ A
25 PRINT A;
30 LET S = S + A
40 NEXT I
45 PRINT
50 PRINT "AVERAGE = " S/I
60 DATA 71,67,73,84,52,58,64,80,68,71
70 END
```

Programs 5-1 and 5-2 process ten DATA values—no more and no less. To allow more flexibility, the first number listed in the DATA could be the *number* of values in the set. This value would be read into location N and used to control the FØR-NEXT loop that reads, prints, and sums the DATA values, as in the following program.

Program 5-3

```
5 READ N
6 REM  N REPRESENTS THE NUMBER ØF ELEMENTS IN
7 REM  THE DATA SET TØ BE AVERAGED.
10 FØR I = 1 TØ N
20 READ A
25 PRINT A;
30 LET S = S + A
40 NEXT I
45 PRINT
50 PRINT "AVERAGE = " S/N
60 DATA 10,71,67,73,84,52,58,64,80,68,71
70 END
```

N *could be changed to* I, *since the last value for* I *is* N.

This is not an element of the set to be averaged but a preliminary numeral signifying the number of elements in the list that follows.

Even the approach on the previous page becomes inconvenient when a large number of values must be processed. It would prove tedious (if not inaccurate) to count 50, 100, or more values for input to the program. To avoid this drawback, use a code number, say 9999. Any number that the programmer knows will not appear in the DATA list may be used as a *sentinel* to signify the end of the set. This idea is implemented in Program 5-4 below. No preliminary number at the head of the list is needed. Simply add 9999 at the end of the DATA. Insert in the program (line 22 below) a decision to test if the 9999 has been reached. When it is read, branch out of the loop that reads, prints, and sums the DATA values and print the average.

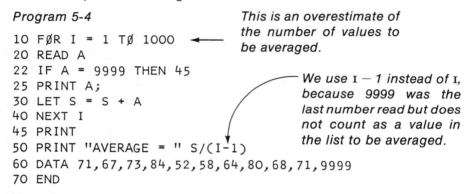

Program 5-4

```
10 FØR I = 1 TØ 1000
20 READ A
22 IF A = 9999 THEN 45
25 PRINT A;
30 LET S = S + A
40 NEXT I
45 PRINT
50 PRINT "AVERAGE = " S/(I-1)
60 DATA 71,67,73,84,52,58,64,80,68,71,9999
70 END
```

This is an overestimate of the number of values to be averaged.

We use $I - 1$ instead of I, because 9999 was the last number read but does not count as a value in the list to be averaged.

If all DATA of a program are positive, then zero or a negative number can be used as an end-of-data sentinel.

EXERCISES 5-1

A   **1.** Steve believes he can write Program 5-4 without using a FØR-NEXT loop. His program is listed below. Will it do the job? If not, what changes can be made (without introducing a FØR-NEXT loop) so that it will give the desired output?

```
10 READ A
20 LET N = N + 1
30 PRINT A;
40 LET S = S + A
50 GØ TØ 10
60 PRINT
70 PRINT "AVERAGE = " S/N
80 DATA 71,67,73,84,52,58,64,80,68,71
90 END
```

2. Input a number x and then a list of twenty numbers. Determine the number of times x occurs in the list.

3. Write a program that accepts a list of numbers and prints the average of the positives and the average of the negatives.

B **4.** Given a list of whole numbers, find the sum of those that are multiples of both three and five.

5. Given a list of whole numbers, find the sum of those that are multiples of either three or five.

6. Given a list of whole numbers, find the sum of those that are even multiples of seven.

7. Trace this program.

```
10 READ X
20 IF X < O THEN 60
30 LET S = S + X
40 LET C = C + 1
50 GØ TØ 10
60 PRINT "AVERAGE IS " S/C
70 DATA 30,20,6,4,-1
80 END
```

Draw a flowchart for each of the following programs.

8. 5-1   **9.** 5-2   **10.** 5-3   **11.** 5-4

5-2 SUBSCRIPTED VARIABLES

Lesson 5-1 developed a program to calculate the average of a set of numbers. We now move a step further.

Example:

Read a list of numbers; compute the average of the set; then determine how far from the average (above or below) each element in the list lies.

In Programs 5-1 to 5-4 on pages 146 through 148, it was possible to use one memory location, A, to hold, one at a time, each input value so that it could be printed and added to the sum S. Since the element was no longer needed, the next number in the list could be read into the same location.

For the problem above, however, this scheme will not work because after the average is computed, we must go back to each element and subtract the average from it. The algorithm might be stated as follows.

1. Read and store a list of numbers.
2. Find the sum of the list.
3. Compute the average of the set.
4. Subtract the average from each number in the list.
5. Print each number and its distance from the average.
6. Stop.

Steps 1 and 2 might be combined into one loop, as in Programs 5-1 through 5-4. Similarly steps 4 and 5 could be combined into another loop, after the average has been computed.

One thought might be to return to using a list of variables. If there are ten DATA items, the following program would work.

Program 5-5

```
10 READ A,B,C,D,E,F,G,H,I,J
20 LET X = (A+B+C+D+E+F+G+H+I+J)/10
30 PRINT A, A-X
40 PRINT B, B-X
50 PRINT C, C-X
60 PRINT D, D-X
70 PRINT E, E-X
80 PRINT F, F-X
90 PRINT G, G-X
100 PRINT H, H-X
110 PRINT I, I-X
120 PRINT J, J-X
130 DATA 71,67,73,84,52,58,64,80,68,71
140 END
```

For a list of ten numbers fourteen statements were required in Program 5-5. No loop was used. For longer lists of values the program quickly gets out of hand. There must be a better way.

The solution lies in using a *subscripted variable.* In mathematics a list of numbers is often designated using subscripts.

$$a_1, a_2, a_3, \ldots, \text{ or in general } a_i$$

These variables are read "*a* sub one," "*a* sub two," and so on, or in general "*a* sub *i.*" In BASIC, since a terminal cannot print actual subscripts below the line, this list is written A(1), A(2), A(3), . . . , A(I). The subscript is placed in parentheses behind the letter being subscripted. The advantage of this notation is that the subscript is itself a variable and can therefore have values as large as needed. For the averaging problem ten numbers could be named A(1), A(2), A(3), . . . , A(10); that is, A(I) with I running from 1 to 10. Ninety-eight numbers could be stored as A(1), A(2), A(3), . . . , A(98); that is, A(I) with I running from 1 to 98. In both cases only two letters are needed: A and I.

A set of values named by one letter with a changing subscript is called a *list, vector,* or **array**. The number of values in the list is called the **dimension** (length) of the array. The variable representing the subscript (I above) is called the **index**. A one-dimensional array has one index; a two-dimensional array needs two indices (plural of "index"); three indices are used for a three-dimensional array, and so forth. For this chapter we limit ourselves to one-dimensional arrays.

Mathematically there is no limit to the number of subscripts a variable may have. In computer programming, however, the size of the machine being used and the rules of the programming language set an upper limit. Most versions of BASIC allow at most *two* subscripts.

In BASIC any one-letter variable may be subscripted. (Some systems may allow a variable such as A1 to be subscripted also.) Any one-letter variable (for example A) or one-letter-one-digit variable (such as A5) may be used as an index. Here are examples of subscripted variables in mathematical and BASIC notations.

Mathematical Notation	BASIC Notation
x_1	X(1)
a_0	A(0)
$R1_5$	Usually not permitted
z_v	Z(V)
p_{n+1}	P(N+1)
r_{2j-1}	R(2*J−1)

In many versions of BASIC a subscript must be a positive integer. Some compilers, however, allow zero subscripts. The subscript may be a constant, a variable, or a legitimate arithmetic expression. For some BASIC compilers the subscript, if it involves operations, must work out to an integer; otherwise an error message is printed and execution stops. For other versions of BASIC, if the computed subscript is positive but not an integer, the INT function is applied and execution continues. For example, if K = 3 and M = 2, then A(K/M) would become A(1).

For each computer there is a maximal value a subscript may attain. The limit is undoubtedly large enough for the programs you will write but if in doubt, consult the manual for your system.

When we wish to display the elements of an array, we do so between brackets. See the example below.

$$x = [31 \quad -6 \quad 1.5 \quad 83 \quad -17]$$

If the array is called x, then mathematically x_1 refers to an individual element. If indexing begins at one, then the elements of array x are $x_1 = 31$, $x_2 = -6$, $x_3 = 1.5$, $x_4 = 83$, and $x_5 = -17$. If the index is started at 0, then $x_0 = 31$, $x_1 = -6$, $x_2 = 1.5$, $x_3 = 83$, and $x_4 = -17$.

x, I, and X(I) are three different variables whose values are stored in three separate locations in memory. Some compilers may not permit the use of x both subscripted and not subscripted in a program. But if both x and X(I) are permitted, then one memory location is reserved for x and separate locations for x(1), x(2), x(3), . . . , to the last element of the array. If I is used as the index, then I itself requires a storage location.

To input the array x on the previous page, use the loop at the right.

```
10 FØR I = 1 TØ 5
20 READ X(I)
30 NEXT I
40 DATA 31,-6,1.5,83,-17
       ⋮
```

Before execution of this loop, the compiler establishes a memory location for I and for x(1), x(2), x(3), x(4), and x(5).

Subscripted variables may be used in algebraic expressions just like other variables and inserted into READ, LET, PRINT, or IF . . . THEN statements. However, a subscripted variable may not be used as the index for a FØR statement or in NEXT statements.

Mathematical Notation	BASIC Notation
$a_1 + a_2 + a_3 + a_4$	A(1) + A(2) + A(3) + A(4)
$x_1{}^2 + x_2{}^2$	X(1) ↑ 2 + X(2) ↑ 2
$(a - r_1)(z - r_2)$	(A − R(1))*(Z − R(2))
$1.5(z_{i+1} - z_i)$	1.5 * (Z(I + 1) − Z(I))

Here are sample BASIC statements involving subscripted variables.

```
10 READ A(I)
20 READ X(1),X(2),X(3)
20 LET Z = X(I)*2
20 LET F(I+1) = F(I) + F(I-1)
25 LET R = SQR(A(J))
30 PRINT X(I);
40 PRINT Z(D+1)/Z(D)
50 PRINT X(1),X(2),X(3)
50 IF X(I) = Z(J) THEN 100
50 IF A(I+1)/A(I) = SQR(A(I)) THEN 80
50 IF INT(R(D)) = INT(B(J))THEN 100
60 FØR X = 0 TØ M(J)
60 FØR S = Y(1) TØ Y(N) STEP .5
60 FØR T = 1 TØ 10 STEP X(I)
```

Subscripted variables may be used in the flow-chart boxes corresponding to these statements.

These may not be allowed on your system.

Let us now return to the problem stated at the beginning of this lesson.

Read a list of numbers; compute the average of the set; then determine how far from the average (above or below) each element in the list lies.

Using a subscript will enable us to save the numbers in the list. The values will be read into an array A. If there are ten numbers to be averaged, they can be stored in ten locations labeled A(1), A(2), A(3), . . . , A(10). The loop to input the list might look like this.

```
10 FØR I = 1 TØ 10
20 READ A(I)
30 NEXT I
```

But, as before, we seek a method to process a list of any size. 9999 can again be used as an end-of-list sentinel. We now have this loop.

```
10 FØR I = 1 TØ 100
20 READ A(I)
30 IF A(I) = 9999 THEN 50
40 NEXT I
50 ...
```

The "100" in line 10 is an intentional overestimate and can be revised if necessary to fit different DATA sets. We must remember that when execution of this loop is complete and control transfers to line 50, 9999 has been entered as the last element of array A. Actually there are only $I - 1$ numbers in the list to be averaged.

As in Programs 5-1 to 5-4 summation of the list can be embedded in the READ loop. With this idea in mind we complete the program as follows.

Program 5-6

```
5 DIM A(100) ◄──────────────────────This statement will
10 FØR I = 1 TØ 100                  be explained in the
20 READ A(I)                         next lesson.
30 IF A(I) = 9999 THEN 50
35 LET S = S + A(I)                  This loop uses N as the
40 NEXT I                            counter-index. A new var-
50 LET X = S/(I-1)                   iable is necessary be-
60 FØR N = 1 TØ I-1 ⎤                cause I − 1 must remain
70 PRINT A(N), A(N)-X ⎥              fixed as the number of
80 NEXT N           ⎦                elements in the array.
90 DATA 71,67,73,84,52,58,64,80,68,71,9999
100 END
```

EXERCISES 5-2

A   Write a BASIC subscripted variable for each of the following mathematical variables.

    1. x_3 **2.** t_i **3.** z_{j+1}
    4. R_0 **5.** q_{2x} **6.** z_{m+n}

Write *Yes* or *No* to show whether each of the following is a legal BASIC subscripted variable.

    7. Z(0)   **8.** J   **9.** X(−3)
   10. K*(I)   **11.** K(A+B+C)   **12.** V(L)
   13. X1(17)   **14.** M(1E6)   **15.** Z(INT(X/Y))

Let the array a be [8   −4   16 −12 2 11] with indexing beginning at one. Give the value of each of the following.

16. a_2 **17.** a_{3-1} **18.** $a_3 - 1$ **19.** $2a_4$

20. $a_1{}^2$ **21.** a_{a_5} **22.** $6 + a_6$ **23.** $a_3 - a_4$

24. Write each expression in Exercises 16 through 23 in BASIC, if it is possible to do so.

For the array a given for Exercises 16 through 23, state which member of each pair has the larger value.

25. a_2, a_1 **26.** $a_{2+1}, a_2 + 1$ **27.** $a_{1+3}, a_1 + a_3$

Let $i = 2$ and $j = 3$. Then for the array a given for Exercises 16 through 23, find the value of each of the following.

28. $a_i \cdot a_j$ **29.** $a_{i \cdot j}$ **30.** a_{i+j} **31.** $a_i + a_j$

32. $2a_i$ **33.** a_{2i} **34.** a_{j+1} **35.** a_{i-1}

36. Write the BASIC equivalent of each expression in Exercises 28 through 35.

37. Write a READ loop and DATA statement to input the array a given for Exercises 16 through 23.

For each mathematical expression write a corresponding BASIC expression.

38. $x_1 + x_2$

39. $\dfrac{y_2 - y_1}{x_2 - x_1}$

40. $a_1 x^n + a_2 x^{n-1}$

41. $\sqrt{s_1{}^2 + s_2{}^2 + s_3{}^2}$

42. $a_3 x^3 + a_2 x^2 + a_1 x + a_0$

43. $c_1 d_1 + c_2 d_2 - c_3 d_3 - c_4 d_4$

44. $|2t_1 - t_2|$

45. $\cos(y_1 + y_2)/\sin(y_1 - y_2)$

46. $b_1{}^2 + c_1{}^2$

47. $(x_1 - x_2)^2 + (y_1 - y_2)^2$

B   **48.** A travelling salesman deals in five items having fixed prices. (In practice the number of items would be much larger.) Suppose the five items are priced respectively at $1.10, $2.20, $.80, $3.40, and $1.90. The salesman would like a program written so that when he receives an order, he can enter as DATA the number ordered of each item and the computer will print the total price of the order. Use two lists (and therefore two subscripted variables): a P-list containing the prices of the items and an N-list consisting of the number ordered of each item.

49. Exercise 2 on page 148 stated: "Input a number x and then a list of twenty numbers. Determine the number of times x occurs in the list." Switch the input so that the list of twenty numbers comes first, followed by x. Now write a program to determine the number of times x occurs in the list.

Suppose that you are given ten numbers; now "push down" the list, that is, replace each element of the set by the element that follows it (move element one to position ten).

50. Write a program that uses a subscripted variable to input the list into an array A and merely prints the list in pushdown order without actually manipulating array A in memory.
51. Write a program that inputs the array A and actually repositions the elements in memory before printing the pushdown list. (Do not use a second subscripted variable.)

5-3 DIM STATEMENTS

"5 DIM A(100)" was the first line of Program 5-6 on page 153. DIM is short for "DIMENSION." BASIC automatically assigns storage space for any list in the program, with subscripts 0 through 10 or 1 through 10, depending on the system. But if longer lists are desired, a DIM statement is needed. The instruction   DIM A(100)   saves 101 memory locations for the values of an array named A: A(0), A(1), A(2), . . . , A(100). (If the system does not use zero subscripts, then 100 locations are reserved: A(1) through A(100).) Any computer possesses only a finite storage capacity and there is a limit to the number and length of the lists a program might require. However, the programs considered in this text should not exceed this limit.

The DIM statement notifies the compiler how many locations to reserve for a subscripted list. No harm results if more locations are reserved than are actually needed (provided the total capacity of the machine is not exceeded). Therefore when the programmer is uncertain of the length of an array, he should set his dimension at a value that is larger than the number of entries expected in the array.

One DIM statement may include more than one array.

Example: 10 DIM A(50), X(100), K(15)

SUMMARY OF RULES GOVERNING DIM STATEMENTS

1. If a subscripted variable is used in a program but the subscript will not take on a value greater than ten, no DIM statement is needed for that array.

2. Whenever a program contains a subscripted variable whose subscript will take on a value greater than ten, that variable must be listed in a DIM statement with a number in parentheses behind it to indicate the maximum size of the index. When in doubt indicate a larger dimension than you expect to use.

3. Since a DIM statement is not executed, it may be entered into the program on any line before END; it is convenient and customary, however, to place DIM statements at the beginning of the program.

A common error involving DIM statements is illustrated by this program.

```
10 DIM I(50)
20 FØR I = 1 TØ 50
30 READ X(I)
40 IF X(I) = 9999 THEN 70
50 LET S = S + X(I)
60 NEXT I
70 PRINT "SUM ØF THE ARRAY IS " S
80 DATA 67,-14,81,40,75,86,104.9,9999
90 END
```

The error lies in line 10. The programmer has confused the variable naming the array (x), with the index for the array (I). Line 10 should read as follows.

```
10 DIM X(50)
```

Some systems allow variables as subscripts in DIM statements.

```
10 READ N
20 DIM A(N)
30 FØR I = 1 TØ N
40 READ A(I)
50 LET S = S + A(I)
60 NEXT I
70 PRINT "THE SUM ØF THE ARRAY IS" S
80 DATA 6,841,732,904,897,684,831
90 END
```

EXERCISES 5-3

A Write the DIM statement that is needed before each of these arrays can be read into the computer.

1. $[x_1 \quad x_2 \quad x_3 \quad \ldots \quad x_{50}]$ **2.** $[t_j]$ where $j = 1, 2, 3, \ldots, 37$
3. $[r_{10} \quad r_{20} \quad r_{30} \quad r_{40}]$ **4.** $[z_{51} \quad z_{52} \quad z_{53} \quad \ldots \quad z_{79}]$
5. $B = [87 \quad 92 \quad 61 \quad 78 \quad 94 \quad 87 \quad 91 \quad 83 \quad 75 \quad 62 \quad 99]$

Correct any errors in the following programs.

6.
```
10DIM X(20)
20 LET X + 1 = X
30 READ B(X)
40 LET S = S + B(X)
50 IF B(X) = 9999 THEN 70
60 GØ TØ 10
70 LET A = S/X
80 PRINT "AVERAGE ØF THE SET IS " A
90 DATA 20,5,2,7,3,8,1,9,11,3,15,20,4,0,10,2,16,9999
100 END
```

7.
```
5 DIM I = 1 TØ 40
10 LET I = O
20 READ K(I+1)
30 IF K(I+1) > O THEN 70
40 LET N = N + K(I+1)
50 GØ TØ 30
70 LET P = P + K(I+1)
80 GØ TØ 30
90 PRINT "SUM ØF THE PØSITIVES IS " P
100 PRINT "SUM ØF THE NEGATIVES IS " N
110 DATA 10,-60,20,17,-3,90,4,-5,-120,-17.8
120 END
```

B In Exercises 8 and 9 consider an array A.

8. Without actually manipulating the array in memory, print A in reverse order. For example, if A = [8 10 3 5] print 5,3,10,8.

9. Create an array B such that the elements of B are the elements of A in reverse order. Print A and B.

5-4 POLYNOMIALS

Polynomials are handled in programming by means of subscripted variables. The general form of a polynomial (in ascending order of powers of the variable x) is

$$a_0 + a_1x + a_2x^2 + a_3x^3 + \cdots + a_{n-1}x^{n-1} + a_nx^n$$

where n is a nonnegative integer called the *degree* of the polynomial and each a_i $(0 \leq i \leq n)$ is a real number constant called the *coefficient* of its term. a_0 is called the *constant term*. We can think of the polynomial as an array

$$[a_0 \quad a_1 \quad a_2 \quad \ldots \quad a_{n-1} \quad a_n]$$

containing the coefficients in ascending powers of x. Note that the x^i's need not be stored because the subscript of each coefficient is the power of x for that term. Of course the variable in the polynomial may be any nonsubscripted variable. Here are examples.

Polynomial	Corresponding Array
$5 + 7x - 6x^2 + x^3$	[5 7 −6 1]
$-7 + .5y^3 + y^5$	[−7 0 0 .5 0 1]
$11c - 7.3c^2 + 3c^4$	[0 11 −7.3 0 3]
$r^2 - 8r^4 + 6r - 3r^3 - 4$	[−4 6 1 −3 −8]
82	[82]

Notice in the second and third examples that 0's are used in the array for missing powers of the variable.

To input the arrays on page 157, the DATA statements at the right can be used, where the first numeral in each line denotes the degree of each polynomial.

```
330 DATA 3,5,7,-6,1
331 DATA 5,-7,0,0,.5,0,1
332 DATA 4,0,11,-7.3,0,3
333 DATA 4,-4,6,1,-3,-8
334 DATA 0,82
```

If the system allows zero subscripts, the READ loop to input the polynomials will appear as shown at the right. N is the degree.

```
10 READ N
20 FØR I = 0 TØ N
30 READ A(I)
40 NEXT I
```

If zero subscripts cannot be used, line 20 will be written in the following way.

```
20 FØR I = 1 TØ N+1
```

This approach makes operations with polynomials awkward since the programmer must remember that for a polynomial of degree N, N + 1 is the index of the last coefficient and the subscript of a coefficient is one more than the power of the variable in that term.

$$a_1 + a_2 x + a_3 x^2 + \cdots + a_n x^{n-1} + a_{n+1} x^n$$

Unfortunately, where a zero subscript is not permitted, there is no alternative to the above form.

Printing a polynomial is tricky. A first thought is to print all of the terms with the following loop (we assume that zero subscripts can be used).

```
50 FØR I = 0 TØ N
60 PRINT A(I) "X↑" I;
70 NEXT I
80 PRINT
```

This loop would produce isolated terms such as the following (using the first two polynomials from the DATA steps listed earlier).

```
 5 X↑ 0   7 X↑ 1 -6 X↑ 2   1 X↑ 3
-7 X↑ 0   0 X↑ 1   0 X↑ 2  .5 X↑ 3   0 X↑ 4   1 X↑ 5
```

There are objections to the form of the above polynomials: **1.** no plus signs connect the terms, **2.** $0 \times {\uparrow} 1$, $0 \times {\uparrow} 2$, and $0 \times {\uparrow} 4$ should not appear, **3.** $5 \times {\uparrow} 0$ should be 5, and $-7 \times {\uparrow} 0$ should be -7, **4.** $7 \times {\uparrow} 1$ should be $7x$, and **5.** $1 \times {\uparrow} 3$ should print as $x {\uparrow} 3$, and $1 \times {\uparrow} 5$ should print as $x {\uparrow} 5$. The polynomials should be in correct form, like this.

```
 5   +   7 X   - 6 X↑ 2   +   X↑ 3
-7   +   .5 X↑ 3   +   X↑ 5
```

On a terminal, of course, we cannot avoid the ↑ to denote exponents.

The following program reads the degree and coefficients from DATA and prints the polynomial as "neatly" as possible. REM statements explain the sections of the program.

Program 5-7: Read and Print a Polynomial
(Assumes zero subscripts are legal.)

```
10 READ N
11 REM      N IS THE DEGREE ØF THE PØLYNØMIAL TØ BE READ.
20 FØR I = O TØ N
30 READ A(I)
40 NEXT I
45 IF N = O THEN 325
49 REM      LINES 50-60 HANDLE THE CØNSTANT TERM.
50 IF A(O) = O THEN 70
60 PRINT A(O);
69 REM      LINES 70-170 PRINT THE X-TERM.
70 IF A(1) = O THEN 180
80 IF A(1) < O THEN 120
90 IF A(1) = 1 THEN 150
98 REM      IF A CØEFFICIENT IS PØSITIVE, PRINT A + SIGN
99 REM      IN FRØNT ØF IT (SEE LINE 220)
100 IF A(O)=O THEN 105
102 PRINT " + " A(1) "X ";
103 GØ TØ 180
105 PRINT A(1) "X ";
110 GØ TØ 180
120 IF A(1)=-1 THEN 170
130 PRINT A(1) "X ";
140 GØ TØ 180
150 IF A(O)=O THEN 155
152 PRINT "+ X ";
153 GØ TØ 180
155 PRINT "X ";
160 GØ TØ 180
170 PRINT " - X";
180 FØR I = 2 TØ N
181 REM      THIS LØØP PRINTS
182 REM      THE REMAINING TERMS.
190 IF A(I) = O THEN 300
200 IF A(I) < O THEN 240
210 IF A(I) = 1 THEN 270
220 PRINT " + "A(I)"X↑"I;
230 GØ TØ 300
240 IF A(I) = -1 THEN 290
250 PRINT A(I) "X↑" I;
260 GØ TØ 300
270 PRINT " + X↑"I;
280 GØ TØ 300
290 PRINT " - X↑"I;
300 NEXT I
310 PRINT
320 GØ TØ 10
325 PRINT A(O)
327 GØ TØ 10
330 DATA 3,5,7,-6,1
331 DATA 5,-7,0,0,.5,0,1
332 DATA 4,0,11,-7.3,0,3
333 DATA 4,-4,6,1,-3,-8
334 DATA 0,82
999 END
```

If your system does not permit zero subscripts, revise Program 5-7 above accordingly.

EXERCISES 5-4

A   Show the array of coefficients (ascending order of powers) for these polynomials.

1. $7 + 3x + 4x^2$ **2.** $11x - x^2 + 5x^4$
3. $.5z^3 - \frac{1}{4}z^2 + 113z - 61.23$ **4.** $6x - 5$
5. 13 **6.** $t + 3t^3 - 2t^2 - 16 + 5t^4$

7. Write the DATA statements for Program 5-7 on page 159 to input the polynomials in Exercises 1 through 6. Number the lines 330 to 335.

Write *Yes* or *No* to show whether each of the following expressions is a polynomial.

8. $\frac{1}{2}$ **9.** $-8y^{100}$ **10.** $\frac{1}{q}$ **11.** $\sqrt{t + 1}$

12. $4m^{-2} - 3m^{-1}$ **13.** $|b^3 - 5b + 6|$ **14.** $\frac{c^2 - 1}{c + 1}$ **15.** a^n

B   List the line numbers of the print section of Program 5-7 in the order in which the statements would be executed after each of these polynomials is entered as input.

Example: $7 - x + 3x^2$
Answer: 45,50,60,70,80,120,170,180,190,200,210,220,230,300,310, 320

16. $2x$ **17.** -6.75 **18.** $8 + x$ **19.** $-17 + 8x^2$ **20.** $-x - 5x^2 - x^3$

5-5 CREATING A SORT ALGORITHM (Optional)

Frequently, in programming, you will need to sort a set of numbers into either ascending or descending order. Usually the sort algorithm is part of a larger program. For example, the monthly sales are computed for each salesman of an organization and then printed in ranked order.

Diagrams will help you understand the sort algorithm. Imagine that we have seven numbers in an array x.

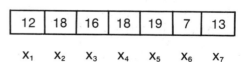

12	18	16	18	19	7	13

X_1 X_2 X_3 X_4 X_5 X_6 X_7

Suppose we must sort this array into descending order. In sorting, you would probably scan the array from left-to-right to determine the largest value, 19. Then you would scan again to decide the second largest, 18. (18 is also the third highest.) You would continue this process until you had completely ordered the array.

The computer, however, cannot "see" the values. It must instead follow a more detailed algorithm. It begins like this: compare the first number to the second; if the first is larger, leave the numbers as they are; if the second element is greater, swap the positions of the two numbers. (If they are equal, leave them as they are.)

Now compare the current first element to element three. If one is greater than or equal to three, retain their present positions; if three is larger, reverse them. Now compare element one to element four in a similar fashion, either leaving them alone or swapping, depending on which is the larger. This compare-swap routine is called one *pass* through the array. After it has been executed one complete time (1-2, 1-3, 1-4, 1-5, 1-6, and 1-7), the element that has finished in the first position is definitely the largest in the array. (There may be another element equal to it but certainly none greater.)

Return to element two and compare it to three, either leaving it in position two (if it is greater or equal) or swapping it with three (if it is smaller). Then make a similar decision for two and four, two and five, two and six, and two and seven. When this second pass is complete, the number in position two is definitely the second largest in the array. Continue the algorithm for positions three through six, at which time the array will be in descending order.

Let us apply the algorithm to the array introduced on page 160.

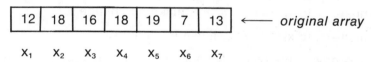

| 12 | 18 | 16 | 18 | 19 | 7 | 13 | ⟵ *original array* |

X_1 X_2 X_3 X_4 X_5 X_6 X_7

The execution of the algorithm would involve these steps (the steps are numbered in a way that emphasizes the cyclic nature of the algorithm).

1-1 Compare x_1 to x_2. Since 12 < 18, reverse their positions. The array stands as shown at the right.

| 18 | 12 | 16 | 18 | 19 | 7 | 13 |

X_1 X_2 X_3 X_4 X_5 X_6 X_7

1-2 Compare x_1 (which is now 18) to x_3. Since 18 > 16, leave these two elements as they are.

1-3 Compare x_1 to x_4. Both presently equal 18; it makes no difference whether we swap or not. To save work, leave them as they are.

1-4 Compare x_1 to x_5. Since 18 < 19, reverse positions. The array stands as shown at the right.

| 19 | 12 | 16 | 18 | 18 | 7 | 13 |

X_1 X_2 X_3 X_4 X_5 X_6 X_7

(We can see that the largest element is now first and that further comparisons will cause no change. But the machine cannot make a judgment like this and must continue the algorithm.)

1-5 Compare x_1 to x_6. Since x_1 is greater, make no change.

1-6 Compare x_1 to x_7. Since x_1 is greater, make no change.

We can now guarantee that element x_1 is the largest in the array. Consequently we can forget about element one and begin cycle two of the algorithm.

2-1 Compare x_2 to x_3. Since $12 < 16$, reverse their positions. The array thus takes this form.

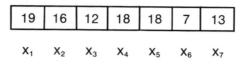

19	16	12	18	18	7	13
x_1	x_2	x_3	x_4	x_5	x_6	x_7

2-2 Compare x_2 (16) to x_4 (18). Since x_4 is greater, swap again, producing this array.

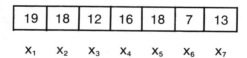

19	18	12	16	18	7	13
x_1	x_2	x_3	x_4	x_5	x_6	x_7

2-3 Compare x_2 to x_5. Since $18 = 18$, leave them as they are.

2-4 Compare x_2 to x_6. Since $18 > 7$, make no change.

2-5 Compare x_2 to x_7. $18 > 13$, again no change.

Location x_2 now contains the second largest element of the array. The algorithm is working and, if followed to completion, will put all elements in their correct order as shown below.

final array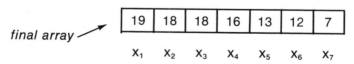

19	18	18	16	13	12	7
x_1	x_2	x_3	x_4	x_5	x_6	x_7

EXERCISES 5-5

A **1.** As in the lesson, list the steps of the algorithm for putting the following array into descending order: 71, 89, 84, 103, 97. Each time a change is made, show the new version of the array.

2. What change(s) must be made in the algorithm if the array is to be put into ascending order?

3. As in the lesson, list the steps for putting this array into *ascending* order: 70, 6, 121, −8, 10, −14.

B **4.** Write a program for the flowchart in Exercise 18 on page 18.

5. Here is an explanation of a sorting method different from the one in the lesson. The method is shown through an example.

Example: Sort A = [6 5 9 2 8] into descending order.
Solution:
  (i) Make pairwise comparisons of consecutive elements (1-2, 2-3, 3-4, 4-5). Switch their positions when a smaller precedes a larger. Thus A undergoes these changes on the first pass.

  original list ⟶ $\left.\begin{array}{ccccc} 6 & 5 & 9 & 2 & 8 \\ 6 & 9 & 5 & 2 & 8 \\ 6 & 9 & 5 & 8 & 2 \end{array}\right\}$ *1st pass*

  (ii) Repeat (i) until a pass finds no switches necessary.

  list after 1st pass ⟶ $\left.\begin{array}{ccccc} 6 & 9 & 5 & 8 & 2 \\ 9 & 6 & 5 & 8 & 2 \\ 9 & 6 & 8 & 5 & 2 \end{array}\right\}$ *2nd pass*

  list after 2nd pass ⟶ $\left.\begin{array}{ccccc} 9 & 6 & 8 & 5 & 2 \\ 9 & 8 & 6 & 5 & 2 \end{array}\right\}$ *3rd pass*

A fourth pass makes no switches and the process ends. Apply this technique to the following list, showing all switches on each pass as above. B = [4 1 7 2 3 5]

6. Here is a revision of the sorting technique explained in Exercise 5. Again use the array A = [6 5 9 2 8].

  (i) 6 > 5? Yes, so continue comparing consecutive elements until a smaller precedes a larger.
  (ii) 5 > 9? No, so swap their positions. The array now looks like this. A = [6 9 5 2 8].
  (iii) Start over (here is where the change occurs in the previous algorithm). 6 > 9? No, so swap and start over.

As the process continues, the array changes like this.

list after step iii ⟶ $\begin{array}{ccccc} 9 & 6 & 5 & 2 & 8 \\ 9 & 6 & 5 & 8 & 2 \\ 9 & 6 & 8 & 5 & 2 \\ 9 & 8 & 6 & 5 & 2 \end{array}$

On the next pass, since no swaps are made, the algorithm stops. Apply this technique to the array B given in Exercise 5, showing the array after each swap.
NOTE: This technique is called "bubble" sorting, probably because the larger numbers "bubble" to the front of the array as the process is repeated.

5-6 THE SORT ALGORITHM IN BASIC (Optional)

We are now ready to program the Sort Algorithm in BASIC. The READ portion of the program can be quickly written as shown below.

```
10 DIM X(100)
20 READ N
30 FØR I = 1 TØ N
40 READ X(I)
50 NEXT I
     . . .
140 DATA ...
```

We can now concentrate on the sort portion of the program.

Recall the pattern of comparisons.

x_1 to x_2	x_2 to x_3	x_3 to x_4	. . .	x_{n-1} to x_n
x_1 to x_3	x_2 to x_4	. . .		
x_1 to x_4	. . .	x_3 to x_n		
. . .	x_2 to x_n			
x_1 to x_n				

We need two indices: one (I) to mark the position of the first number being compared and the second (J) to indicate the position of the second. I will run from 1 to N − 1; J runs from I + 1 to N. Thus the sort requires a nested loop.

```
60 FØR I = 1 TØ N-1
70 FØR J = I+1 TØ N
     . . .
120 NEXT J
130 NEXT I
```

Once we set the indices, we write the statement for comparison.

```
80 IF X(I) >= X(J) THEN 120
```

If the answer is "no" to the question of the IF clause, we must swap X(I) and X(J). It would seem that this operation would require only these two statements.

```
90 LET X(J) = X(I)
100 LET X(I) = X(J)
```

But careful analysis proves otherwise. Suppose X(I) is 10 and X(J) is 14. Then, since X(I) < X(J), the two elements must be reversed. After the machine executes   90 LET X(J) = X(I)   , X(J) equals 10.

| 10 | 14 | $\longrightarrow$ | 10 | 10 |

X(I)   X(J)   X(I)   X(J)

The '14' has been lost. Consequently when   100 LET X(I) = X(J)   is executed, the swap is not effected and instead both X(I) and X(J) end up equal to 10.

To avoid this difficulty, a "dummy" third location is needed. Call it Z. Both diagrams below will illustrate what must be done.

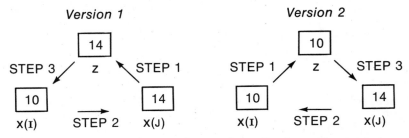

The corresponding BASIC steps for each method are shown below.

Version 1

```
9O LET Z = X(J)
100 LET X(J) = X(I)
110 LET X(I) = Z
```

Version 2

```
9O LET Z = X(I)
100 LET X(I) = X(J)
110 LET X(J) = Z
```

The completed sort sequence looks like this.

```
6O FØR I = 1 TØ N-1
7O FØR J = I+1 TØ N
8O IF X(I) >= X(J) THEN 12O
9O LET Z = X(J)
100 LET X(J) = X(I)
110 LET X(I) = Z
12O NEXT J
13O NEXT I
```

The PRINT segment of the program can be accomplished in either of two ways. The most obvious is with a separate loop.

```
14O FØR I = 1 TØ N
15O PRINT X(I);
16O NEXT I
17O PRINT
```

The second method capitalizes on the fact that each time the J-loop is completed, one more element of the array has fallen into its proper position and consequently can be printed immediately before NEXT I is executed.

```
12O NEXT J
125 PRINT X(I);
13O NEXT I
```

However, line 60 must be changed to read FØR I = 1 TØ N so that the last element will be printed. Since this second method saves steps, we use it in the complete program which will be shown on the next page.

Program 5-8: Sort an array into descending order

```
10 DIM X(100)
20 READ N
30 FØR I = 1 TØ N
40 READ X(I)
50 NEXT I
60 FØR I = 1 TØ N
70 FØR J = I+1 TØ N
80 IF X(I) >= X(J) THEN 120
90 LET Z = X(J)
100 LET X(J) = X(I)
110 LET X(I) = Z
120 NEXT J
125 PRINT X(I);
130 NEXT I
140 DATA 7,12,18,16,18,19,7,13
150 END
```

NOTE: there are many sort algorithms. This one was chosen because it is among the easiest to understand.

EXERCISES 5-6

A 1. What change(s) must be made in Program 5-8 if the array must be sorted into ascending order?
2. Modify Program 5-8 so that it prints the original array, skips a line, and then prints the array in descending order.
3. What would be the output of Program 5-8 if line 60 were left as
    60 FOR I = 1 TØ N − 1   ?

For the DATA in line 140 of Program 5-8, how many times will each of these statements be executed?

4. 20   **5.** 40   **6.** 120   **7.** 125   **8.** 130

B 9. Prepare a flowchart for Program 5-8.

10. Ellen claims that she can write Program 5-8 without using index J. She keeps the first five lines and changes the rest of the program as shown at the right. Will the new program do the job? If not, where is it erroneous?

```
60 FØR I = 1 TØ N-1
70 IF X(I) >= X(I+1) THEN 110
80 LET Z = X(I+1)
90 LET X(I+1) = X(I)
100 LET X(I) = Z
110 NEXT I
120 FØR I = 1 TØ N
130 PRINT X(I);
140 NEXT I
150 DATA 7,12,18,16,18,19,7,13
160 END
```

CHAPTER REVIEW

Write *Yes* or *No* to show whether each of the following is a BASIC subscripted variable for your system.

1. Z4(I)   **2.** M(X + 1)   **3.** N(−1)   **4.** M(0)
5. J*(T)   **6.** A(A)   **7.** X(3/2)   **8.** R(1E2)

For each mathematical expression write a BASIC expression.

9. $a_2y^2 + a_1y + a_0$ **10.** $\dfrac{1}{s_1s_2} + \dfrac{1}{s_3}$ **11.** m_{i+j} **12.** b_{2n}

13. $\sqrt{x_2{}^2 - x_1{}^2}$ **14.** $a|2r_1 + r_2|$ **15.** x^{a_i} **16.** $d_2{}^2$

17. Apply the Sort Algorithm of Lesson 5-5 on pages 160 through 162 to put the following list into descending order. Each time a change is made, show the new version of the array.

$$\mathbf{R} = [6 \quad 14 \quad 20 \quad 3 \quad 15 \quad 12]$$

Write DATA statements to input these polynomials to Program 5-7 on page 159.

18. $134 - 91x - 5x^2$ **19.** $8 + m^3$ **20.** $17x$
21. $9y^4 - 15y^2 + y$ **22.** $-1812 + \frac{1}{2}k$ **23.** -9.7

24. Write a program to input an array X and two additional real numbers A and B (A < B). Then print all elements of X that are greater than A and less than B.

25. Write a program to input an array X and two additional real numbers A and B (A < B). Then print all elements of X that are less than A or greater than B.

26. What is the output of the program at the right.

27. Prepare a flowchart for the program at the right.

```
10 DIM T(20)
20 FØR J = 1 TØ 20
30 READ T(J)
40 IF T(J) = 999   THEN 60
50 NEXT J
60 FØR C = 1 TØ (J-1)/2
70 LET T(2*C) = 2*T(C)
80 NEXT C
90 FØR C = 1 TØ J-1
100 PRINT T(C);
110 NEXT C
120 DATA 2,3,7,8,10,6,5,1,999
130 END
```

28. Program the sort algorithm in Exercise 5 on page 163.

29. Program the sort algorithm in Exercise 6 on page 163.

*This exercise covers optional material from the chapter.

ROUND FIVE: PROGRAMS FOR STUDENT ASSIGNMENT

GENERAL INSTRUCTION:

In each exercise on pages 168 through 175, write a program that will do what is specified in the exercise.

ALGEBRA ONE

In Exercises 1 and 2, accept a list of numbers and print every other number (second, fourth, sixth, and so forth).

1. Write the program using a subscripted variable.

2. Write the program without using a subscripted variable.

In Exercises 3 through 10, input sets A and B by first reading M, the number of elements in A, and then the elements, stored as A(1), A(2), . . . , A(M). Then read N, the number of elements of B, then B(1), B(2), . . . , B(N). (If M = 0, then A = ∅; if N = 0, B = ∅.)

3. Determine whether the sets are equivalent.

4. Is A = B?

5. Decide whether either set is a subset of the other.

6. Print A ∪ B. In choosing DATA, include these possibilities: **(a)** A ⊆ B, **(b)** B ⊆ A, **(c)** A = B, **(d)** A ∩ B = ∅, **(e)** A = ∅, and **(f)** B = ∅.

7. Print A ∩ B. Include the same possibilities as Exercise 6.

8. Consider A to be the universal set and B, one of its subsets. Print the complement of B with respect to A.

9. Define a "set subtraction" as follows. Print A − B and B − A.
A − B = {x| $x \in$ A and $x \notin$ B}

10. Print A × B, the "Cartesian" or "cross product" of A and B, and B × A.

11. Change a repeating decimal to the ratio (in lowest terms) of two integers. For example, for $.\overline{45}$ (.454545 . . .) print 5 / 11. Input the repeating decimal with three DATA items: **(a)** the number of decimal places before the repeating block, **(b)** the number of digits in the repeating block, and **(c)** the decimal up to the place where repeating begins. For example, the DATA for $.12\overline{345}$ would be 2, 3, .12345. For $.\overline{45}$ use 0, 2, .45.

12. Factor over the integers, if possible, quadratic polynomials of the form $x^2 + $ B$x + $ C (B and C integers).

13. Factor over the integers (if possible) quadratic polynomials of the form A$x^2 + $ B$x + $ C (A, B, and C integers with A ≠ 0).

14. Multiply a one-variable polynomial by a constant.

15. Add pairs of one-variable polynomials. Assume that the variable is the same in both polynomials but do not assume that the polynomials are the same degree.

The Texxacon chain of service stations is sponsoring a lucky number drawing in your city with tickets numbered 1 to 1000.

16. Given a ticket number, check the list of ten lucky numbers to see if the ticket is a winner.

17. Complicate matters by introducing different prizes. Given a ticket number, decide if it is a $100 winner, a $10 winner, a $1 winner, or none of these. There are only five $100 winners, ten $10 winners, and twenty $1 winners, and no number can win in more than one category.

18. Read a list of numbers. Place the positive numbers sequentially (as they occur in the input list) into array P and the negatives into array N. Then print P and N.

Arnold has played in twelve golf tournaments this year. Given his scores in the four rounds of each tournament (he "made the cut" every time), do Exercises 19 through 22.

19. Print his average score for each tournament.

20. Print his average for all forty-eight rounds this year.

21. Print his lowest and highest rounds of the year.

22. Print his lowest and highest tournament averages.

23. Input a list of numbers in which an element may occur more than once. Print the list with duplications eliminated.

GEOMETRY

Input the coordinates of the vertices of an n-gon (polygon with n sides) in the Cartesian plane. If the vertices are (x_1, y_1), (x_2, y_2), . . . , (x_n, y_n), then store the coordinates in two arrays, X and Y.

24. Find the perimeter.   25. Decide whether the n-gon is equilateral.

For two n-gons (polygons with n sides) read N, the number of sides, the lengths of the sides of the first polygon, and the lengths of the corresponding sides of the second.

26. Decide whether the n-gons have congruent sides.

27. Decide whether the n-gons have a common ratio between the sides of the first and the corresponding sides of the second.

28. Do Exercises 26 and 27 with the n-gons in the coordinate plane. Instead of accepting the lengths of the sides of the polygons, input the coordinates of the vertices. Store the x-coordinates in an x-array and the y-coordinates in a Y-array.

In Exercises 29 through 31, read N, the number of sides of a polygon. Then input the measures of N − 1 angles.

29. Compute the measure of the Nth angle.

30. Decide whether the polygon is equiangular.

31. Also read the measures of N − 1 corresponding angles of a second N-gon. Decide whether the polygons are similar.

ALGEBRA TWO

32. Accept an array x(1), x(2), . . . , x(20). Print the array with the following elements swapped: x(1) and x(20), x(2) and x(19), x(3) and x(18), . . . , x(10) and x(11).

33. Given ten National Merit composite scores, print that score of the ten which is nearest to the average of the set.

Find the point(s) of intersection (if any) of the circle $x^2 + y^2 = r^2$ and the conic section with each of the following equations.

34. $y = ax^2 + bx + c$

35. $(x - h)^2 + (y - k)^2 = r_1^2$

36. $\dfrac{x^2}{a^2} + \dfrac{y^2}{b^2} = 1$

37. $\dfrac{x^2}{a^2} - \dfrac{y^2}{b^2} = 1$

38. Given the number of pins he knocked down with each ball in each frame, compute a bowler's score.

39. Input a table of common logarithms for the integers 1 to 20, inclusive. That is, $L(1) = \log_{10}1$, $L(2) = \log_{10}2$, . . . , $L(20) = \log_{10}20$. Use the table to perform calculations with these integers. Invent a code for the operations of multiplication, division, and exponentiation (taking roots can be handled as exponentiation). For example, if the computation to be performed is 2×3^2, list as DATA 3, 2, 23, 2, 21, 99, where '23' means exponentiation, '21' denotes multiplication, and '99' is an end-of-problem sentinel. Remember that the answer to every problem must be an integer from 1 to 20—otherwise the computer cannot find the antilogarithm.

40. In an array of twelve numbers, find the longest sequence of nondecreasing numbers. For example, for the list 17, 31, 40, 5, 6, 10, 46, 37, 53, 12, 9, 86, the longest string of nondecreasing numbers is 5, 6, 10, 46. If two or more sequences tie for longest, print all of them. Thus for 17, 31, 40, 5, 6, 10, 3, 37, 53, 12, 9, 86, print   17, 31, 40   and   5, 6, 10   and   3, 37, 53   .

41. Accept a sequence of numbers. Print the first, second, and third differences of consecutive terms.

Example 1:

original sequence ⟶   1   4   9   16   25   36

first differences ⟶   3   5   7   9   11

second differences ⟶   2   2   2   2

third differences ⟶   0   0   0

Example 2:

original sequence ⟶   3   −2   16   5   −1   0   27

first differences ⟶   −5   18   −11   −6   1   27

second differences ⟶   23   −29   5   7   26

third differences ⟶   −52   34   2   19

ADVANCED MATHEMATICS

42. Evaluate sin x by this series and compare with the SIN(X) of BASIC.

$$\sin x = x - \frac{x^3}{3!} + \frac{x^5}{5!} - \frac{x^7}{7!} + \ldots \; (x \text{ in radians})$$

43. Evaluate cos x using this series and compare with CØS(X) of BASIC.

$$\cos x = 1 - \frac{x^2}{2!} + \frac{x^4}{4!} - \frac{x^6}{6!} + \ldots \; (x \text{ in radians})$$

44. Use the Taylor series below to evaluate arctan x and check answers with ATN(X) of BASIC.

$$\arctan x = x - \tfrac{1}{3}x^3 + \tfrac{1}{5}x^5 - \tfrac{1}{7}x^7 + \ldots \; (-1 < x < 1)$$

In Exercises 45 and 46, input a vector A of dimension D.

45. Read N (N $\leq$ D) and assign zero to **(a)** A_N, **(b)** the first N elements of A, and **(c)** the last N elements of A.

46. Find the maximum of the absolute values of the components of A. Print the component with largest absolute value and its position in the vector. For example, if A = (13, −21, 0, 17), print   −21 2   .

Descartes' Rule of Signs establishes a connection between the number of sign changes between consecutive terms of a polynomial P and the number of possible real roots of $P = 0$. In Exercises 47 and 48, input the degree and coefficients of a polynomial. (See Ex. 84 and 85, p. 140.)

47. Count the number of sign changes and print the number of possible positive real roots the equation may have. For example, for $2 - 3x + x^2 + 7x^3 - 5x^4 + x^5 = 0$ there are 4, 2, or 0 positive real roots.

48. Decide the number of possible negative real roots.

In Exercises 49 through 51, a polynomial P is given.

49. A function f is *even* if, for each x in the domain, $f(x) = f(-x)$. A function f is *odd* if $f(x) = -f(-x)$ for each x in the domain. Decide whether the function determined by P is even, odd, or neither.

50. Print the first derivative of the function determined by P.

51. Print the second derivative.

52. For a quadratic polynomial function, use the first and second derivatives to find the critical point and whether this critical point is a relative maximum or a relative minimum.

53. For a cubic polynomial function, find the critical point(s), if any, and determine whether each is a relative maximum or relative minimum.

54. Expand Exercise 53 to find inflection points.

55. Consider the sequence 1, 2, 3, 6, 18, 78, 438, . . . , where the average of the first n terms is the (n − 1)st term for n > 2. Find the kth term.

56. Print the quotient and the remainder when polynomial P is divided by polynomial Q. Assume the variable is the same in both polynomials but do not presume that the degree of P is greater than the degree of Q.

57. Use Newton's Method to approximate an irrational zero of a polynomial function, given the two consecutive integers between which the root lies. Newton's Method is based on the iteration formula
$$x_{n+1} = x_n - \frac{f(x_n)}{f'(x_n)}$$
for n = 1, 2, 3, . . . , where $f'(x_n)$ is the first derivative of f at x_n.

NUMBER THEORY

The Fibonacci Sequence begins 1, 1, 2, 3, 5, 8, 13, . . . , and each term from the third on is the sum of the two preceding terms.

58. Read N and print the first N terms of the Fibonacci Sequence.

59. Given A and B, print all terms of the Fibonacci Sequence that lie between A and B.

60. Find N such that the sum of the first N Fibonacci numbers exceeds 10^8.

61. What happens to the ratio of consecutive Fibonacci numbers as the number of terms becomes very large?

A whole number expressed in base ten can also be shown as a numeral in another base and vice-versa. Solve the problems below.

62. Given the base ten numeral for a whole number, convert it to a base-n numeral (n is a whole number such that $2 \le n < 10$).

63. Count to thirty-one in base two.

64. Given an octal (base eight) numeral for a whole number, print the same number in binary form.

65. Given the binary representation of a whole number, convert to octal.

66. Add pairs of binary whole numbers. Do not convert to decimal.

67. Add pairs of base-n whole numbers (n a whole number such that $2 \le n < 10$). Do not convert to decimal.

The Lucas numbers are similar to the Fibonacci numbers but the sequence begins differently: 1, 3, 4, 7, 11, 18, 29, 47, ... Do Exercises 68 and 69.

68. Accept N and print the first N Lucas numbers.

69. Which of the first fifty Lucas numbers are divisible by five?

70. Print the first fifty primes. As the primes are found, store them in an array so that they may be used to test later integers. Also gain efficiency by immediately printing 2 as the first prime (and storing it as the first element of the array) and then testing only odd numbers greater than two. (See Ex. 106, p. 143.)

71. Another method of finding primes is the Sieve of Erastothenes. Simulate the Sieve for the integers 1 to 100. Print 0's in place of the composites (and in place of one).

72. Print a table giving the number and percent of primes in the intervals 2–100, 101–200, 201–300, . . . , 901–1000.

73. Fermat proposed that all numbers of the form $2^{2^n} + 1$ ($n = 0,1,2,3$, . . .) are primes. Show that the statement is true for $n = 0,1,2,3,4$ but not for $n = 5$.

74. A rich man wants to give away a sum of money by dividing the sum equally among a number of needy families. (The sum is below $10,000 and he will calculate the equal division to pennies.) If he kept a penny, he could divide it equally among 31 families; if he kept a nickel, he could divide it among 32 families; if he kept a dime, he could divide it among 33 families; and if he kept a quarter, he could divide it equally among 35 families. How much money does he have to give away? (Use a trial-and-error method.)

75. Mersenne primes are of the form $2^p - 1$ where p is a prime. For every Mersenne prime there is a corresponding perfect number $2^{p-1}(2^p - 1)$. Find three Mersenne primes and the corresponding perfect numbers.

76. Use Zeller's Congruence Law to determine the day of the week for a given date from the past or future.

77. Find the *LCM* and *GCF* for a set of N positive integers.

78. Decide whether a set of N positive integers are relatively prime.

79. Program the computer to play the game of "Buzz." That is, count from 1 to 100 but for any number containing the digit 7 or any number divisible by 7, say "Buzz" instead of saying the number. For numbers that contain the digit 7 and are also divisible by 7, say "Buzz-Buzz."

80. Divide pairs of base-ten whole numbers by over-and-over subtraction, giving the quotient and the remainder. For example, for 73 and 6, print a quotient of 12 and remainder 1.

STATISTICS

These problems utilize common statistical methods for analyzing an array of data. Finding the average or *mean* was explained in the chapter.

81. The **median** of a list of numbers is that element such that when the numbers are arranged in either ascending or descending order, half the elements lie above it and half below. This can happen only when there are an odd number of elements in the list. If the array contains an even number of items, the median is the average of the two numbers in the middle. Input an array and print the median.

82. The **mode** of a list of numbers is that value which occurs most often. An array may have more than one mode. Write a program to accept an array and print the mode(s) and the number of times each mode occurs.

83. A set of data (for example, test results) can be summarized by a *frequency distribution chart*. For example, if the list is 90, 85, 100, 85, 60, 70, 80, 80, 95, 80, 75, 70, 95, 80, 65, 80, 75, 80, 75, the frequency distribution chart looks like the one at the right. Write a program to input the raw scores and print the frequency distribution chart.

Value	Frequency
100	1
95	2
90	1
85	2
80	6
75	3
70	2
65	1
60	1

84. The *standard deviation* of a list of data measures how "spread out" or "scattered" the data is. Specifically, to find the standard deviation do the following:
   (a) compute the mean;
   (b) subtract each item in the list from the mean and square this difference;
   (c) sum the squared differences of (**b**);
   (d) divide this sum by n, the number of values in the list;
   (e) take the square root of the quotient from (**d**).
   Write a program to accept a list of data and print the standard deviation.

When you take a standardized test, your score is reported by *percentile* rank. If you rank at the 90th percentile, then your score on the test was equal to or better than 90% of the students who took the test.

85. Accept a list of test scores and the number of students who made each score and print the percentile table for the test.

86. Given the raw scores from a test, output the percentile table. Now the program must organize the data before percentiles can be computed.

87. The mean and standard deviation of a list of raw scores are used to convert the scores to "z-scores" (also called "*t*-scores" or "standard scores"). Reducing data to standard scores allows results of different tests to be compared because an array of z-scores has a mean of zero and standard deviation of one. A standard score in effect tells how many standard deviation units above or below the mean a given raw score lies. (For national tests z-scores are often further converted by multiplying by ten and adding fifty. This creates a scale where 50 is the mean and the standard deviation is ten; no score is negative.) Convert raw scores to z-scores.

88. The *relative error* of a measurement is the ratio $\dfrac{\text{maximum error}}{\text{measurement}}$
   For example, a measurement of .26 has a maximum error of .005. Hence the relative error of the measurement is

$$\frac{.005}{.26} = \frac{5}{260} = \frac{1}{52} \approx .0192 \approx 1.92\%$$

Given a measurement and the unit of measurement, compute the relative error and percent of error. For example, for .26 input .26, .01. For 93,000,000 miles input 93E6, 1E6.

89. Write a test-correcting program for multiple-choice tests. Assume there are twenty questions with five possible answers for each question. Count the number of questions each student gets right, the number wrong, and the number he does not answer.

6

MATRICES

6-1 WHAT IS A MATRIX?

Tables (rectangular arrays of numbers) often arise in business, science, and everyday life.

Example 1:

Table 6-1 lists the distances between certain cities.

Table 6-1 Distances Between Cities (in miles)

	New Orleans	New York	Miami	Denver	St. Paul	Los Angeles
New Orleans	0	1325	875	1282	1241	1901
New York	1325	0	1330	1851	1253	2915
Miami	875	1330	0	2046	1770	2712
Denver	1282	1851	2046	0	841	1134
St. Paul	1241	1253	1770	841	0	1940
Los Angeles	1901	2915	2712	1134	1940	0

Example 2:

Hiram orders an inventory of his clothing store. Table 6-2 summarizes the number of pairs of men's pants of each size and color.

Table 6-2 Hiram's Clothing Store: Inventory of Men's Pants

	Blue	Gray	Black	Red	White	Brown
small	27	15	22	4	6	32
medium	46	21	39	11	12	49
large	33	16	37	7	15	37

A rectangular array of numbers is called a **matrix**. In mathematical work the elements of a matrix are displayed between brackets. (Some texts enclose matrices in parentheses.) For example, Table 6-1 on page 176 includes the following matrix.

$$
\mathbf{A} = \begin{bmatrix}
0 & 1325 & 875 & 1282 & 1241 & 1901 \\
1325 & 0 & 1330 & 1851 & 1253 & 2915 \\
875 & 1330 & 0 & 2046 & 1770 & 2712 \\
1282 & 1851 & 2046 & 0 & 841 & 1134 \\
1241 & 1253 & 1770 & 841 & 0 & 1940 \\
1901 & 2915 & 2712 & 1134 & 1940 & 0
\end{bmatrix}
$$

A matrix is named by a variable, say **A**. Matrix **A** above is a 6×6 matrix; that is, **A** has six **rows** (horizontal) and six **columns** (vertical). The number of rows and the number of columns (in that order) are the **dimensions** of the matrix. A particular element is specified by a double subscript. The first subscript names the row; the second subscript gives the column. For example, in the matrix above,

$$A_{1,1} = 0 \qquad A_{3,2} = 1330 \qquad A_{6,2} = 2915.$$

row 1   column 1   row 3   column 2   row 6   column 2

In general, an element of matrix **A** can be referred to as $A_{i,j}$ where i denotes the row and j, the column.

A matrix such as the 6×6 matrix above is called a **square matrix** because the number of rows equals the number of columns. For an $n \times n$ matrix, n is called the *order* of the matrix. Thus the order of **A** is six.

A square matrix has a *main diagonal* consisting of the elements $A_{i,i}$. In Table 6-1 the main diagonal contains all zeros, each representing the distance from a city to itself.

A square matrix may be **symmetric**, like matrix **A**, in which case each element $A_{i,j}$ equals $A_{j,i}$. This is illustrated in the following diagram.

$$
\begin{bmatrix}
0 & 1325 & 875 & 1282 & 1241 & 1901 \\
1325 & 0 & 1330 & 1851 & 1253 & 2915 \\
875 & 1330 & 0 & 2046 & 1770 & 2712 \\
1282 & 1851 & 2046 & 0 & 841 & 1134 \\
1241 & 1253 & 1770 & 841 & 0 & 1940 \\
1901 & 2915 & 2712 & 1134 & 1940 & 0
\end{bmatrix}
$$

In a symmetric matrix row i equals column i.

A matrix does not have to be square (see Example 2 on page 176). Here are other examples of matrices, with the dimensions of each.

(a) $\begin{bmatrix} 4 & 6 & 0 \\ -3 & 2 & 1 \end{bmatrix}$ 2×3 **(b)** $[8 \quad 61 \quad 14 \quad -7]$ 1×4

(c) $\begin{bmatrix} 7 & 16 \\ .5 & 8 \\ -.01 & .4 \end{bmatrix}$ 3×2 **(d)** $\begin{bmatrix} 0 \\ 4 \\ -2 \\ 5 \end{bmatrix}$ 4×1

Example **b** shows that the concept of "matrix" includes the idea of an "array" or "list" studied in the last chapter. A matrix that has exactly one row or one column is often called a **vector**. A distinction is made between a "row vector" or "row matrix" (see Example **b**), and a "column vector" or "column matrix" (Example **d**).

EXERCISES 6-1

A Which of the following are mathematically accepted ways of denoting matrices?

1. 6, 8, −3

2. {6, 8, −3}

3. [6 8 −3]

4. $\begin{bmatrix} 6 \\ 8 \\ -3 \end{bmatrix}$

5. $\begin{bmatrix} 1 & 0 \\ 0 & 1 \end{bmatrix}$

6. ∅

Give the dimensions of each matrix.

7. [3 2]

8. $\begin{bmatrix} 7 \\ 10 \end{bmatrix}$

9. $\begin{bmatrix} 6 & 0 & -1 \\ 3 & -2 & 7 \end{bmatrix}$

10. $\begin{bmatrix} 1 & 0 & 0 & 0 & 1 \\ 0 & 1 & 0 & 1 & 0 \\ 0 & 0 & 1 & 0 & 0 \\ 1 & 1 & 0 & 1 & 0 \end{bmatrix}$

11. $\begin{bmatrix} 6 & 0 \\ 2 & 17 \\ 1 & .5 \end{bmatrix}$

12. [0]

13. Which matrices in Exercises 7 through 12, if any, are row vectors? Which are column vectors? Which are square matrices?

Let **T** be the matrix of the table in Example 2 on page 176. Give the number named by each of the following.

14. $T_{1,2}$ **15.** $T_{3,5}$ **16.** $T_{2,1}$ **17.** $T_{1+2,4}$ **18.** $T_{1,6-1}$

6-2 MATRIX INPUT-OUTPUT

In BASIC, as in mathematics, two subscripts are used to name an element of a matrix. The subscripts are written inside parentheses behind the letter naming the matrix. The first subscript gives the row; the second designates the column.

As an example, let $\mathbf{A} = \begin{bmatrix} 4 & 6 & 0 \\ -3 & 2 & 1 \end{bmatrix}$. Then in BASIC

$$A(1,2) = 6 \qquad A(2,1) = -3 \qquad A(1,3) = 0.$$

row column   row column   row column

The DIM statement for this array would be   10 DIM A(2,3)   . As with one-dimensional arrays, however, if neither of the subscripts exceeds ten, the DIM statement for that array may be omitted on most systems.

A matrix name must be a single letter. For example, X, Y, and Z are valid names for matrices but A1, B7, and M4 are not.

A matrix is read and stored by means of a nested loop.

```
10 DIM A(2,3)
20 FØR I = 1 TØ 2
30 FØR J = 1 TØ 3
40 READ A(I,J)
50 NEXT J
60 NEXT I
70 DATA 4,6,0,-3,2,1
     . . .
```

Matrix **A**, above, is used as DATA. Note that elements are listed by rows since J, the column subscript, is nested and varies faster than the row subscript, I.

For larger matrices, such as the one in Table 6-1 on page 176, it is a good idea to list each row in a separate DATA statement.

```
100 DATA 0,1325,875,1282,1241,1901
101 DATA 1325,0,1330,1851,1253,2915
102 DATA 875,1330,0,2046,1770,2712
103 DATA 1282,1851,2046,0,841,1134
104 DATA 1241,1253,1770,841,0,1940
105 DATA 1901,2915,2712,1134,1940,0
```

The READ loop above handles only 2×3 matrices. It can be generalized by first reading R and C, which give the number of rows and the number of columns, respectively, of the matrix that follows in the DATA. The loop is shown at the top of the next page.

```
10 DIM A(20,20)
20 READ R,C
21    REM    R = NØ. ØF RØWS IN THE MATRIX
22    REM    C = NØ. ØF CØLUMNS IN THE MATRIX
30 FØR I = 1 TØ R
40 FØR J = 1 TØ C
50 READ A(I,J)
60 NEXT J
70 NEXT I
80 DATA 2,3
81 DATA 4,6,0
82 DATA -3,2,1
   . . .
```

As mentioned for one-dimensional arrays, some systems allow variable subscripts in DIM statements, as in the following program.

```
10 READ R,C
20 DIM A(R,C)
30 FØR I = 1 TØ R
40 FØR J = 1 TØ C
50 READ A(I,J)
60 NEXT J
70 NEXT I
   . . .
```

A nested loop is also used to print a matrix.

```
                    . . .
100 FØR I = 1 TØ R
110 FØR J = 1 TØ C
120 PRINT A(I,J);
130 NEXT J
140 PRINT
150 NEXT I
                    . . .
```

A semicolon is added at the end of line 120 so that all elements of each row will print on one line. The purpose of line 140 is to get off that line before the next row is printed.

However, the semicolon of line 120 often causes a format problem. We like the elements of a matrix to be in straight columns. But the semicolon will not necessarily do this. For example, the matrix of Table 6-1 on page 176 would print crooked columns like the one at the top of the next page.

```
O   1325  875   1282  1241  1901
1325  O   1330  1851  1253  2915
875  1330  O   2046  1770  2712
1282 1851  2046  O    841   1134
1241 1253  1770  841   O    1940
1901 2915  2712  1134  1940  O
```

A comma at the end of line 120 instead of a semicolon would output the elements in aligned columns but would correctly print only matrices with five columns or fewer. (The TAB function discussed in the next chapter can be used to print the matrix neatly in columns even when there are more than five of them.)

SUMMARY: when printing matrices with five or fewer columns, use a comma after "PRINT A(I,J)". If the matrix has more than five columns, a semicolon will have to be used.

EXERCISES 6-2

A   Let $S = \begin{bmatrix} 7 & -3 & 2 \\ 0 & 4 & 16 \\ -5 & 9 & -1 \end{bmatrix}$. Use a BASIC subscripted variable to name each of these elements of the matrix.

Example: 0   **Answer:** s(2,1)

   1. −3   **2.** 4   **3.** 16   **4.** −5   **5.** −1

Write a BASIC subscripted variable for each of these mathematical variables.

Example: $a_{i,j}$ **Answer:** A(I,J)

   6. $x_{1,4}$ **7.** $y_{i+1,j}$ **8.** $b_{2x,2y}$ **9.** $k_{r,c}$
   10. $m_{1,d}$ **11.** $g_{i,i}$ **12.** $a_{r-1,c+1}$ **13.** $d_{10,6}$

14. To read the matrix on the right, a programmer writes this loop.

$\begin{bmatrix} 8 & 3 & 1 & 2 \\ -1 & 7 & 4 & 0 \\ 10 & -6 & 3 & 5 \end{bmatrix}$

```
5 DIM M(3,4)
10 FØR J = 1 TØ 4
20 FØR I = 1 TØ 3
30 READ M(I,J)
40 NEXT I
50 NEXT J
```

Write the DATA step(s) he needs to input this matrix properly with this loop.

15. Write a program to read the matrix on the right and print the matrix that results when all the elements are multiplied by two.

$$\begin{bmatrix} 9 & .3 & -1 & 7 \\ 2 & 0 & 4 & 3 \\ -.1 & 7 & 2 & 11 \end{bmatrix}$$

16. Will the READ loop and DATA steps below properly input the matrix at the right?

$$\begin{bmatrix} 7 & 13 & 6 \\ -4 & 21 & -2 \\ 0 & 10 & 9 \end{bmatrix}$$

```
5 DIM B(5,5)
10 FØR I = 1 TØ 3
20 READ B(I,1),B(I,2),B(I,3)
30 NEXT I
       . . .

200 DATA 7,13,6,-4,21,-2,0,10,9
210 END
```

Consider the partial program at the right. Show the output when each of the following sets of statements is added to this partial program.

```
10 DIM X(3,4)
20 FØR I = 1 TØ 3
30 FØR J = 1 TØ 4
40 READ X(I,J)
60 NEXT J
70 NEXT I
80 DATA 71,-18,24,6,121,62,-5
82 DATA 141,.08,1.2,7.35,-1.5
90 . . .
```

17. 50 PRINT X(I,J);

18. 50 PRINT X(I,J);
    65 PRINT

19. 50 PRINT X(I,J),
    65 PRINT

B **20.** Prepare a flowchart for the loop at the top of page 180.
   21. Prepare a flowchart for the third loop on page 180.
   22. Rewrite the loop in Exercise 21 to output the matrix double-spaced.
   23. $r \times c$ matrices **A** and **B** are equal if all corresponding elements are equal: A(1,1) = B(1,1), A(1,2) = B(1,2), . . . , A(R,C) = B(R,C). Write a program to decide whether two $r \times c$ matrices are equal.
   24. The "transpose" of matrix **A**, represented by $\mathbf{A}^T$, is the matrix formed by reversing the rows and columns: the first row becomes the first column, the second row becomes the second column, and so forth. Write a program to read a matrix and print its transpose.

6-3 ADDING MATRICES

Table 6-2 on page 176 listed the inventory of men's pants at Hiram's Clothing Store. Let us suppose that Hiram orders a new supply. Table 6-3 summarizes his new order.

Table 6-3 Hiram's Order for Men's Pants

	Blue	Grey	Black	Red	White	Brown
small	12	9	10	2	6	20
medium	12	15	16	0	12	11
large	24	8	5	2	15	13

After the new shipment arrives, what is Hiram's total inventory by size and color?

The answer is found by performing *matrix addition.*

$$\begin{bmatrix} 27 & 15 & 22 & 4 & 6 & 32 \\ 46 & 21 & 39 & 11 & 12 & 49 \\ 33 & 16 & 37 & 7 & 15 & 37 \end{bmatrix} + \begin{bmatrix} 12 & 9 & 10 & 2 & 6 & 20 \\ 12 & 15 & 16 & 0 & 12 & 11 \\ 24 & 8 & 5 & 2 & 15 & 13 \end{bmatrix} = \begin{bmatrix} 39 & 24 & 32 & 6 & 12 & 52 \\ 58 & 36 & 55 & 11 & 24 & 60 \\ 57 & 24 & 42 & 9 & 30 & 50 \end{bmatrix}$$

previous inventory   +   new shipment   =   updated inventory

The boxed elements shown in the matrix addition above are examples of the following rule.

RULE FOR ADDING MATRICES

Two matrices with the same dimensions are added by adding corresponding elements. Matrices with different dimensions cannot be added.

This rule fits Hiram's problem perfectly since corresponding elements of the two matrices represent the same size and color pants.

Here are further examples of matrix addition.

1. $\begin{bmatrix} 6 & 2 & 3 \\ 4 & -1 & -5 \end{bmatrix} + \begin{bmatrix} 10 & -6 & 4 \\ 3 & 2 & 7 \end{bmatrix} = \begin{bmatrix} 16 & -4 & 7 \\ 7 & 1 & 2 \end{bmatrix}$

2. $\begin{bmatrix} 3 & 0 \\ 1 & -5 \end{bmatrix} + \begin{bmatrix} 7 & -3 \\ 4 & 0 \end{bmatrix} = \begin{bmatrix} 10 & -3 \\ 5 & -5 \end{bmatrix}$

3. $\begin{bmatrix} 6 & 2 & 3 \\ 4 & -1 & -5 \end{bmatrix}$ and $\begin{bmatrix} 3 & 0 \\ 1 & -5 \end{bmatrix}$ cannot be added.

For any set of $r \times c$ matrices, the additive identity matrix or **zero matrix**, is the $r \times c$ matrix each of whose elements is 0. Examples are shown below and at the top of the next page.

4. The 2×2 zero matrix is $\begin{bmatrix} 0 & 0 \\ 0 & 0 \end{bmatrix}$. Thus, $\begin{bmatrix} 3 & 0 \\ 1 & -5 \end{bmatrix} + \begin{bmatrix} 0 & 0 \\ 0 & 0 \end{bmatrix} = \begin{bmatrix} 3 & 0 \\ 1 & -5 \end{bmatrix}$

5. The 1×5 zero matrix is $[0 \quad 0 \quad 0 \quad 0 \quad 0]$.

To program matrix addition, we logically need these steps.

1. Read the elements of matrix **A** (dimensions $r \times c$).
2. Read the elements of matrix **B** (also $r \times c$).
3. Add the elements of matrices **A** and **B**.
4. Print the sum.
5. Return to step 1 for new DATA.

The computer can begin adding the elements of the matrices as soon as it has read the latest element of Matrix **B**. Hence the loops for reading **B**, adding **A** and **B**, and printing the sum can be combined. Here is a program for the algorithm above with the entries of Examples 1 and 2 on page 183 as DATA.

Program 6-1: Adding Two $r \times c$ Matrices

```
10 DIM A(5,5),B(5,5)
20 READ R,C
30 FØR I = 1 TØ R
40 FØR J = 1 TØ C
50 READ A(I,J)
60 NEXT J
70 NEXT I
80 FØR I = 1 TØ R
90 FØR J = 1 TØ C
100 READ B(I,J)
110 PRINT A(I,J) + B(I,J),
120 NEXT J
130 PRINT
140 NEXT I
145 PRINT
150 GØ TØ 20
160 DATA 2,3,6,2,3,4,-1,-5,10,-6,4,3
161 DATA 2,7,2,2,3,0,1,-5,7,-3,4,0
170 END
```

EXERCISES 6-3

A Add, if possible, the following matrices.

1. $\begin{bmatrix} 1 \\ -2 \end{bmatrix}, \begin{bmatrix} 5 \\ 6 \end{bmatrix}$

2. $\begin{bmatrix} 2 & -1 \\ 3 & 4 \end{bmatrix}, \begin{bmatrix} 0 & 6 \\ -8 & -12 \end{bmatrix}$

3. $\begin{bmatrix} 0 & 2 & 1 \\ -1 & 3 & 5 \end{bmatrix}, \begin{bmatrix} 7 & 9 \\ -8 & 11 \\ 30 & -10 \end{bmatrix}$

4. $\begin{bmatrix} 5 & -.04 & 13 \\ 21 & 11 & -2 \end{bmatrix}, \begin{bmatrix} 10 & -.01 & -5 \\ .5 & -3 & 9 \end{bmatrix}$

5. Show the output of Program 6-1 on page 184.
6. Would Program 6-1 yield the same results if line 110 were changed from "PRINT A(I,J) + B(I,J)," to "PRINT B(I,J) + A(I,J),"? What property of matrix addition applies here?

B

7. Change Program 6-1 so that it prints matrix **A**, skips a line, prints matrix **B**, skips a line, and then prints their sum.
8. Modify Program 6-1 to handle the situation where the two matrices to be read do not necessarily have the same dimensions. Have the computer print the two matrices, followed by their sum, or by the message CANNØT BE ADDED.
9. Write a program to read two 2×2 matrices, print them *side-by-side,* skip a line, and then print their sum.
10. Prepare a flowchart for Program 6-1.
11. Prepare a flowchart for the program of Exercise 8 above.
12. Write a program to add three matrices. Allow the possibility that the matrices cannot be added. (See Ex. 8.)
13. Write a program to add N $r \times c$ matrices, where N is read from DATA.

C

14. Addition of real numbers is closed, commutative, associative, and has identity and inverse elements. Which of these properties does addition of matrices of the same dimensions possess? If the identity property holds, what is the additive identity for $r \times c$ matrices? If the inverse property holds, what is the additive inverse of a particular $r \times c$ matrix?

6-4 SCALAR MULTIPLICATION; MATRIX SUBTRACTION

Let us change the example of the last lesson. Suppose that Hiram wishes to double his inventory of men's pants. This idea corresponds to **scalar multiplication** of the matrix of Table 6-2 on page 176. A **scalar** is any real number. In this case the scalar is two.

$$2\begin{bmatrix} 27 & 15 & 22 & 4 & 6 & 32 \\ 46 & 21 & 39 & 11 & 12 & 49 \\ 33 & 16 & 37 & 7 & 15 & 37 \end{bmatrix} = \begin{bmatrix} 54 & 30 & 44 & 8 & 12 & 64 \\ 92 & 42 & 78 & 22 & 24 & 98 \\ 66 & 32 & 74 & 14 & 30 & 74 \end{bmatrix}$$

RULE FOR SCALAR MULTIPLICATION
To multiply a matrix by a scalar k, multiply each element of the matrix by k.

Here are some more examples.

1. $-3\begin{bmatrix} 3 & -1 & 4 \\ -2 & 0 & 7 \end{bmatrix} = \begin{bmatrix} -9 & 3 & -12 \\ 6 & 0 & -21 \end{bmatrix}$

2. $.5\begin{bmatrix} 4 & 0 \\ 3 & 1 \\ -2 & 5 \end{bmatrix} = \begin{bmatrix} 2 & 0 \\ 1.5 & .5 \\ -1 & 2.5 \end{bmatrix}$

3. $-5\begin{bmatrix} 6 & -1 & 4 & .8 \end{bmatrix} = \begin{bmatrix} -30 & 5 & -20 & -4.0 \end{bmatrix}$

We can now define **matrix subtraction** by using the scalar -1. If **A** and **B** are $r \times c$ matrices, then

$$\mathbf{A} - \mathbf{B} = \mathbf{A} + (-1)\mathbf{B}.$$

Examples:

1. If $\mathbf{A} = \begin{bmatrix} 8 & 2 \\ 0 & -5 \end{bmatrix}$ and $\mathbf{B} = \begin{bmatrix} 12 & 0 \\ 1 & 13 \end{bmatrix}$, then $\mathbf{A} - \mathbf{B} = \mathbf{A} + (-1)\mathbf{B} =$

$$\begin{bmatrix} 8 & 2 \\ 0 & -5 \end{bmatrix} + (-1)\begin{bmatrix} 12 & 0 \\ 1 & 13 \end{bmatrix} = \begin{bmatrix} 8 & 2 \\ 0 & -5 \end{bmatrix} + \begin{bmatrix} -12 & 0 \\ -1 & -13 \end{bmatrix} = \begin{bmatrix} -4 & 2 \\ -1 & -18 \end{bmatrix}$$

2. Hiram's inventory of men's pants at the beginning of a month is shown below.

	blue	grey	black	red	white	brown
small	39	24	32	6	12	52
medium	58	36	55	11	24	60
large	57	24	42	9	30	50

The sales for the month are given by this table.

	blue	grey	black	red	white	brown
small	8	6	5	1	3	15
medium	12	6	14	3	10	13
large	10	4	7	0	9	8

Then the inventory at the end of the month can be found by matrix subtraction.

$$\begin{bmatrix} 39 & 24 & 32 & 6 & 12 & 52 \\ 58 & 36 & 55 & 11 & 24 & 60 \\ 57 & 24 & 42 & 9 & 30 & 50 \end{bmatrix} - \begin{bmatrix} 8 & 6 & 5 & 1 & 3 & 15 \\ 12 & 6 & 14 & 3 & 10 & 13 \\ 10 & 4 & 7 & 0 & 9 & 8 \end{bmatrix} =$$

$$\begin{bmatrix} 31 & 18 & 27 & 5 & 9 & 37 \\ 46 & 30 & 41 & 8 & 14 & 47 \\ 47 & 20 & 35 & 9 & 21 & 42 \end{bmatrix}$$

The matrix $(-1)\mathbf{B}$ can also be written as $-\mathbf{B}$ and is the **additive inverse** of **B** since the sum of **B** and $-\mathbf{B}$ is the $r \times c$ zero matrix.

$$\mathbf{B} + (-\mathbf{B}) = \begin{bmatrix} 12 & 0 \\ 1 & 13 \end{bmatrix} + \begin{bmatrix} -12 & 0 \\ -1 & -13 \end{bmatrix} = \begin{bmatrix} 0 & 0 \\ 0 & 0 \end{bmatrix}$$

In a similar fashion the additive inverse of **L** is $-\mathbf{L}$.

$$\mathbf{L} = \begin{bmatrix} 6 & -1 & 0 \\ -7 & 5 & .5 \end{bmatrix} \qquad -\mathbf{L} = \begin{bmatrix} -6 & 1 & 0 \\ 7 & -5 & -.5 \end{bmatrix}$$

EXERCISES 6-4

A   Let $\mathbf{A} = \begin{bmatrix} 2 & 0 \\ -1 & 3 \end{bmatrix}$, $\mathbf{B} = \begin{bmatrix} 1 & 5 \\ 0 & -6 \end{bmatrix}$, and $\mathbf{C} = \begin{bmatrix} -2 & 0 \\ -4 & 7 \end{bmatrix}$. Compute each of the following.

1. $2\mathbf{A}$
2. $-4\mathbf{B}$
3. $-\mathbf{C}$
4. $\mathbf{A} - \mathbf{C}$
5. $\mathbf{B} + \mathbf{C} - \mathbf{A}$
6. $2\mathbf{A} - 4\mathbf{B}$
7. $\mathbf{C} - 3\mathbf{A}$
8. $\mathbf{B} + (-1)\mathbf{B}$
9. $2\mathbf{C} - (\mathbf{A} + \mathbf{B})$
10. $\frac{1}{2}(\mathbf{C} - \mathbf{B})$
11. $2(3\mathbf{A})$
12. $(2 \cdot 3)\mathbf{A}$
13. $3(\mathbf{A}^{\mathsf{T}})$ (See Ex. 24, p. 182.)
14. $(3\mathbf{A})^{\mathsf{T}}$
15. $\mathbf{A}^{\mathsf{T}} + \mathbf{B}^{\mathsf{T}}$
16. $(\mathbf{A} + \mathbf{B})^{\mathsf{T}}$
17. $\mathbf{B}^{\mathsf{T}} - \mathbf{C}^{\mathsf{T}}$
18. $(\mathbf{B} - \mathbf{C})^{\mathsf{T}}$

19. This table represents the prices of a pair of each type of pants at Hiram's Clothing Store.

	blue	grey	black	red	white	brown
small	8.98	9.50	8.98	8.98	9.98	8.98
medium	7.98	9.00	7.98	9.50	9.50	7.98
large	8.98	9.50	8.98	9.98	9.98	8.98

Hiram plans a sale. The price reduction for each size and color pants is given by this table.

	blue	grey	black	red	white	brown
small	1.00	1.50	1.00	1.50	1.50	1.00
medium	1.00	1.00	1.00	1.50	1.00	1.00
large	1.00	1.50	1.00	1.50	1.50	1.00

Give the table showing Hiram's net pants prices for the sale.

B   20. Is matrix subtraction a commutative operation? associative?
21. Write a program to input a matrix and print its additive inverse.
22. Write a program to input $r \times c$ matrices $\mathbf{A}$ and $\mathbf{B}$ and print $\mathbf{A} - \mathbf{B}$.
23. Write a program to input *and print* $r \times c$ matrices $\mathbf{A}$ and $\mathbf{B}$ and then print $\mathbf{A} - \mathbf{B}$.

Which of the following properties hold in a system of $r \times c$ matrices? ($\mathbf{A}$ and $\mathbf{B}$ are $r \times c$ matrices and m and n are scalars.)

24. $m(n\mathbf{A}) = (mn)\mathbf{A}$
25. $m(\mathbf{A} + \mathbf{B}) = m\mathbf{A} + m\mathbf{B}$
26. $m(\mathbf{A} - \mathbf{B}) = m\mathbf{A} - m\mathbf{B}$
27. $(m + n)\mathbf{A} = m\mathbf{A} + n\mathbf{A}$

28. Write a program to multiply any given matrix by any given scalar.

6-5 INNER PRODUCT OF VECTORS

Example 1:

A customer at Hiram's Clothing Store buys five pairs of medium-size pants: two blue pairs @ $7.98 each, one grey pair @ $9.00, and two white @ $9.50 each. The customer's total bill (before tax) can be computed by taking the inner product of two vectors. Let the order be expressed as the row vector $[2 \quad 1 \quad 2]$ and list the prices (per pair) in a column vector: $\begin{bmatrix} 7.98 \\ 9.00 \\ 9.50 \end{bmatrix}$. Then the *inner product* is a scalar which is computed as follows.

$$[2 \quad 1 \quad 2]\begin{bmatrix} 7.98 \\ 9.00 \\ 9.50 \end{bmatrix} = \begin{matrix} 2(7.98) + 1(9.00) + 2(9.50) = \\ 15.96 \quad + \quad 9.00 \quad + \quad 19.00 \quad = \$43.96 \end{matrix}$$

The **inner product** of a $1 \times r$ matrix (row vector) and an $r \times 1$ matrix (column vector) equals the sum of the products of the corresponding elements of the matrices. Using letters to express general formulas, we have the following.

$r = 1$: $[a][b] = ab$

$r = 2$: $[a \quad b]\begin{bmatrix} c \\ d \end{bmatrix} = ac + bd$

$r = 3$: $[a \quad b \quad c]\begin{bmatrix} d \\ e \\ f \end{bmatrix} = ad + be + cf$

$r = 4$: $[a \quad b \quad c \quad d]\begin{bmatrix} e \\ f \\ g \\ h \end{bmatrix} = ae + bf + cg + dh$

Here are some other instances of inner products.

(a) $[6 \quad -4]\begin{bmatrix} 3 \\ 5 \end{bmatrix} = 18 - 20 = -2$

(b) $[5 \quad 3 \quad 10]\begin{bmatrix} 2.00 \\ 1.00 \\ 2.00 \end{bmatrix} = 10.00 + 3.00 + 20.00 = 33.00$

(c) $[0 \quad 0 \quad 0]\begin{bmatrix} 871 \\ -43 \\ 61.5 \end{bmatrix} = 0 + 0 + 0 = 0$

The "inner product of $[6 \quad -4]$ and $\begin{bmatrix} 13 \\ -11 \\ 10 \end{bmatrix}$" cannot be taken.

Example 2:

In baseball the total bases produced by a hitter is expressed as follows.

$$1 \times \begin{pmatrix} \text{Number of} \\ \text{singles} \end{pmatrix} + 2 \times \begin{pmatrix} \text{Number of} \\ \text{doubles} \end{pmatrix} + 3 \times \begin{pmatrix} \text{Number of} \\ \text{triples} \end{pmatrix} + 4 \times \begin{pmatrix} \text{Number of} \\ \text{home runs} \end{pmatrix}$$

This formula can be expressed as the inner product of the vector [1 2 3 4], which gives the number of bases for each type of hit, with a column vector which gives the number of singles, doubles, triples, and homers of a player (in that order). For example, if Joe Slobotnik has 23 singles, 8 doubles, 2 triples, and 5 home runs, his total bases are as shown below.

$$\begin{bmatrix} 1 & 2 & 3 & 4 \end{bmatrix} \begin{bmatrix} 23 \\ 8 \\ 2 \\ 5 \end{bmatrix} = 23 + 16 + 6 + 20 = 65$$

To program the inner product operation, first input a $1 \times r$ vector **A** and an $r \times 1$ vector **B**. Then, since a sum must be accumulated, initialize to 0 a location s. In a FOR-NEXT loop compute the products of corresponding elements of the vectors and add these products to s.

Program 6-2: Compute Inner Product of Vectors

```
10 DIM A(1,20),B(20,1)
20 READ R
30 FØR I = 1 TØ R
40 READ A(1,I)
50 NEXT I
60 FØR I = 1 TØ R
70 READ B(I,1)
80 NEXT I
90 LET S = O
100 FØR I = 1 TØ R
110 LET S = S + A(1,I) * B(I,1)
120 NEXT I
130 PRINT "INNER PRØDUCT = " S
140 GØ TØ 20
150 DATA ...
200 END
```

EXERCISES 6-5

A   Give the inner product of [2 −3 4] and each of the following.

1. $\begin{bmatrix} 8 \\ -10 \\ -6 \end{bmatrix}$ **2.** $\begin{bmatrix} 1 \\ 0 \\ 1 \end{bmatrix}$ **3.** $\begin{bmatrix} 7 \\ -1 \\ 2 \end{bmatrix}$ **4.** $[2 \; -3 \; 4]^\mathsf{T}$
(See Ex. 24, p. 182.)

Give the inner product, if possible, for each pair of vectors.

5. $\begin{bmatrix} 6 & 5 \end{bmatrix} \begin{bmatrix} 20 \\ 30 \end{bmatrix}$

6. $\begin{bmatrix} 13 & 31 & 29 \end{bmatrix} \begin{bmatrix} 7 \\ 11 \\ -9 \\ 23 \end{bmatrix}$

7. $\begin{bmatrix} 1 & 0 & 3 & 2 \end{bmatrix} \begin{bmatrix} -16 \\ 42 \\ -5 \\ 6 \end{bmatrix}$

B
8. A customer in a grocery buys 2 quarts of milk @ 64¢/quart, 3 boxes of cereal @ 24¢/box, 2 dozen eggs @ 65¢/dozen, and a jar of mayonnaise @ 57¢/jar. Use the inner product of two vectors to compute the customer's total charge (without tax).
9. Use the inner product of two vectors to calculate the total bases of a baseball hitter with 10 singles, 4 doubles, 1 triple, and 2 home runs.
10. A steel company makes three alloys. 1.5% of alloy A is iron ore, 1.7% of alloy B is iron ore, and 2% of alloy C is iron ore. Use an inner product to calculate the total amount of iron ore needed to produce 500 tons of alloy A, 200 tons of alloy B, and 350 tons of alloy C.
11. Prepare a flowchart for Program 6-2 on page 189.
12. Revise Program 6-2 so that it handles A and B as one-dimensional arrays, that is, with one subscript instead of two.

6-6 MULTIPLYING MATRICES

We introduce matrix multiplication by means of several examples.

Example 1:

Big Brain Computer Corporation maintains an armada of automobiles and trucks for its sales and maintenance forces. Table 6-4 gives the operating costs per vehicle per year.

Table 6-4   Annual Operating Costs Per Vehicle

	Automobiles	Trucks
Depreciation	$500	$900
Taxes	50	95
Maintenance	800	650

Table 6-5 lists the number of each type of vehicle owned by BBCC for four years.

Table 6-5   Number of Motor Vehicles Owned by BBCC

	1970	1971	1972	1973
Automobiles	20	25	35	50
Trucks	5	10	15	25

MATRICES   **191**

Here are some questions about Big Brain's vehicle costs.

Question 1: How much did automobile depreciation cost in 1970?

Answer: $\begin{pmatrix} \text{Amount of} \\ \text{depreciation} \end{pmatrix} \times \begin{pmatrix} \text{Number of} \\ \text{cars in 1970} \end{pmatrix} = \$500(20) = \$10,000$

Question 2: What was the amount of taxes on trucks in 1972?

Answer: $\begin{pmatrix} \text{Taxes per} \\ \text{truck} \end{pmatrix} \times \begin{pmatrix} \text{Number of} \\ \text{trucks in 1972} \end{pmatrix} = \$95(15) = \$1425$

Question 3: What was the total maintenance cost for both automobiles and trucks in 1973?

Answer: $800 × 50 + $650 × 25 =

$\begin{pmatrix} \text{Maintenance} \\ \text{per car} \end{pmatrix}$ $\begin{pmatrix} \text{Number of} \\ \text{cars in 1973} \end{pmatrix}$ $\begin{pmatrix} \text{Maintenance} \\ \text{per truck} \end{pmatrix}$ $\begin{pmatrix} \text{Number of} \\ \text{trucks in 1973} \end{pmatrix}$

$40000 + $16250 = $56250

$\begin{pmatrix} \text{Total auto} \\ \text{maintenance} \end{pmatrix}$ $\begin{pmatrix} \text{Total truck} \\ \text{maintenance} \end{pmatrix}$ $\begin{pmatrix} \text{Total maintenance} \\ \text{in 1973} \end{pmatrix}$

This last calculation is the inner product $\begin{bmatrix} 800 & 650 \end{bmatrix} \begin{bmatrix} 50 \\ 25 \end{bmatrix}$.

These questions and others like them can all be answered easiest from a table summarizing vehicle costs over the four year period. This table results from matrix multiplication. Let C = the cost matrix of Table 6-4 and N = the number-of-vehicles matrix from Table 6-5.

$$C = \begin{bmatrix} 500 & 900 \\ 50 & 95 \\ 800 & 650 \end{bmatrix} \qquad N = \begin{bmatrix} 20 & 25 & 35 & 50 \\ 5 & 10 & 15 & 25 \end{bmatrix}$$

The product $C \times N$ is calculated as follows.

$$C \times N = \begin{bmatrix} 500 & 900 \\ 50 & 95 \\ 800 & 650 \end{bmatrix} \times \begin{bmatrix} 20 & 25 & 35 & 50 \\ 5 & 10 & 15 & 25 \end{bmatrix} =$$

$$\begin{bmatrix} 500(20) + 900(5) & 500(25) + 900(10) & 500(35) + 900(15) & 500(50) + 900(25) \\ 50(20) + 95(5) & 50(25) + 95(10) & 50(35) + 95(15) & 50(50) + 95(25) \\ 800(20) + 650(5) & 800(25) + 650(10) & 800(35) + 650(15) & 800(50) + 650(25) \end{bmatrix}$$

$$= \begin{bmatrix} 14500 & 21500 & 31000 & 47500 \\ 1475 & 2200 & 3175 & 4875 \\ 19250 & 26500 & 37750 & 56250 \end{bmatrix}$$

Matrix multiplication consists of a sequence of inner products, with each inner product (a scalar) forming an entry in the product matrix. Each row of matrix **C** is a vector and each column of **N** is a vector. To multiply **C** times **N**, take each row of **C** and compute its inner product with each column of **N**. For example, the inner product of the *second* row of **C** with the *third* column of **N** gives the element in the second row, third column of the product matrix (3175). The answer to Question 3 earlier is found in the third row, fourth column of **C** × **N**.

$$
\begin{bmatrix} 500 & 900 \\ 50 & 95 \\ 800 & 650 \end{bmatrix} \times \begin{bmatrix} 20 & 25 & 35 & 50 \\ 5 & 10 & 15 & 25 \end{bmatrix} = \begin{bmatrix} 14500 & 21500 & 31000 & 47500 \\ 1475 & 2200 & 3175 & 4875 \\ 19250 & 26500 & 37750 & 56250 \end{bmatrix}
$$

The product **C** × **N** can be displayed in tabular form with rows and columns labeled.

Table 6-6 Total Vehicle Costs for BBCC (1970–73)

	1970	*1971*	*1972*	*1973*
Total depreciation	$14500	$21500	$31000	$47500
Total taxes	1475	2200	3175	4875
Total maintenance	19250	26500	37750	56250

The multiplication process requires that the number of columns of the first matrix equal the number of rows of the second matrix. Otherwise the matrices cannot be multiplied. Thus, in Example 1 on page 191 **C** × **N** is possible but **N** × **C** is not.

RULE FOR MULTIPLICATION OF MATRICES
If matrix **A** has dimensions $m \times n$ and matrix **B** has dimensions $p \times q$, then **A** and **B** can be multiplied if and only if $n = p$. The product will have dimensions $m \times q$.

If $n = p$, the matrices are said to be **conformable** or **compatible**.

Check the dimensions of the matrices in Example 1 to see that the rule holds.

$$
\begin{bmatrix} 500 & 900 \\ 50 & 95 \\ 800 & 650 \end{bmatrix} \times \begin{bmatrix} 20 & 25 & 35 & 50 \\ 5 & 10 & 15 & 25 \end{bmatrix} = \begin{bmatrix} 14500 & 21500 & 31000 & 47500 \\ 1475 & 2200 & 3175 & 4875 \\ 19250 & 26500 & 37750 & 56250 \end{bmatrix}
$$

3×2 *These must be equal.* 2×4 3×4

m n p q m q

Multiplication of polynomials can be accomplished by matrix multiplication. Compare the "long multiplication" of algebra with matrix multiplication.

Example 2: $(4x^3 - 6x^2 + x + 3) \cdot (x^2 + 2x - 1)$

Solution: "Long Multiplication"

$$
\begin{array}{r}
4x^3 - 6x^2 + x + 3 \\
\underline{x^2 + 2x - 1} \\
4x^5 - 6x^4 + x^3 + 3x^2 \\
8x^4 - 12x^3 + 2x^2 + 6x \\
\underline{- 4x^3 + 6x^2 - x - 3} \\
4x^5 + 2x^4 - 15x^3 + 11x^2 + 5x - 3
\end{array}
$$

Matrix Multiplication

$$
\begin{bmatrix} 1 & 2 & -1 \end{bmatrix}
\begin{bmatrix}
4 & -6 & 1 & 3 & 0 & 0 \\
0 & 4 & -6 & 1 & 3 & 0 \\
0 & 0 & 4 & -6 & 1 & 3
\end{bmatrix}
= \begin{bmatrix} 4 & 2 & -15 & 11 & 5 & -3 \end{bmatrix}
$$

Matrix for   "Staggered" matrix for   Matrix for
$x^2 + 2x - 1$ $4x^3 - 6x^2 + x + 3$ $4x^5 + 2x^4 - 15x^3 + 11x^2 + 5x - 3$
(1×3) (3×6) (1×6)

A closer examination of the two methods reveals why they yield the same result. Examine closely the third column of terms in the "long multiplication" and the inner product of the row vector and third column of the "staggered" matrix in the matrix multiplication.

$$
\begin{array}{r}
4x^3 - 6x^2 + x + 3 \\
\underline{x^2 + 2x - 1} \\
4x^5 - 6x^4 + x^3 + 3x^2 \\
8x^4 - 12x^3 + 2x^2 + 6x \\
\underline{- 4x^3 + 6x^2 - x - 3} \\
4x^5 + 2x^4 - 15x^3 + 11x^2 + 5x - 3
\end{array}
$$

$$
\begin{bmatrix} 1 & 2 & -1 \end{bmatrix}
\begin{bmatrix}
4 & -6 & \boxed{1} & 3 & 0 & 0 \\
0 & 4 & \boxed{-6} & 1 & 3 & 0 \\
0 & 0 & \boxed{4} & -6 & 1 & 3
\end{bmatrix} =
$$

$$
\begin{bmatrix} 4 & 2 & \underbrace{1 + (-12) + (-4)} & 11 & 5 & -3 \end{bmatrix}
$$

same coefficients being
added

For 2×2 matrices, since there are so few terms, multiplication can be reduced to a formula.

$$
\begin{bmatrix} a & b \\ c & d \end{bmatrix} \times \begin{bmatrix} e & f \\ g & h \end{bmatrix} = \begin{bmatrix} ae + bg & af + bh \\ ce + dg & cf + dh \end{bmatrix}
$$

In general, matrix multiplication is not commutative. For the 2×2 case just given,

$$
\begin{bmatrix} e & f \\ g & h \end{bmatrix} \times \begin{bmatrix} a & b \\ c & d \end{bmatrix} = \begin{bmatrix} ea + fc & eb + fd \\ ga + hc & gb + hd \end{bmatrix} \neq \begin{bmatrix} a & b \\ c & d \end{bmatrix} \times \begin{bmatrix} e & f \\ g & h \end{bmatrix}.
$$

In other instances the fact that matrix multiplication is not commutative is even more obvious because matrices conformable in one order cannot even be multiplied when reversed. For example,

$$\begin{bmatrix} 2 & -3 \\ 4 & 0 \end{bmatrix} \times \begin{bmatrix} 8 & 7 & 0 \\ -2 & 1 & 4 \end{bmatrix} = \begin{bmatrix} 22 & 11 & -12 \\ 32 & 28 & 0 \end{bmatrix}$$ but

$$\begin{bmatrix} 8 & 7 & 0 \\ -2 & 1 & 4 \end{bmatrix} \times \begin{bmatrix} 2 & -3 \\ 4 & 0 \end{bmatrix}$$ cannot be multiplied.

An odd fact, offered here without explanation, is that, although matrix multiplication is not commutative, it is associative, that is if **A**, **B**, and **C** are matrices and if (**A** × **B**) × **C** exists, then (**A** × **B**) × **C** = **A** × (**B** × **C**).

Like real numbers, square matrices can be raised to powers. For example, if $\mathbf{A} = \begin{bmatrix} 1 & 3 \\ -1 & 2 \end{bmatrix}$, then

$$\mathbf{A}^2 = \mathbf{A} \times \mathbf{A} = \begin{bmatrix} 1 & 3 \\ -1 & 2 \end{bmatrix} \times \begin{bmatrix} 1 & 3 \\ -1 & 2 \end{bmatrix} = \begin{bmatrix} -2 & 9 \\ -3 & 1 \end{bmatrix}$$

$$\mathbf{A}^3 = \mathbf{A}^2 \times \mathbf{A} = \begin{bmatrix} -2 & 9 \\ -3 & 1 \end{bmatrix} \times \begin{bmatrix} 1 & 3 \\ -1 & 2 \end{bmatrix} = \begin{bmatrix} -11 & 12 \\ -4 & -7 \end{bmatrix}$$

$$\mathbf{A}^4 = \mathbf{A}^3 \times \mathbf{A} = \begin{bmatrix} -11 & 12 \\ -4 & -7 \end{bmatrix} \times \begin{bmatrix} 1 & 3 \\ -1 & 2 \end{bmatrix} = \begin{bmatrix} -23 & -9 \\ 3 & -26 \end{bmatrix}$$ and so forth.

We have already seen that a set of $r \times c$ matrices possesses an additive identity element, namely the $r \times c$ zero matrix. It is natural to ask whether a class of matrices can have a *multiplicative* identity element playing a role similar to the number one.

The answer is that only a set of square matrices has a multiplicative identity. The identity for each order n consists of 1's on the main diagonal and 0's everywhere else. Thus $\begin{bmatrix} 1 & 0 \\ 0 & 1 \end{bmatrix}$ is the 2 × 2 identity; $\begin{bmatrix} 1 & 0 & 0 \\ 0 & 1 & 0 \\ 0 & 0 & 1 \end{bmatrix}$

is the order-3 identity; $\begin{bmatrix} 1 & 0 & 0 & 0 \\ 0 & 1 & 0 & 0 \\ 0 & 0 & 1 & 0 \\ 0 & 0 & 0 & 1 \end{bmatrix}$ is the 4 × 4 identity, and so forth.

Examples:

$$\begin{bmatrix} 6 & -10 \\ -5 & 7 \end{bmatrix} \times \begin{bmatrix} 1 & 0 \\ 0 & 1 \end{bmatrix} = \begin{bmatrix} 1 & 0 \\ 0 & 1 \end{bmatrix} \times \begin{bmatrix} 6 & -10 \\ -5 & 7 \end{bmatrix} = \begin{bmatrix} 6 & -10 \\ -5 & 7 \end{bmatrix}$$

$$\begin{bmatrix} 1 & 0 & 0 \\ 0 & 1 & 0 \\ 0 & 0 & 1 \end{bmatrix} \times \begin{bmatrix} 11 & 0 & -3 \\ 5 & 9 & -1 \\ -2 & 1 & 7 \end{bmatrix} = \begin{bmatrix} 11 & 0 & -3 \\ 5 & 9 & -1 \\ -2 & 1 & 7 \end{bmatrix} \times \begin{bmatrix} 1 & 0 & 0 \\ 0 & 1 & 0 \\ 0 & 0 & 1 \end{bmatrix} = \begin{bmatrix} 11 & 0 & -3 \\ 5 & 9 & -1 \\ -2 & 1 & 7 \end{bmatrix}$$

EXERCISES 6-6

A   Multiply, if possible, each of the following pairs of matrices in the order shown.

1. $\begin{bmatrix} 1 & 6 \\ -6 & 1 \end{bmatrix}, \begin{bmatrix} 3 & -2 \\ 2 & 3 \end{bmatrix}$ **2.** $\begin{bmatrix} 5 & 1 & -7 \\ 0 & -3 & 6 \end{bmatrix}, \begin{bmatrix} 2 & 1 \\ 0 & -6 \end{bmatrix}$

3. $\begin{bmatrix} 2 & 1 \\ 0 & -6 \end{bmatrix}, \begin{bmatrix} 5 & 1 & -7 \\ 0 & -3 & 6 \end{bmatrix}$ **4.** $\begin{bmatrix} 61 & -47 & 92 \\ 113 & 27 & -18 \\ -9 & 86 & 59 \end{bmatrix}, \begin{bmatrix} 1 & 0 & 0 \\ 0 & 1 & 0 \\ 0 & 0 & 1 \end{bmatrix}$

5. $[16 \quad -4 \quad 0], \begin{bmatrix} 0 & 2 \\ -3 & 5 \end{bmatrix}$ **6.** $\begin{bmatrix} 2 & -4 & 6 \\ 0 & 1 & -3 \end{bmatrix}, \begin{bmatrix} -5 \\ 1 \\ 7 \end{bmatrix}$

7. $\begin{bmatrix} -3 & 5 \\ 1 & -2 \end{bmatrix}, \begin{bmatrix} -2 & -5 \\ -1 & -3 \end{bmatrix}$ **8.** $\begin{bmatrix} 2 & -1 \\ 2 & -1 \end{bmatrix}, \begin{bmatrix} 3 & 4 \\ 6 & 8 \end{bmatrix}$

9. $\begin{bmatrix} 2 & -1 \\ 3 & 4 \end{bmatrix}, \begin{bmatrix} 2 & -1 \\ 3 & 4 \end{bmatrix}^{\mathsf{T}}$ **10.** $\begin{bmatrix} 5 & -9 & 23 \\ 16 & -7 & 91 \end{bmatrix}, \begin{bmatrix} 0 & 0 \\ 0 & 0 \\ 0 & 0 \end{bmatrix}$

(See Ex. 24, p. 182.)

Let $\mathbf{A} = \begin{bmatrix} 2 & 0 \\ -1 & 3 \end{bmatrix}$, $\mathbf{B} = \begin{bmatrix} 1 & 5 \\ 0 & -6 \end{bmatrix}$, and $\mathbf{C} = \begin{bmatrix} -2 & 0 \\ -4 & 7 \end{bmatrix}$. Compute, if possible, each of the following.

11. AB   **12. BC**   **13. AC**
14. A(B + C)   **15. AB + AC**   **16. B(A + C)**
17. C(B − A)   **18. AB + C**   **19. (AB)C**
20. A(BC)   **21. B + A**   **22. A²**
23. B² + 2C   **24. 3A − C²**   **25. A² − C²**
26. A³   **27. A²B**   **28. B²C²**

Let $\mathbf{L} = \begin{bmatrix} 0 & 2 & -1 \\ 3 & 1 & 5 \end{bmatrix}$, $\mathbf{M} = \begin{bmatrix} 4 & 0 \\ -6 & 4 \\ -2 & 7 \end{bmatrix}$, $\mathbf{N} = \begin{bmatrix} 10 & 8 & -3 \\ -5 & 0 & 1 \end{bmatrix}$. Compute, if possible, the following.

29. LM   **30. MN**   **31. LN**   **32. L²**
33. 4L + N   **34. 2(LM)** **35. L(2M)** **36. (2L)M**
37. Lᵀ + M (See Ex. 24, p. 182.) **38. LᵀMᵀ** **39. (LM)ᵀ** **40. (ML)ᵀ**

Compute these powers.

41. $\begin{bmatrix} 1 & 1 \\ -1 & -1 \end{bmatrix}^2$ **42.** $\begin{bmatrix} \frac{1}{3} & \frac{1}{3} & \frac{1}{3} \\ \frac{1}{3} & \frac{1}{3} & \frac{1}{3} \\ \frac{1}{3} & \frac{1}{3} & \frac{1}{3} \end{bmatrix}^3$ **43.** $\begin{bmatrix} 1 & 0 \\ 2 & -1 \end{bmatrix}^2$

44. $\begin{bmatrix} 1 & 0 \\ 0 & 1 \end{bmatrix}^5$ **45.** $\begin{bmatrix} -1 & 0 \\ 0 & -1 \end{bmatrix}^4$ **46.** $\begin{bmatrix} -1 & 0 \\ 0 & 1 \end{bmatrix}^2$ **47.** $\begin{bmatrix} 1 & 0 \\ 0 & -1 \end{bmatrix}^2$

B **48.** Hiram's Clothing Store deals with a company that makes three types of women's coats. The materials needed (in square inches) for each style are shown at the right.

	Coat A	Coat B	Coat C
Dacron	30	35	15
Cotton	10	20	10
Wool	40	15	50

Hiram orders 20 of coat A, 15 coat B, and 12 coat C. Use matrix multiplication to determine how much dacron, cotton, and wool the company will need to fill Hiram's order.

49. This table gives the percentage of each element used to produce three different alloys of steel.

	Iron ore	Scrap	Manganese	Limestone	Coke
Alloy A	1.5	0.3	0.7	2.1	1.3
Alloy B	1.7	0	0.5	2.4	2.7
Alloy C	2.0	0.2	0	2.5	1.7

This next table gives the production schedule for each alloy over the next three weeks.

	Alloy (in tons)		
	A	B	C
Week 1	250	150	50
Week 2	200	200	150
Week 3	350	250	0

Use matrix multiplication to produce a matrix that gives the number of units of each component that will be needed each week. Label the rows and columns to complete the table. (Note: A process using matrix multiplication that determines the needed amounts of component parts is called an "explosion" process.)

Use matrices to multiply these polynomials.

50. $(2x - 1)(3x + 5)$

51. $(x^2 - 2x + 3)(x - 1)$

52. $(2x^3 - 2x^2 + 5x - 4)(x + 1)$

53. $(2x^3 - 4x^2 + 5)(x^2 + 3x + 2)$

6-7 MATRIX MULTIPLICATION IN BASIC

Study the pattern of matrix multiplication shown below.

$$
\mathbf{A}\ (m \times n) \qquad\qquad\qquad \mathbf{B}\ (n \times q)
$$

$$
\begin{bmatrix}
A(1,\,1) & A(1,\,2) & \ldots & A(1,\,N) \\
A(2,\,1) & A(2,\,2) & \ldots & A(2,\,N) \\
\cdot & & & \cdot \\
\cdot & & & \cdot \\
\cdot & & & \cdot \\
A(M,\,1) & A(M,\,2) & \ldots & A(M,\,N)
\end{bmatrix}
\times
\begin{bmatrix}
B(1,\,1) & B(1,\,2) & \ldots & B(1,\,Q) \\
B(2,\,1) & B(2,\,2) & \ldots & B(2,\,Q) \\
\cdot & & & \cdot \\
\cdot & & & \cdot \\
\cdot & & & \cdot \\
B(N,\,1) & B(N,\,2) & \ldots & B(N,\,Q)
\end{bmatrix}
=
$$

$$
\mathbf{C}\ (m \times q)
$$

$$
\begin{bmatrix}
C(1,\,1) & C(1,\,2) & \ldots & C(1,\,Q) \\
C(2,\,1) & C(2,\,2) & \ldots & C(2,\,Q) \\
\cdot & & & \cdot \\
\cdot & & & \cdot \\
\cdot & & & \cdot \\
C(M,\,1) & C(M,\,2) & \ldots & C(M,\,Q)
\end{bmatrix}
$$

where

$$C(1,\,1) = A(1,\,1) \cdot B(1,\,1) + A(1,\,2) \cdot B(2,\,1) + \ldots + A(1,\,N) \cdot B(N,\,1)$$
$$C(1,\,2) = A(1,\,1) \cdot B(1,\,2) + A(1,\,2) \cdot B(2,\,2) + \ldots + A(1,\,N) \cdot B(N,\,2)$$
$$\ldots \qquad \ldots \qquad \ldots \qquad \ldots \qquad \ldots \qquad \ldots \qquad \ldots$$

$$C(1,\,Q) = A(1,\,1) \cdot B(1,\,Q) + A(1,\,2) \cdot B(2,\,Q) + \ldots + A(1,\,N) \cdot B(N,\,Q)$$
$$C(2,\,1) = A(2,\,1) \cdot B(1,\,1) + A(2,\,2) \cdot B(2,\,1) + \ldots + A(2,\,N) \cdot B(N,\,1)$$
$$C(2,\,2) = A(2,\,1) \cdot B(1,\,2) + A(2,\,2) \cdot B(2,\,2) + \ldots + A(2,\,N) \cdot B(N,\,2)$$
$$\ldots \qquad \ldots \qquad \ldots \qquad \ldots \qquad \ldots \qquad \ldots \qquad \ldots \qquad \ldots$$

$$C(2,\,Q) = A(2,\,1) \cdot B(1,\,Q) + A(2,\,2) \cdot B(2,\,Q) + \ldots + A(2,\,N) \cdot B(N,\,Q)$$
$$\ldots \qquad \ldots \qquad \ldots \qquad \ldots \qquad \ldots \qquad \ldots \qquad \ldots \qquad \ldots$$

$$C(M,\,1) = A(M,\,1) \cdot B(1,\,1) + A(M,\,2) \cdot B(2,\,1) + \ldots + A(M,\,N) \cdot B(N,\,1)$$
$$C(M,\,2) = A(M,\,1) \cdot B(1,\,2) + A(M,\,2) \cdot B(2,\,2) + \ldots + A(M,\,N) \cdot B(N,\,2)$$
$$\ldots \qquad \ldots \qquad \ldots \qquad \ldots \qquad \ldots \qquad \ldots \qquad \ldots \qquad \ldots$$

$$C(M,\,Q) = A(M,\,1) \cdot B(1,\,Q) + A(M,\,2) \cdot B(2,\,Q) + \ldots + A(M,\,N) \cdot B(N,\,Q)$$

To program this procedure, these steps must be generalized. Each $C(I, J)$ is a sum and hence the LET statement to compute each entry of the product will take this form.

```
LET C(I,J) = C(I,J) + A(?,?)*B(?,?)
```

The step at the bottom of the previous page will be imbedded in nested **FOR-NEXT** loops.

```
FØR I = 1 TØ M
FØR J = 1 TØ Q
        .
        .
        .

NEXT J
NEXT I
```

Returning to the steps on page 197 for computing $c(1, 1)$, $c(2, 1)$, . . . , note that in each term the *second* subscript of the A-factor matches the *first* subscript of the B-factor. We need a third index, say K, to occupy these two positions. The complete multiplication loop thus looks like this.

```
130 FØR I = 1 TØ M⎤          Recall the dimensions.
140 FØR J = 1 TØ Q⎥          A: m × n
150 LET C(I,J) = O ⎥──────▶  B: n × q
160 FØR K = 1 TØ N⎦          the product C: m × q
170 LET C(I,J) = C(I,J) + A(I,K)*B(K,J)
180 NEXT K
190 PRINT C(I,J),
200 NEXT J
210 PRINT
220 NEXT I
```

Line 150 is included so that when the program loops back to read the elements of the next two matrices in the DATA, the C-sums are cleared to zero.

The heart of the multiplication program has now been written. Adding the read loops and the DIM, DATA, and END statements gives the complete program. This is shown as Program 6-3 on the next page.

EXERCISES 6-7

A 1. Expand Program 6-3 (see next page) so that it reads matrix **A** ($m \times n$) and matrix **B** ($p \times q$), then tests whether **A** and **B** are conformable. If they are not, print a suitable message. If they are conformable, print the product **AB**.

2. Write a program to read conformable matrices **A** and **B** and print **A** and **B** and their product in this form: skip a line, print "A =", skip a line, print A, skip a line, print "B =", skip a line, print B, skip a line, print "A × B =", skip a line, and print A × B. Assume that neither **A** nor **B** has more than five columns.

B   3. Prepare a flowchart for Program 6-3.
   4. Write a program to test whether multiplication of conformable square matrices is commutative. (See Ex. 23, p. 182.)
   5. Write a program to test whether multiplication of conformable square matrices is associative. (See Ex. 23, p. 182.)
   6. If $\mathbf{A}^\mathsf{T}$ represents the "transpose" of $\mathbf{A}$ (see Ex. 24, p. 182), write a program to verify that

$$(\mathbf{AV})^\mathsf{T} = \mathbf{V}^\mathsf{T}\mathbf{A}^\mathsf{T}$$

   where $\mathbf{A}$ and $\mathbf{V}$ are order-n square matrices.
   7. Write a program that reads a scalar k and conformable matrices $\mathbf{A}$ and $\mathbf{B}$ and tests whether $(k\mathbf{A})\mathbf{B} = k(\mathbf{AB})$.

Program 6-3: Multiplication of Conformable Matrices

```
10 DIM A(10,10),B(10,10),C(10,10)
20 READ M,N,Q
30 FØR I = 1 TØ M
40 FØR J = 1 TØ N
50 READ A(I,J)
60 NEXT J
70 NEXT I
80 FØR I = 1 TØ N
90 FØR J = 1 TØ Q
100 READ B(I,J)
110 NEXT J
120 NEXT I
130 FØR I = 1 TØ M
140 FØR J = 1 TØ Q
150 LET C(I,J) = O
160 FØR K = 1 TØ N
170 LET C(I,J) = C(I,J) + A(I,K)*B(K,J)
180 NEXT K
190 PRINT C(I,J),
200 NEXT J
210 PRINT
220 NEXT I
225 PRINT
230 GØ TØ 20
240 DATA ...
300 END
```

6-8 "MAT" COMMANDS

Matrix operations occur so frequently in programming that the creators of BASIC developed a special set of twelve instructions for such computations. They all start with "MAT" and are summarized below.

MAT READ A,B,C,...   Read matrices **A**, **B**, **C**, ... All elements of **A** are read from DATA first, in row-wise sequence, then all elements of **B**, then **C**, ...

MAT PRINT A,B;C...   Print the matrices **A**, **B**, **C**, . . . with **A** and **C** in regular format (one entry per zone per line) but matrix **B** closely packed.

MAT C = (K)*A   Multiply matrix **A** by scalar k; store the result as matrix **C**. K (any valid arithmetic expression) must be in parentheses.

MAT B = A   Set the matrix **B** equal to the matrix **A**. (On some systems this command is not allowed. However, the same result can be achieved by the statement MAT B = (1)*A.)

MAT C = A + B   Add the matrices **A** and **B** and store the result as matrix **C**. **A** and **B** must have the same dimensions.

MAT C = A - B   Subtract matrix **B** from matrix **A** and store the result as matrix **C**. **A** and **B** must have the same dimensions.

MAT C = A * B   Multiply the matrix **A** times the matrix **B** and store the result as matrix **C**. **A** and **B** must be conformable.

MAT C = IDN   Set **C** equal to the multiplicative identity matrix. **C** must be a square matrix.

MAT C = TRN(A)   Transpose the matrix **A** and store the resulting matrix in **C**. If **A** is an $r \times c$ matrix, **C** must be a $c \times r$ matrix.

MAT C = INV(A)   Form the multiplicative inverse of the square matrix **A** (if it exists) and store it as **C**.

MAT C = ZER   Set each element of matrix **C** to zero.

MAT C = CØN   Set each element of matrix **C** to one. ("CON" means "constant.")

A BASIC compiler has available in storage a library of routines similar to those we have written in this chapter: a routine to read a matrix, a routine to add matrices, a routine to print a matrix, and so forth. When a program contains one of the "shorthand" MAT commands, the compiler pulls the necessary statements from the library and inserts them into the program before translating to machine language and executing.

Depending on the system, there are several ways of stating the dimensions of matrices involved in MAT commands.

1. DIM statement(s)
2. Putting dimensions in the MAT READ, ZER, CØN, and IDN statements
3. Both 1 and 2 above

A difficulty with all of these methods is that some BASIC compilers begin the row and column subscripts with zero, while other versions start numbering rows and columns with ones. Consult your manual and run experimental programs to determine the rules your system follows. To compare the possibilities, suppose a 3×5 matrix **A** is to be read. If your system begins rows and columns at zero, you must use the statement 10 DIM A(2, 4)   . But if the system starts rows and columns at one, use 10 DIM A(3, 5)

Matrices may also be dimensioned in the MAT READ statement itself.

Examples: 10 MAT READ A(2,4)   30 MAT READ B(2,6)
20 MAT READ M(1,5)

(Note that the statement   10 MAT READ A(2,4)   does *not* mean that only the element in the second row, fourth column is read.) For this method of dimensioning a matrix, as for the DIM statement, some systems begin subscripts at zero and others start at one.

Other MAT statements may contain dimensions, as in these examples.

20 MAT C = ZER(4,3)   30 MAT C = CØN(5,6)
50 MAT C = IDN(10,10)

On some systems, variables may be used to dimension matrices, as in this program segment.

```
10 READ R,C
20 MAT READ A(R,C)
30 MAT B = IDN(R,R)
40 MAT D = ZER(R,C)
. . . . . . . . .

100 DATA
110 END
```

Some systems require that all matrices used in a program be listed in a DIM statement even if dimensions are also stated in the MAT statements themselves. For such systems the above program segment would need this statement.

$$15 \ DIM \ A(R,C), \ B(R,R), \ D(R,C)$$

If a DIM statement is used and dimensions are listed in a MAT statement later in the program, the MAT dimensions may not exceed the number of locations reserved by the DIM statement. Here are examples.

Incorrect Combination	Correct Combination
10 DIM A(3,3)	10 DIM A(10,10)
20 MAT READ A(5,4)	20 MAT READ A(5,5)

Another error to be avoided is putting dimensions to the left of the equal sign in a MAT calculation. All these statements are *incorrect*.

```
30 MAT C(5,5) = A + B
40 MAT R(2,2) = IDN
50 MAT X(R,C) = A * B
```

It is also erroneous to combine more than one MAT operation in a computation step.

Incorrect

```
20 MAT C = A + B - X
40 MAT Y = R * S + T
```

These calculations must be broken into several steps.

20 MAT C = A + B - X	becomes	20 MAT D = A + B
		25 MAT C = D - X
40 MAT Y = R * S + T	becomes	40 MAT Z = R * S
		45 MAT Y = Z + T

"D" and "Z" were introduced for temporary storage of intermediate results.

A MAT READ may read more than one matrix, as in these examples.

```
20 MAT READ A(R,C), B(R,C)
40 MAT READ M,N,R
50 MAT READ X(2,3), Y(3,4)
```

There is no question here of alternating values of the matrices being read. The statement   20 MAT READ A,B   will go to the DATA lists and first read the entire matrix **A** and then read the entire matrix **B**.

Matrices may be printed in various ways. Consider the 3 × 3 matrix at the right.

$$A = \begin{bmatrix} 197 & 106 & 15 \\ 361 & 27 & 192 \\ 0 & 1 & 10 \end{bmatrix}$$

50 MAT PRINT A   would product this result.

197	106	15
361	27	192
0	1	10

Thus   50 MAT PRINT A   is equivalent to   50 MAT PRINT A,

On the other hand,   50 MAT PRINT A;   would output matrix **A** like this.

107	106	15
361	27	192
0	1	10

NOTE: Some systems double-space the rows of the matrix.

More than one matrix may be printed. If $X = \begin{bmatrix} 71 & -13 & 4 & 19 \\ 10 & 0 & 1 & -5 \end{bmatrix}$ and

$Y = \begin{bmatrix} 11 & 0 & 10 \\ 3 & 14 & 9 \\ -1 & -7 & 4 \end{bmatrix}$, then   50 MAT PRINT X,Y   would produce this result.

71	-13	4	19
10	0	1	-5

11	0	10
3	14	9
-1	-7	4

50 MAT PRINT X;Y   would cause this output.

71 -13 4 19
10 0 1 -5

11	0	10
3	14	9
-1	-7	4

50 MAT PRINT X;Y;   would yield the following output.

71 -13 4 19
10 0 1 -5

11 0 10
3 14 9
-1 -7 4

Note that the commands   50 MAT PRINT X,Y   or   50 MAT PRINT X;Y
do *not* mean that X and Y will be printed side-by-side.

In the list of MAT commands at the beginning of this lesson the explanation for "MAT C = (K)*A" says that scalar K may be either a number or
an expression. The examples below clarify this point.

```
10 MAT F = (2)*G       50 MAT Q = (2.89+M)*Q
             75 MAT B = (N)*A
```

On most systems the same matrix may occur on both sides of a MAT
assignment in case of addition, subtraction, or scalar multiplication
but not in any of the other instructions. Thus the following examples
are all legal on some systems.

```
MAT A = A + B       MAT A = (K)*A
        MAT A = B - A
```

However, the following are usually illegal.

```
MAT A = B * A       MAT A = INV(A)
        MAT A = TRN(A)
```

Row vectors and column vectors are permissible in MAT instructions.
As with all other matrices, the dimensions are explicitly stated prior to
their use in a MAT command. Row vectors are considered to be $1 \times n$
matrices and column vectors are considered to be $n \times 1$ matrices.

Example:
```
10 DIM A(1,5),B(5,1)
20 MAT READ A,B
30 MAT C = A*B
         . . .
```

EXERCISES 6-8

A   Classify each of these MAT statements as legal or illegal for your
BASIC system.

1. 40 MAT D = C
2. 10 MAT READ A
3. 30 MAT READ A(3,5)
4. 20 MAT C = ZER(2,2)
5. 15 MAT READ C(0,4)
6. 30 MAT B = IDN(N,N)
7. 50 MAT C = A + B - D
8. 15 MAT PRINT A,B
9. 65 MAT PRINT A;B
10. 95 MAT C = CØN(N,N-1)
11. 80 MAT F = (A+B)*Y
12. 90 MAT X = X * Y
13. 60 MAT X1 = X + Y
14. 35 MAT R = INV(R)
15. 50 MAT PRINT X;
16. 91 MAT A = A + X
17. 60 MAT C=MAT A - MAT B
18. 72 MAT L(2,3) = CØN
19. 50 MAT M = C * (2*L+1)
20. 90 MAT B = A + A

Use MAT commands in writing these programs.

21. Add two matrices.
22. Multiply two matrices.
23. Multiply any given matrix by any given scalar.
24. Multiply a matrix by its transpose.
25. Multiply a square matrix by its inverse.
26. Multiply an order-n square matrix by the order-n multiplicative identity.
27. Multiply a $p \times q$ matrix by the $q \times p$ constant matrix.

B　**28.** Test matrix addition for the commutative property. Assume that the matrices to be added have the same dimensions.
29. Test matrix addition for the associative property. Assume that the matrices to be added have the same dimensions.
30. Test matrix multiplication for the commutative property. Assume that the matrices are all of order n.
31. Test matrix multiplication for the associative property. Assume that the matrices are all of order n.
32. Test the distributive law of multiplication over addition for square matrices; that is, if **A**, **B**, and **C** are $n \times n$ matrices, is "$A(B + C) = AB + AC$" true?
33. If **A** and **B** are $n \times n$ matrices, which of the following equations is true: "$(AB)^T = A^T B^T$" or "$(AB)^T = B^T A^T$"?

CHAPTER REVIEW

Write a BASIC subscripted variable corresponding to each of these mathematical variables.

1. $y_{2,3}$　　　**2.** $m_{r,c}$　　　**3.** $b_{i+1, j-1}$　　　**4.** $a_{k,k}$　　　**5.** $s_{m+n, p}$

6. Nifty Cleaners has three stores in the city. Each store reports its sales for the first quarter of the year as follows:

	Fremont Avenue Store			Oakmont Mall Store			Canal Street Store		
	Jan.	Feb.	Mar.	Jan.	Feb.	Mar.	Jan.	Feb.	Mar.
shirts	$1083	$1103	$1027	$1214	$1286	$ 989	$523	$517	$482
pants	725	813	737	853	817	761	289	253	207
coats	314	375	212	450	492	376	192	189	154

The head of the Nifty chain wishes a report giving the total sales in each category for each month for the entire chain. What matrix operation should be used to generate this data? Perform this operation and form the table that can serve as the report the head of the chain desires.

7. Read positive integers R and C. Print the R $\times$ C zero matrix. Do not use any MAT commands.

Let $\mathbf{R} = \begin{bmatrix} 4 & 1 & 0 \\ -3 & 2 & 1 \end{bmatrix}$, $\mathbf{S} = \begin{bmatrix} 0 & 6 \\ -2 & 4 \\ 1 & -3 \end{bmatrix}$, and $\mathbf{U} = \begin{bmatrix} -4 & 1 & 2 \\ 2 & -5 & 0 \end{bmatrix}$. Give, if possible, each of the following matrices.

8. RS   **9. SR**   **10. R + U**
11. U − R   **12. S + U**   **13. 3R**
14. −7S   **15. R²**   **16. (RS)²**
17. Rᵀ   **18. R(Uᵀ)**   **19. RᵀU**

20. Use matrices to multiply $2x^2 + 3x - 1$ and $x^3 - 7x + 5$.

21. Let $\mathbf{I} = \begin{bmatrix} 1 & 0 \\ 0 & 1 \end{bmatrix}$. What is (a) the additive inverse of $\mathbf{I}$; (b) the multiplicative inverse of $\mathbf{I}$?

In each of the following (true) statements, 0, 1, x, y, and z are real numbers. Convert each equation to a matrix equation by replacing 0 with $\bar{0}$, the 2 × 2 zero matrix, 1 by $\mathbf{I}$, the 2 × 2 multiplicative identity, and x, y, and z by $\mathbf{X}$, $\mathbf{Y}$, and $\mathbf{Z}$, respectively, 2 × 2 matrices. Which of the resulting statements are true?

22. $x + 0 = 0 + x = x$ **23.** $x \cdot 0 = 0 \cdot x = 0$
24. $(x + y) + z = x + (y + z)$ **25.** $(xy)z = x(yz)$
26. $x + y = y + x$ **27.** $xy = yx$
28. $x \cdot 1 = 1 \cdot x = x$ **29.** $x(y + z) = xy + xz$
30. $y(z - x) = yz - yx$ **31.** $x - (y + z) = x - y - z$

Compute each of the following powers.

32. $\begin{bmatrix} \frac{1}{2} & \frac{1}{2} \\ \frac{1}{2} & \frac{1}{2} \end{bmatrix}^2$ **33.** $\begin{bmatrix} 0 & -1 \\ -1 & 0 \end{bmatrix}^4$

34. Write the DATA steps so that the matrix below will be properly read by this program segment at the right.

$\mathbf{A} = \begin{bmatrix} 61 & -9 & 17 & 0 \\ -6 & -1 & 0 & 14 \\ 83 & 13 & 9 & -2 \\ -4 & 1 & 8 & -1 \end{bmatrix}$

```
10 DIM A(10,10)
20 READ M,N
30 FØR K = 1 TØ M
40 FØR L = 1 TØ N
50 READ A(K,L)
60 NEXT L
70 NEXT K
80 DATA ...
  · · ·
```

Show the output when matrix **A** of Exercise 34 is printed by each of the following statements.

35. 100 MAT PRINT A   **36.** 100 MAT PRINT A,
37. 100 MAT PRINT A;

Use MAT commands in writing the following programs.
38. Read an $r \times c$ matrix **A**, multiply it by its transpose, and then take and print the inverse of this product.
39. Read $n \times n$ matrices **P**, **Q**, and **R**, and compute $\mathbf{PQ} - \mathbf{R}$.

ROUND SIX: *PROGRAMS FOR STUDENT ASSIGNMENT*

Unlike the first five rounds, the programs in this round are not classified by subject matter. Matrices are not a common topic in algebra one, geometry, or algebra two. Some programs below do require advanced mathematical knowledge (Pascal's Triangle, truth tables, analytic geometry, and so forth,) but most can be programmed from the information given in this chapter and in the problem itself.

Do not use any MAT commands unless the problem specifically allows them.

GENERAL INSTRUCTION:

In each exercise on pages 207 through 215, write a program that will do what is specified in the exercise.

1. Given a matrix, sum each column and print the results as a one-dimensional array.

   For example, for the matrix $\begin{bmatrix} 6 & -4 & 3 \\ 7 & 0 & -9 \\ -11 & 13 & 2 \end{bmatrix}$ print   2 9 -4

2. Given a matrix find the sum of each row and print the results as a one-dimensional array.

3. Search a given matrix for its largest value. Print that value together with its row and column indices.

A finite relation can be stored as a set of n ordered pairs in an $n \times 2$ matrix where the first column holds the x-values and the second column holds the corresponding y-values.

4. Determine whether a given relation is a function.

5. Functions f and g are equal if they have the same domain and if $f(x) = g(x)$ for each x in the domain. Given the ordered pairs of two functions, decide whether they are equal.
   Note: The functions $\{(1, 2), (3, 4), (5, 6)\}$ and $\{(3, 4), (5, 6), (1, 2)\}$ are equal even though the pairs are in different sequences.

In Exercises 6 and 7, build Pascal's Triangle to the tenth row. Print in the fashion at the right.

```
        1
       1 1
      1 2 1
     1 3 3 1
        . . .
```

6. Use an $r \times c$ matrix with $r > 1$ and $c > 1$.

7. Use a $1 \times c$ matrix.

8. Read thirty numbers fed five per line for six DATA lines. Print these values five per line but in the reverse order from which they were read.

In Exercises 9 through 11, input a matrix.

9. Compute the average of all elements of the matrix.

10. Compute the average of all elements in row L (L read from DATA).

11. Compute the average of all elements in column M.

12. Using 1 for true and 0 for false, build truth tables for $p \wedge q$ (p and q) and $p \vee q$ (p or q) and prove tautologies.

13. Extend Exercise 12 to three variables, p, q, and r.

14. In a branch of mathematics called "game theory," a matrix is said to have a *saddle point* if one of its elements is both (a) the smallest value in its row and (b) the largest value in its column. Read an $r \times c$ matrix and determine whether it has a saddle point. If it does, print the value and its indices.

15. Print the first ten rows of a table according to the following rules.

   (a) The table has four columns called N, A, B, C.
   (b) The values in the first row are 0, 1, 1, 1.
   (c) In any row the value of N is one greater than its value in the preceding row.
   (d) In any row the value of A is one greater than its value in the preceding row.
   (e) In any row the value of B is one greater than the sum of the values of A to and including the preceding row.
   (f) In any row the value of C is one greater than the sum of the values of B to and including the preceding row.

16. A square matrix is *stochastic* if (a) each element is nonnegative and (b) the sum of every row equals one. Input a square matrix and decide whether it is stochastic.

In Exercises 17–19 let the set G consist of the following matrices.

$$\begin{bmatrix} 1 & 0 & 0 \\ 0 & 1 & 0 \\ 0 & 0 & 1 \end{bmatrix} \begin{bmatrix} 1 & 0 & 0 \\ 0 & 0 & 1 \\ 0 & 1 & 0 \end{bmatrix} \begin{bmatrix} 0 & 1 & 0 \\ 0 & 0 & 1 \\ 1 & 0 & 0 \end{bmatrix} \begin{bmatrix} 0 & 1 & 0 \\ 1 & 0 & 0 \\ 0 & 0 & 1 \end{bmatrix} \begin{bmatrix} 0 & 0 & 1 \\ 1 & 0 & 0 \\ 0 & 1 & 0 \end{bmatrix} \begin{bmatrix} 0 & 0 & 1 \\ 0 & 1 & 0 \\ 1 & 0 & 0 \end{bmatrix}$$

All three exercises can be solved by producing the multiplication table for G. Give letter names to each matrix.

(Note that all the matrices in G have 0 and 1 entries such that there is exactly one 1 in each row and in each column. Such matrices are called *permutation matrices*.)

17. Show that G is closed under multiplication.

18. Show that G has an identity element for multiplication.

19. Show that each element of G has a multiplicative inverse in G.

20. Given a matrix, print the matrix with row L and row M interchanged (L and M read from DATA).

21. Given a matrix, add to row L two times row M and print the resulting matrix.

22. Given a matrix, find the entry x in row L having the largest absolute value; divide every element in this row by x and print the resulting matrix.

In Exercises 23 and 24, read N, a positive integer greater than 1.

23. Create and print an order N square matrix having 0's in the main diagonals and 1's everywhere else.

24. Print the unit matrix (multiplicative identity matrix) of order N.

25. A square matrix **A** is *upper triangular* if $A_{i,j} = 0$ for $i > j$ and *lower triangular* if $A_{i,j} = 0$ for $i < j$. Read the order of a square matrix and a code number that determines whether the matrix is upper or lower triangular. Then input the nonzero elements and print the complete matrix.

26. Input a square matrix. Find and print the largest element on each diagonal.

The sum of the elements of the main diagonal in a square matrix is called the *trace* of the matrix. The trace of matrix **X** is symbolized by tr(**X**). Input square matrices **A** and **B** and verify each of the following.

27. tr(**A** + **B**) = tr(**A**) + tr(**B**)

28. tr(**AB**) = tr(**BA**)

29. tr(k**A**) = k tr(**A**) where k is a scalar.

30. Input a square matrix **A** and print **A**, **A**^{2}, **A**^{3}, and **A**^{4}.

31. Matrix **A** is *idempotent* if **A**^{2} = **A**. Input a square matrix **A** and decide whether it is idempotent. (The biggest challenge is to find DATA that yield an idempotent matrix. Do research or use trial-and-error.)

32. A square matrix **A** of order n is *nilpotent* if there exists a positive integer k such that **A**^{k} = $\overline{0}$ (where $\overline{0}$ is the zero matrix of order n). Input a matrix and test whether it is nilpotent. Since this could be an infinite process, limit the search to $k \le 5$. Two nilpotent matrices are shown below.

$$\begin{bmatrix} 1 & 1 & 1 \\ -1 & -1 & -1 \\ 1 & 1 & 0 \end{bmatrix} \qquad \begin{bmatrix} 1 & 1 \\ -1 & -1 \end{bmatrix}$$

33. Let **A** be an $n \times n$ matrix of the following form.

$$\mathbf{A} = \begin{bmatrix} 0 & 1 & 0 & 0 & \ldots & 0 & 0 \\ 0 & 0 & 1 & 0 & \ldots & 0 & 0 \\ 0 & 0 & 0 & 1 & \ldots & 0 & 0 \\ . & . & . & . & \ldots & . & . \\ 0 & 0 & 0 & 0 & \ldots & 0 & 1 \\ 0 & 0 & 0 & 0 & \ldots & 0 & 0 \end{bmatrix}$$

That is, **A**'s entries are all zero except on the "super-diagonal." For various values of n, show that $\mathbf{A}^n = \overline{0}$ but $\mathbf{A}^{n-1} \neq \overline{0}$ (where $\overline{0}$ is the $n \times n$ zero matrix). **A** will thus be proved nilpotent (see Ex. 32, p. 209). n is called the "index of nilpotence."

34. If an order n matrix **A** is triangular (see Ex. 25, p. 209) and all entries in the main diagonal are 0, show that $\mathbf{A}^n = \overline{0}$.

A *diagonal matrix* is a square matrix with all elements zero except those on the main diagonal.

35. Given the order n of a diagonal matrix, read just the entries on the main diagonal and print the complete matrix.

36. Input and print an order n square matrix and decide whether it is a diagonal matrix.

37. By a *scalar matrix* is meant any diagonal matrix having equal diagonal entries. Given an order n square matrix, decide whether it is a scalar matrix.

38. If a matrix has an even number of rows and an even number of columns, it can be subdivided into four matrices of equal size. Here is an example.

$$\left[\begin{array}{ccc|ccc} 2 & 8 & 17 & -5 & 23 & 81 \\ -1 & .2 & 0 & 16 & 4 & -92 \\ \hline 0 & -4 & 8 & 12 & 11 & -101 \\ 5 & -2 & 9 & -4 & 15 & 16 \end{array} \right]$$

Given a matrix, decide whether it can be subdivided. If it can, print the subdivisions as four separate matrices.

Recall that $\mathbf{A}^\mathsf{T}$ represents the *transpose of* **A**. (See Ex. 24, p. 182.)

39. A matrix **A** is said to be *symmetric* if $\mathbf{A}^\mathsf{T} = \mathbf{A}$ and *skew-symmetric* if $\mathbf{A}^\mathsf{T} = -\mathbf{A}$. Input a square matrix **A** (do you see why a nonsquare matrix can be neither symmetric or skew-symmetric?) and decide

whether it is symmetric, skew-symmetric, or neither.
(Note: If a matrix is skew-symmetric, the entries on its main diagonal are zero.)

40. Show that $(\mathbf{A} + \mathbf{B})^{\mathsf{T}} = \mathbf{A}^{\mathsf{T}} + \mathbf{B}^{\mathsf{T}}$.

41. Show that $(k\mathbf{A})^{\mathsf{T}} = k\mathbf{A}^{\mathsf{T}}$ where k is a scalar.

The *determinant* of a square matrix is a number computed from the elements of the matrix in a special way. For example, for a 2 × 2 matrix $\begin{bmatrix} a & b \\ c & d \end{bmatrix}$ the determinant is $ad - bc$. The determinant is often symbolized by showing the elements of the matrix between vertical segments. Thus $\begin{vmatrix} a & b \\ c & d \end{vmatrix} = ad - bc$. Determinants are important in many applications of matrices, particularly in the solution of systems of linear equations, and methods have been developed to find the determinant of any given matrix of order n.

42. The easiest way to compute a 3 × 3 determinant is to study an example. Suppose that $\begin{vmatrix} 2 & 0 & 1 \\ -1 & 6 & -2 \\ 3 & 4 & 1 \end{vmatrix}$ must be computed.

(i) Rewrite the first two columns alongside the determinant.

$$\begin{vmatrix} 2 & 0 & 1 \\ -1 & 6 & -2 \\ 3 & 4 & 1 \end{vmatrix} \begin{matrix} 2 & 0 \\ -1 & 6 \\ 3 & 4 \end{matrix}$$

(ii) Add the products of the main diagonals: $12 + 0 + (-4) = 8$

(iii) Add the products of the other diagonals: $0 + (-16) + 18 = 2$

(iv) Subtract (iii) from (ii). Thus $8 - 2 = 6$

$$\begin{vmatrix} 2 & 0 & 1 \\ -1 & 6 & -2 \\ 3 & 4 & 1 \end{vmatrix} = 6$$

Simulate this procedure for any 3 × 3 determinant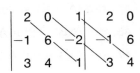

43. Unfortunately, computing a determinant of an order higher than 3 is very complicated. To facilitate matters a technique has been devised that involves the *minor* of an element of the matrix. The **minor** of $A_{i,j}$ is the matrix formed by deleting the *i*th row and *j*th column. For example, in $\begin{bmatrix} 2 & 0 & 1 & 10 \\ -1 & 6 & -2 & 0 \\ 3 & 4 & 1 & 8 \\ 0 & 5 & -7 & -11 \end{bmatrix}$ the minor of 6 (that is, of $A_{2,2}$) is $\begin{bmatrix} 2 & 1 & 10 \\ 3 & 1 & 8 \\ 0 & -7 & -11 \end{bmatrix}$. Input a square matrix A and I and J. Print the minor of A(I,J).

44. The algorithm for computing the determinant of a 4 × 4 matrix **A** is as follows. Pick a row or column.
   (i) Multiply each element $A_{i,j}$ by the determinant $D_{i,j}$ of its minor. (Notice that each minor is a 3 × 3 matrix whose determinant can be computed by the method of Exercise 42.)
  (ii) For each element $A_{i,j}$ if $i + j$ is odd, multiply $A_{i,j}D_{i,j}$ (the product obtained in (i)) by -1; that is, change the sign of the product; if $i + j$ is even, do not change the sign of $A_{i,j}D_{i,j}$.
 (iii) Sum the products $A_{i,j}D_{i,j}$ (half of which have had their signs changed in (ii)); this sum is the determinant of **A**.

Use a complete algorithm that computes the determinant of a 2 × 2, 3 × 3, or 4 × 4 matrix to test the theorems about determinants in Exercises 45-54. "det **A**" is read "the determinant of **A**." (See Ex. 42-44.)

45. det $(\mathbf{A} + \mathbf{B}) \neq$ det **A** + det **B**

46. det $(\mathbf{AB}) = ($det **A**$)($det **B**$)$

47. det $(\mathbf{A}^{\mathsf{T}}) =$ det **A** (For $\mathbf{A}^{\mathsf{T}}$ see Ex. 24, p. 182).

48. The determinant of a diagonal matrix (see Ex. 35 through 37, p. 210) equals the product of its main diagonal elements. (What does this imply about the determinant of a scalar matrix?)

49. If any row or any column of matrix **A** consists entirely of 0's, then det **A** = 0.

50. det **I** = 1 where **I** is the order-*n* unit matrix (multiplicative identity matrix).

51. If two rows of matrix **A** are equal, det **A** = 0.

52. The determinant of a triangular matrix (see Ex. 25, p. 209) is the product of the entries in its main diagonal.

53. If two rows of a matrix are interchanged, the sign of the determinant is changed.

54. Adding a multiple of one row to another row of the matrix does not change the value of the determinant.

55. Use *Cramer's Rule* to solve a system of three linear equations in three variables. Let the system be

$$\begin{cases} a_{1,1}x_1 + a_{1,2}x_2 + a_{1,3}x_3 = b_1 \\ a_{2,1}x_1 + a_{2,2}x_2 + a_{2,3}x_3 = b_2 \\ a_{3,1}x_1 + a_{3,2}x_2 + a_{3,3}x_3 = b_3 \end{cases}$$

where the $a_{i,j}$ and b_i are real number constants and the x_i are the variables of the system.

To implement Cramer's Rule, first compute D, the "determinant of the system." If D = 0, print NØ UNIQUE SØLUTION.

$$D = \begin{vmatrix} a_{1,1} & a_{1,2} & a_{1,3} \\ a_{2,1} & a_{2,2} & a_{2,3} \\ a_{3,1} & a_{3,2} & a_{3,3} \end{vmatrix}$$

If $D \neq 0$, then $x_1 = \dfrac{D_{x_1}}{D}$, $x_2 = \dfrac{D_{x_2}}{D}$, and $x_3 = \dfrac{D_{x_3}}{D}$, where D_{x_i} is the determinant formed by replacing the *i*th column of D with $\begin{matrix} b_1 \\ b_2 \\ b_3 \end{matrix}$.

56. Given the coordinates of three points of a circle in the *xy*-plane, print an equation of the circle in the form

$$x^2 + y^2 + cx + Dy + E = 0.$$

(Finding the equation involves solving a system of three linear equations. See Ex. 42 through 55, pp. 211–213.)

A square matrix does not necessarily possess a multiplicative inverse. If matrix **A** does have an inverse, it is denoted by A^{-1} and **A** is called *invertible* or *nonsingular.* It turns out that **A** has an inverse if and only if det **A** $\neq 0$ (see Ex. 42 through 54, pp. 211–213).

57. Input a square matrix of order 2, 3, or 4, and decide whether it is invertible.

58. Finding the inverse (if it exists) of a 2×2 matrix is not difficult. For $A = \begin{bmatrix} a & b \\ c & d \end{bmatrix}$ where det **A** $\neq 0$ (that is, $ad - bc \neq 0$),

$$A^{-1} = \frac{1}{\det A} \begin{vmatrix} d & -b \\ -c & a \end{vmatrix} = \begin{vmatrix} \dfrac{d}{\det A} & \dfrac{-b}{\det A} \\ \dfrac{-c}{\det A} & \dfrac{a}{\det A} \end{vmatrix}.$$

(From this formula you can see why it is necessary that det **A** $\neq 0$.) Given a 2×2 matrix **A**, print A^{-1} if it exists.

59. For higher order matrices the best method for finding the inverse can be explained using as an example, the matrix at the right. To find the inverse of **A**, place the 3×3 identify matrix **I** alongside **A**.

$$\mathbf{A} = \begin{bmatrix} 2 & 1 & 3 \\ 3 & 2 & 1 \\ 1 & -1 & 0 \end{bmatrix}$$

The strategy is to use row transformations to convert **A** into **I**. At the same time these transformations are also applied to **I**. When **A** has been changed into **I**, then **I** alongside it will have been changed into $\mathbf{A}^{-1}$. The particular steps are shown below.

$$\left[\begin{array}{ccc|ccc} 2 & 1 & 3 & 1 & 0 & 0 \\ 3 & 2 & 1 & 0 & 1 & 0 \\ 1 & -1 & 0 & 0 & 0 & 1 \end{array}\right]$$

Divide row 1 by the scalar 2 and row 2 by the scalar 3.

$$\left[\begin{array}{ccc|ccc} 1 & \frac{1}{2} & \frac{3}{2} & \frac{1}{2} & 0 & 0 \\ 1 & \frac{2}{3} & \frac{1}{3} & 0 & \frac{1}{3} & 0 \\ 1 & -1 & 0 & 0 & 0 & 1 \end{array}\right]$$

Let row 2 = row 2 − row 3 and row 3 = row 1 − row 3.

$$\left[\begin{array}{ccc|ccc} 1 & \frac{1}{2} & \frac{3}{2} & \frac{1}{2} & 0 & 0 \\ 0 & \frac{5}{3} & \frac{1}{3} & 0 & \frac{1}{3} & -1 \\ 0 & \frac{3}{2} & \frac{3}{2} & \frac{1}{2} & 0 & -1 \end{array}\right]$$

Let row 1 = row 1 − $\frac{1}{3}$ × row 3; divide row 2 by $\frac{5}{3}$ and row 3 by $\frac{3}{2}$.

$$\left[\begin{array}{ccc|ccc} 1 & 0 & 1 & \frac{1}{3} & 0 & \frac{1}{3} \\ 0 & 1 & \frac{1}{5} & 0 & \frac{1}{5} & -\frac{3}{5} \\ 0 & 1 & 1 & \frac{1}{3} & 0 & -\frac{2}{3} \end{array}\right]$$

Let row 3 = row 3 − row 2.

$$\left[\begin{array}{ccc|ccc} 1 & 0 & 1 & \frac{1}{3} & 0 & \frac{1}{3} \\ 0 & 1 & \frac{1}{5} & 0 & \frac{1}{5} & -\frac{3}{5} \\ 0 & 0 & \frac{4}{5} & \frac{1}{3} & -\frac{1}{5} & -\frac{1}{15} \end{array}\right]$$

Row 1 = row 1 − $\frac{5}{4}$ × row 3

Row 2 = row 2 − $\frac{1}{4}$ × row 3

Divide row 3 by $\frac{4}{5}$.

$$\left[\begin{array}{ccc|ccc} 1 & 0 & 0 & -\frac{1}{12} & \frac{1}{4} & \frac{5}{12} \\ 0 & 1 & 0 & -\frac{1}{12} & \frac{1}{4} & -\frac{7}{12} \\ 0 & 0 & 1 & \frac{5}{12} & -\frac{1}{4} & -\frac{1}{12} \end{array}\right]$$

$$\underbrace{\qquad}_{\mathbf{I}} \qquad \underbrace{\qquad\qquad}_{\mathbf{A}^{-1}}$$

Write a program that uses this method in finding the inverse of a square matrix.

Test the following statements about inverses. (See Ex. 59, p. 214.)

60. $(\mathbf{A}^{-1})^\mathsf{T} = (\mathbf{A}^\mathsf{T})^{-1}$ (See Ex. 24, p. 182.)

61. $\det(\mathbf{A}^{-1}) = (\det \mathbf{A})^{-1}$ (See Ex. 42 through 54, pp. 211–213.)

62. A permutation matrix (see Ex. 17 through 19, p. 208) is invertible and its inverse is a permutation matrix.

63. If **A** is triangular (see Ex. 25, p. 209) and no entry on the main diagonal is zero, then **A** is invertible; if an entry on the main diagonal is zero, then **A** is singular.

64. If **A** is invertible, then for all matrices **B** of the same order as **A**, $\det(\mathbf{ABA}^{-1}) = \det \mathbf{B}$. (See Ex. 42 through 54, pp. 211–213.)

65. A linear equation over the real numbers takes the form $ax + b = c$ where a, b, and c are constants and x is the variable. Similarly there is the matrix equation $\mathbf{AX} + \mathbf{B} = \mathbf{C}$, where **A**, **B**, **C**, and **X** are all 2×2 matrices or all 3×3 matrices. Given **A**, **B**, and **C**, solve for **X**. Do not assume that a solution always exists. Mimic the steps used in solving $ax + b = c$.

$$ax + b = c$$
$$ax = c - b$$
$$\tfrac{1}{a}(ax) = \tfrac{1}{a}(c - b)$$
$$\left(\tfrac{1}{a} \cdot a\right)x = \tfrac{1}{a}(c - b)$$
$$1 \cdot x = \tfrac{1}{a}(c - b)$$
$$x = \tfrac{1}{a}(c - b)$$

Subtract b.
Multiply by $\dfrac{1}{a}$
(assuming $a \neq 0$).

$$\mathbf{AX} + \mathbf{B} = \mathbf{C}$$
$$\mathbf{AX} = \mathbf{C} - \mathbf{B}$$
$$\mathbf{A}^{-1}(\mathbf{AX}) = \mathbf{A}^{-1}(\mathbf{C} - \mathbf{B})$$
$$(\mathbf{A}^{-1}\mathbf{A})\mathbf{X} = \mathbf{A}^{-1}(\mathbf{C} - \mathbf{B})$$
$$\mathbf{I}\,\mathbf{X} = \mathbf{A}^{-1}(\mathbf{C} - \mathbf{B})$$
$$\mathbf{X} = \mathbf{A}^{-1}(\mathbf{C} - \mathbf{B})$$

Subtract **B**.
Multiply by $\mathbf{A}^{-1}$
(if it exists).

ADDITIONAL FEATURES OF BASIC

Countless variations of the BASIC language have been developed by computer manufacturers, time-sharing firms, and universities and each variation offers its own special features. This chapter introduces some of those features. The ones discussed are available on most systems and are either useful or necessary for certain types of programs, including some of the programs in Round 7.

7-1 "INPUT" STATEMENTS

The READ statement causes data to be read from a DATA list in the program. The INPUT statement allows a user to enter data via the terminal at the appropriate point while the program is being run.

Examples:

```
10 INPUT X(I)     20 INPUT A,B,C     50 INPUT R1,R2
```

When the computer reaches the INPUT statement in the program, it types a question mark on the terminal and waits for the user to type the required number of values. Once these values are entered, the program execution can be completed.

Often the INPUT statement is preceded in the program by one or more PRINT statements that will produce explanatory messages to the user. For example, consider this program.

Program 7-1

```
10 PRINT "PRØGRAM CØMPUTES PERIMETER ØF A RECTANGLE."
20 PRINT "GIVE THE LENGTH AND WIDTH ØF THE RECTANGLE."
30 INPUT L,W
40 PRINT "THE PERIMETER IS " 2*L + 2*W
50 END
```

Lines 10 and 20 would inform the user that he is to type two values and what these values signify. When executed, the program would produce this output.

```
PRØGRAM CØMPUTES PERIMETER ØF A RECTANGLE.
GIVE THE LENGTH AND WIDTH ØF THE RECTANGLE.
?
```

At this point the user types two numerals separated by commas. (Some systems allow numerals to be separated by blanks when an INPUT command is being executed.) Then he hits the RETURN key. The remainder of the program is then executed. A printout from Program 7-1 might look like this.

```
PRØGRAM CØMPUTES PERIMETER ØF A RECTANGLE.
GIVE THE LENGTH AND WIDTH ØF THE RECTANGLE.
? 7,6
THE PERIMETER IS 26
```

If "45 GO TO 30" were inserted into Program 7-1, the computer would type another "?" and wait for new values for L and W. The program would contain an infinite loop. On most time-sharing systems, the program could be terminated by striking the 'ESC' key or the 'S' key.

The INPUT statement is ideally suited for use in game programs, such as tic-tac-toe, blackjack, and football, which involve a player's entering his move or play. Other common uses are teaching programs that require responses from the student, or problems related to business or engineering that require specific input from managers, engineers, clerks, and other personnel who have little or no programming training. Such programs are usually written by one person and require another person to enter the data.

The user must be careful what he types in response to the '?' of the INPUT command. First, the number of numerals typed should match the number of variables in the INPUT statement. Most systems require the numerals to be separated by commas (as in a DATA statement). If the number of numerals typed is greater than the number of variables in the INPUT command, most systems ignore the additional values. For example, suppose that INPUT A, B, C is executed and that the user types "10,−8,12,23,16" after the computer types "?"; thus,

$$? \ 10,-8,12,23,16$$

followed by a carriage return. Then 10 would be assigned to A, −8 to B, 12 to C, and 23 and 16 ignored, or, on some systems, held until the next INPUT command.

Now suppose that fewer values are supplied than called for. For example, suppose INPUT A, B, C gets the following response followed by a carriage return.

$$? \; 10,-8$$

Most systems would assign 10 to A, −8 to B, and 0 to C. Thus, zero is assumed for all values not explicitly typed.

CAUTION: Some systems interpret the typing of too many or too few values for the number of variables in an INPUT command as an error. The execution of the program is thus disrupted. Consult the manual for your system.

A user must enter only numerals to an INPUT command. For example, if a program asks the question

WHAT IS YØUR AGE?

the response should be just   18   and not   I AM 18   or   18 YEARS OLD   . Most systems would respond to either of the latter two inputs with   ILLEGAL CHARACTER   or some such error message. Some versions of BASIC would then stop the program while others would repeat the INPUT command and give the user another chance to give a valid response.

If the programmer anticipates a verbal response, such as "YES" or "NØ," he should tell the user a code to use, as in the next example. This example also illustrates the suppressing of line feed to keep the response on the same line as the question.

```
. . .
30 PRINT "DØ YØU WISH TØ CØNTINUE (1=YES,O=NØ)";
31     REM   NØ ? IS INCLUDED INSIDE THE QUØTES IN
32     REM   LINE 30 BECAUSE A ? WILL AUTØMATICALLY
33     REM   BE PRINTED BY LINE 40 BELØW.
40 INPUT N
50 IF N = O THEN 999
60 PRINT
70 PRINT "I WILL DEAL;YØUR FIRST CARD IS ";
   . . .

999 END
```

A sample printout from this program segment might look like this.

```
DØ YØU WISH TØ CØNTINUE (1=YES,O=NØ) ? 1
I WILL DEAL;YØUR FIRST CARD IS TWØ ØF CLUBS.
   . . .
```

EXERCISES 7-1

A Write *Yes* or *No* to show whether each of the following is a valid
BASIC statement for your system.

1. 10 INPUT X; **2.** 5 INPUT D;E
3. 15 INPUT R(I) **4.** 20 INPUT C?
5. 30 MAT INPUT Z **6.** 45 MAT INPUT M(3,3)
7. 15 INPUT A,B,C **8.** 25 MAT INPUT X,Y

Below are computer-user dialogs with each "?" signalling the
execution of the command INPUT N. What is wrong with each
response?

9. HØW MANY CHILDREN DØ YØU HAVE? I HAVE 4.
10. WHAT IS YØUR ANNUAL INCØME? $9000
11. WHAT IS YØUR ANNUAL INCØME? 8,500

7-2 "DEF" STATEMENTS

Functions other than the standard mathematical functions can be defined using a DEF statement. If a function will be needed often, it can
be defined near the beginning of the program and used throughout.

Examples:

```
30 DEF FNA(X) = X↑3 - X↑2
100 DEF FNB(X,Y) = SQR(X↑2 + Y↑2)
```

It is possible to define up to 26 functions in a program: FNA, FNB, . . . ,
FNZ. Once the functions have been defined, later steps are made easier.
Thus, in the examples just shown,   150 LET Y = FNA(.1)   means that
.1 will be substituted for X in the expression X ↑ 3 − X ↑ 2 and Y will be
set equal to the result of the evaluation. Similarly,   180 LET Z =
FNB(7, −4)   means that 7 will be substituted for X and −4 for Y in the
formula SQR(X ↑ 2 + Y ↑ 2) and the result stored in location Z. The statement   200 LET U = FNA(R)   will cause the current value of the variable R to be substituted for X in the expression X ↑ 3 − X ↑ 2 and the result assigned to location U.

In these examples FNA was a function of one variable (X); FNB was a
function of two variables (X and Y). On some systems a DEF function
may have up to sixteen such "dummy" variables. X and Y are referred
to as dummy variables because in the formula they are simply place-
holders identified between parentheses on the left side of the equal sign
in the DEF statement.

In the statement

$$90 \quad DEF \quad FNX(X,Y,Z) = A*X + B*Y - C*Z$$

X, Y, and Z are dummy variables, whereas A, B, and C are references to variables given values elsewhere in the program. Thus A, B, and C play the roles of constants. Do not confuse the dummy variable X with the X being used to name the function ("FNX").

The DEF statement may occur anywhere in the program, and the expression to the right of the equal sign may be any formula that fits on one line. It may include any combination of other functions, including ones defined by other DEF statements, and it can involve variables other than the ones denoting the arguments of the function.

Examples: 20 DEF FNC(X) = SIN(X)*CØS(X)/360
55 DEF FNR(A,B) = FNC(A) + FNC(B)
80 DEF FNG(R,S,T) = R*S*T/(M-N)

"FN" expressions may be used in LET, IF . . . THEN, and PRINT statements.

Examples: 40 LET Q = FNA(R) * X - Z
90 IF FNP(X) = 3.14159 THEN 180
55 PRINT X, FNA(X), FNB(X)
65 IF FNR(3.7) = FNM(2.6) THEN 10

EXERCISES 7-2

A   Write *Yes* or *No* to show whether each of the following is a legal BASIC statement on your system.

1. 50 DEF FNA(X) = 3 * X - 7
2. 10 DEF FN(Y) = 4/Y + Y/4
3. 30 DEF FNZ(A) = 9 * X - 13
4. 81 DEF FNC(R,S) = (R + 7)/3.14159
5. 20 IF FNA(I) <FNA(I+1) THEN 40
6. 90 PRINT "F("A") = " FNZ(A)
7. 80 LET R = FNX(2*R)
8. 50 DEF G(X) = X*X - X/2

B   **9.** On most systems a defined function must fit on one line. Assume that the following function is too long for one line and break it into two or more functions in DEF statements.

$$g(x,y) = \frac{ax^3 + bx^2 + cx + d}{ex^2 + fx + g} - |y^3 + y^2 + y - 100|$$

7-3 STRINGS AND STRING VARIABLES

Many computer applications involve processing alphabetic and numeric data (or so-called alphanumeric data), particularly names, addresses, categories, and so forth. As an example consider this table of National Football League Passing Data.

Player, Team	Atts	Comp	Yds Gained	TD	Had Int
Cook, Cincinnati	197	106	1854	15	11
Namath, New York	361	185	2734	19	17
Lamonica, Oakland	426	221	3302	34	25
Livingston, Kansas City	161	84	1123	4	6
Hadl, San Diego	324	158	2253	10	11

To store the names of the players and their teams, "string variables" are used. A "string" is any sequence of alphanumeric characters (excluding certain special control characters). "NAMATH", "CINCINNATI", and "YDS GAINED" are examples of strings, as are "1781 MADISØN AVENUE", "MRS JAMES BRØØKS" and "3302".

A *string variable* is denoted by a letter followed by a "$". Up to twenty-six string variables can be used in a program: A$, B$, C$, . . . , Z$. A **string variable** names a memory location that will store alphanumeric characters.

On some systems the size of a string is limited to fifteen characters, including blanks. Longer strings must be broken into parts. Thus, for "1781 MADISØN AVENUE", A$ could store "1781 MADISØN AV" and B$ could hold "ENUE". Furthermore, some systems require that strings contain at least six characters. Blanks must be used to extend shorter strings. Thus "CØØK" must be handled as "CØØK   ".

String variables may appear in INPUT, LET, IF . . . THEN, and PRINT statements. Strings may occur in LET, IF . . . THEN, and PRINT statements.

An INPUT statement may contain string variables intermixed with ordinary BASIC variables.

Examples: 1O INPUT A$
                 7O INPUT C$,X,Y

To respond to   70 INPUT C$,X,Y   the user might type (after the question mark typed by the computer)

        ? NAMATH,361,185   or   "NAMATH",361,185

depending on the computer system used.

The quotation marks will not be stored as part of the string NAMATH but rather act as in a PRINT statement to show where the string begins and ends, since blanks and commas can be valid parts of a string. (On these systems, since double quotation marks enclose a string, only single quotation marks can be used within a string.)

Some versions of BASIC allow strings in DATA lines and therefore allow string variables in READ statements.

Example: 10 READ C$,X,Y

.

.

.

90 DATA CØØK ,197,106,NAMATH,361,185
100 END

Other systems allow strings in DATA statements but only if each string is enclosed in double quotation marks.

Example: 10 READ C$,X,Y

.

.

.

90 DATA "CØØK ",197,106,"NAMATH",361,185
100 END

On systems where strings are not allowed in DATA statements, strings are often read from and written to external data files, as will be explained in the next lesson.

Strings and string variables may appear in only two forms of the LET statement. The first is used to replace a string variable with the contents of another string variable.

Example: 50 LET G$ = H$

The second form is used to assign a string to a string variable.

Examples: 60 LET J$ = "YDS GAINED"
75 LET X$ = "LAMØNICA"

Arithmetic operations may not be performed on strings or on string variables.

A string or string variable is allowed on each side of the equals sign in the IF clause of an IF . . . THEN statement. All six of the standard relations (=, <, >, <>, <=, >=) are permitted.

Examples: 100 IF N$ = "SMITH" THEN 105
                  120 IF X$ = "END ØF FILE" THEN 9999
                  80 IF A$ <> B$ THEN 205
                  300 IF "JUNE" < M$ THEN 305
                  40 IF D$ >= "FRIDAY" THEN 60

A letter is "less than" another letter if it is closer to the beginning of the alphabet. Thus "A" < "B" < "C" < "D" < . . . < "Z". When strings of different lengths are compared, the shorter string and the corresponding part of the longer string are used. Thus, "ANDERSEN" < "ATWOOD". If all letters compared are the same, the shorter string is taken to be the lesser of the two. Thus if names are being sorted into alphabetical order, "SMITH" will be placed ahead of "SMITHSON", as desired.

PRINT statements may contain string variables and strings intermixed with ordinary BASIC variables.

Examples: 35 PRINT A,B$,C$;N
                  100 PRINT "THE WINNERS ARE" X$;Y$

A semicolon after a string variable in a PRINT statement causes the string to be printed and the variable following that string to be directly connected to it. Thus, in the earlier example where "1781 MADISØN AVENUE" had to be broken into two variables, A$ ("1781 MADISØN AV") and B$ ("ENUE"), the string could be printed correctly with the following statement.

                  90 PRINT A$;B$

The output would be   1781 MADISØN AVENUE   as desired.

On most systems strings can be set up as one-dimensional arrays only. Requests for two or three-dimensional arrays are not allowed and, when encountered, will initiate an error comment. Any string array with more than ten entries must be dimensioned. Here are examples of statements involving subscripted string variables.

                  10 DIM A(20),C$(20),A$(12),D(10,5)
                  20 INPUT C$(10)
                  5 INPUT M$,N$(I)
                  30 IF M$(I) = R$(J) THEN 75
                  100 LET X$(100) = "ØUT ØF DATA"

Some systems allow string arrays in MAT READ, MAT INPUT, and MAT PRINT statements. Here are some examples.

```
20 MAT READ A$,X$      15 MAT INPUT C$
10 MAT PRINT R$        90 MAT PRINT B$;
           85 MAT PRINT T$,W$
```

When using string variables, remember that x and x$ are two different variables. Location x holds a number; x$ stores a string. x(I) would be still another variable representing an element of the one-dimensional numeric array x. x$(I) might be a fourth variable representing an element of the one-dimensional string array x$. Your system may not allow x and x$ to be both subscripted and not subscripted in the same program.

EXERCISES 7-3

A   Write *Yes* or *No* to show whether each of the following is a valid statement on your system.

1. 10 READ A$
2. 5 DIM R$(20),X(15)
3. 15 LET M$ = T$ + 1
4. 53 PRINT C$,C
5. 8 READ N$(J)
6. 84 DIM M$(10,10)
7. 17 INPUT J1$
8. 15 MAT READ A$
9. 20 MAT READ A$(10)
10. 10 MAT INPUT X$,Y$
11. 35 PRINT Z$;
12. 35 MAT PRINT Z$;
13. 35 MAT PRINT Z$
14. 100 LET N$ = "RØY"
15. 20 LET A = "THE END"
16. 30 IF X$ = Y$ THEN 100
17. 92 IF B$ = "ENDFILE" THEN 99
18. 85 IF K$ = 9999 THEN 1000
19. 70 PRINT D$ " IS THE WINNER"
20. 19 LET Z$ = "CØMPLETIØNS"
21. 100 DATA SMITH ,JØNES ,71, 87
22. 100 DATA "SMITH ","JØNES ",71,87
23. 100 LET M$ = "AUTENSPERGER, CHARLES"

B   Write each program to conform to the rules of your system.
24. Read the names of ten students and their test scores. Print the list of students and scores from the highest scoring to the lowest.
25. Read ten names. Print only the name that should come first in alphabetical order.
26. Count the number of times each vowel occurs in a sample text.
27. Merge two lists, each of which is in alphabetical order, into one list that is in alphabetical order.

7-4 EXTERNAL FILE OPERATIONS

A time-sharing user may use an external file to save a program, a data list, or both. There is great variability among systems in the commands used to read and write such files. Consult the manual for your system. This lesson explains one method of gaining access to external files and shows a program in which such files are used.

Suppose a program must be written to rank the seniors of a large high school. The input file contains the code number, last name, and grade-point average (in that order) of each senior. Let us assume there are 305 students in the graduating class. The data file should be entered (by paper tape or directly from the keyboard) into the computer system. This file must be given a name, say SENIØR. (On many systems file names are limited to a maximum of six characters.) When the entire list has been inputted, the SAVE command should be given. This causes the file to be written into auxiliary storage, usually on a disk.

Data files usually require the following format: line number of up to five digits (some systems do not use line numbers for data files), blank, then the items separated by commas, as in DATA statements in a program. (The word DATA, though, is not used.) Thus the file SENIØR might be entered like this.

```
1  1003,AARØN  ,2.63
2  1010,ARMBRUSTER A,3.02
3  1011,ARMBRUSTER L,2.31
4  1023,ATTWATER,1.89
5  1031,BARFIELD,3.92

.  .  .  .  .  .  .  .  .  .  .  .

303  1973,WITTINGHAM,2.47
304  1985,YEAGER,3.52
305  1992,ZINN  ,2.64
SAVE
```

Once SENIØR has been stored, the actual program for ranking is entered. This program would contain a segment such as the following.

```
40 FØR I = 1 TØ 305
50 INPUT:SENIØR:C(I),N$(I),G(I)
51    REM   C(I) IS THE CODE NUMBER.
52    REM    N$(I) IS THE STUDENT NAME.
53    REM   G(I) IS THE GPA.
60 NEXT I
         .
         .
         .
```

In line 50 on the previous page the file name is listed between colons, followed by the particular variables being read. Data are entered in the same manner as with READ and DATA combinations, for example, one item at a time. This means that, if we had wished, the file SENIOR could have been entered in the following format.

```
1 1003,AARØN ,2.63,1010,ARMBRUSTER A,3.02,1011,
2 ARMBRUSTER L,2.31,1023,ATTWATER,1.89,1031,BARFIELD,...
. . . . . . . . . . .

75 WITTINGHAM,2.47,1985,YEAGER,3.52,1992,ZINN  ,2.64
```

Here are further examples of INPUT:FILE: statements.

```
 90 INPUT:ABC:A1,A2
 50 MAT INPUT:BUFFER:A(2,3)
105 INPUT:LIST:N,X(N),Y(N)
```

MAT INPUT:FILE: works like MAT READ. Thus

```
 50 MAT INPUT:BUFFER:A(2,3)
```

will read six numbers from the file named BUFFER naming these elements A(0,0), A(0,1), A(0,2), A(1,0), A(1,1), A(1,2). The next INPUT statement directed to read from BUFFER will read the seventh number of the file.

A program can write data into a file by means of statements such as the following.

```
100 PRINT:ABC:A;B,C(I)
 60 PRINT:ØUTPUT:"THE FØRECAST FØR JUNE 10 IS"
130 MAT PRINT:CØST:A,B
```

A caution here is that the file being written into must already have been "opened," that is, saved under the file name. For example, if a programmer plans to print the output from a program into a file named RESULT, before running the program he must save a blank file called RESULT. Disk space would then be reserved under this name so that any PRINT:RESULT: statement in the program could be executed.

EXERCISES 7-4

B   **1.** Recall Exercise 24 on page 224. Revise the program to read from an external file the names of twenty students and their test scores. Then rewrite the file with the names of the students rearranged in order from highest-scoring to lowest.

   2. Recall Exercise 27 on page 224. Revise the program to read the two alphabetical lists from two external data files. Then write the merged list on a third external file.

7-5 "TAB" FUNCTION

On a typewriter, "tab" stops can be set so that when the tabulator key is struck, the carriage jumps to the next tabbed position to the right. BASIC has a TAB function that can be used in PRINT statements to accomplish a similar result on the terminal output line. The reader is warned that TAB acts differently from one BASIC system to another—and not always in the manner the reference manual says. Here is an example.

$$60 \ PRINT \ TAB(10);X;TAB(22);Y$$

Line 60 gives the following output format: the first nine print positions are skipped; X is printed beginning in position 10 (recall, however, that the first position in a numeric zone is reserved for a possible negative sign); Y is printed beginning in position 22. Thus if X = 1.2 and Y = −13, the output from line 60 would appear as follows.

10   22

1.2   −13

The argument may be either a variable or an expression here.

The argument of TAB may be a variable. Thus, 50 PRINT X; TAB(N);Y means that X is printed, then the machine moves to the print position corresponding to the current value of INT(N) and prints Y.

As in both examples above, semicolons are used to separate TAB expressions from the adjacent items. If the terminal has already passed the print position of the TAB argument, the TAB is ignored and the semicolon format prevails. If the argument of TAB is greater than the number of the rightmost print position on the terminal line, usually the carriage is returned to the beginning of the next line.

Below is an example of a program using TAB. The corresponding output with print positions is noted at the top of the next page.

Program 7-2

```
10 PRINT "LENGTH";TAB(20);"WIDTH";TAB(40);"PERIMETER"
15 PRINT
20 FØR I = 1 TØ 4
30 READ L,W
40 PRINT L;TAB(20);W;TAB(40);2*L+2*W
50 NEXT I
60 DATA 6,8,3,7,10,5,2,11
70 END
```

Output

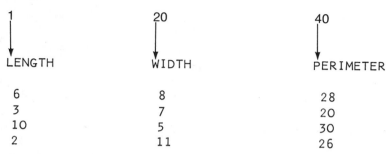

1	20	40
↓	↓	↓
LENGTH	WIDTH	PERIMETER

6	8	28
3	7	20
10	5	30
2	11	26

Here are some more examples using TAB in PRINT statements.

```
50 PRINT X;TAB(20);X*Y+3
85 PRINT TAB(15);A(I)
30 PRINT "RATE";TAB(25);"TIME";TAB(50);"DISTANCE"
100 PRINT:ØUTPUT:TAB(I);X,Y,Z
```

The last example above uses TAB in printing to an external file ØUTPUT.

EXERCISES 7-5

A   **1.** Write a statement that would print the word PAGE on your terminal, starting with "P" in column 65.

In Exercises 2 through 4 assume that A = 10 and B = −5. Show the output, with key columns labeled, of each PRINT statement.

2. 5 PRINT TAB(5);"A";TAB(15);"B";TAB(25);"A/B"
3. 20 PRINT A;TAB(10);B
4. 5 PRINT "A=";A;TAB(20);"B=";B;TAB(35);"A/B=";A/B

B   Write a program using TAB's to print each pattern on the terminal.

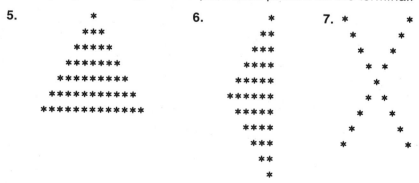

8. In the spirit of Exercises 5 through 7 write a program to print a pattern of your choice. Possibilities are your initials, a numeral, a figure, etc.

7-6 RANDOM NUMBERS AND THE "RND" FUNCTION

Random events, such as tossing a coin, rolling dice, and dealing cards, can be simulated by a computer by means of the RND function. When it is used, a value is randomly selected from the interval zero to one. That

is, if   LET X = RND(I)

is executed, x will be set equal to a six-digit decimal number greater than 0 and less than 1.

The exact method used to generate the random number varies from computer to computer but it can be compared to spinning a roulette wheel: the number on which the ball ultimately comes to rest depends on the number on which the ball was placed when the wheel was spun and the amount of force expended in whirling the wheel. The argument of the RND function corresponds to the position of the ball when spinning begins. If the argument is zero, the function will generate a random number. If the RND function is executed again in the program, a second number is produced and so on. However, the next time that program is run, the computer will generate the *same* sequence of numbers.

On many systems if a different starting number is desired each time the program is executed (as is usually the case for programs simulating games or sports), a negative argument must be used for RND. A negative argument causes the RND function first to produce a random number, which is then used as the starting point for producing additional random numbers. If a positive argument is used, a random number based on its value is generated. Thus, a negative argument produces the "most random" numbers. (The rule just mentioned is not universal; on some systems the argument of RND is purely a "dummy" value or variable and has no effect on the random number generation so that the same sequence of numbers is produced every time the program is run. Another possibility is the RANDØMIZE command explained on page 230.)

As an example consider this program to generate five random numbers. Two separate runs of the program are shown.

```
10 FØR I = 1 TØ 5
20 PRINT I, RND(-I)
21 REM NØTE THE NEGATIVE ARGUMENT FØR RND IN LINE 20.
30 NEXT I
40 END
```

First Run		Second Run	
1	.897334	1	.803628
2	.673334	2	.737032
3	3.14714E-2	3	.130812
4	.114375	4	.612766
5	.157887	5	.788928

On some systems the command RANDØMIZE (or perhaps RANDOM) can be placed at the beginning of a program to initialize the system's random number generator (perhaps by using the time on the system clock). The effect will be to give different sets of random numbers each time the program is executed.

If $A = $ RND($-$I), then A is just as likely to be less than $\frac{1}{2}$ as greater than $\frac{1}{2}$. Hence we may simulate tossing a coin by executing RND($-$I) and testing whether the result is less than $\frac{1}{2}$, as in this program segment.

```
10 IF RND(-I) < .5 THEN 50
20 PRINT "TAILS"
.  .  .  .  .  .  .  .  .  .  .  .  .  .

50 PRINT   "HEADS"
.  .  .  .  .  .  .  .  .  .  .  .  .  .
```

Coin-tossing could also be simulated by generating a random number, multiplying by ten, and taking the INT part of the result.

```
50 LET C = INT(10*RND(X))
```

C will thus be a member of {0, 1, 2, 3, 4, 5, 6, 7, 8, 9}. Test if C is even or odd and arbitrarily equate "even" with "heads" and "odds" with "tails" (or vice-versa).

Now suppose we want to examine the results of numerous rolls of a die. This means we want to generate the integers 1 to 6 at random with equal probability. To accomplish this result, divide the interval 0 to 1 into six equal parts. The table below shows one way to distribute the die faces.

Random numbers	Die faces
.000000 to .166666	1
.166667 to .333333	2
.333334 to .499999	3
.500000 to .666666	4
.666667 to .833332	5
.833333 to .999999	6

To "roll" two dice, generate two random numbers, convert to integers as above, and add the integers together.

For card games the random number generator can be used to "shuffle" the "deck." First produce a random number that converts to one of the four suits (diamonds, hearts, clubs, spades); then generate a second random number to decide the card within the suit (ace, deuce, . . . , ten, jack, queen, king). A special problem here is that a list of cards already dealt in the hand must be stored in order to avoid dealing the same card twice. After generating two random numbers giving the suit and card, the program must check the array of previously used cards. If this card has already appeared, discard it and generate another card.

Coin tossing, rolling a die, and dealing a card are experiments that are relatively easy to simulate since each outcome is equally probable. This is not the case with more complicated games such as boxing, football, and baseball simulations that have recently become popular. A good baseball program, for example, must weight the random numbers to produce a realistic proportion of hits, walks, and outs for particular hitters against particular pitchers. A crude approach, just to illustrate this point, would be to allow ten possible numbers to be produced by the random number generator; for a .300 hitter (one who hits safely 30% of the time) seven of the numbers would represent outs and three would represent hits. Whether the hit is a single, double, triple, or home run could depend on the results of another random generation, weighted according to the hitter's power statistics collected from his past performance.

EXERCISES 7-6

A   What value might be assigned to Y by the following statements?

Example: 50 LET Y $=$ INT(10*RND(X))

Answer: An integer from 0 to 9, inclusive

1. 50 LET Y = INT(6*RND(X) + 1)
2. 50 LET Y = 10*INT(RND(X))
3. 50 LET Y = INT(6*RND(X)) + 1
4. 50 LET Y = INT(10*RND(X)) - 2*INT(10*RND(X)/2)

Write a LET statement involving the RND function that will assign to Y a value from each set.

5. A random number between 1 and 2.
6. A random number between 0 and 10.
7. A random even integer from 0 to 18, inclusive.

B   Write programs for your system to execute the random events described in Exercises 8, 9, and 10.

8. Generate 1000 random digits (0 to 9) and count the number of times each digit occurs.

Flip a coin 1000 times and count the number of heads and the number of tails.

9. Use the first method explained in the lesson, that is, decide if the random number is less than .5 or greater than .5.
10. Use the second method: convert the random number to an integer and decide if the integer is even or odd.

7-7 ADDITIONAL FUNCTIONS: EXP, LØG, SGN

Several standard mathematical functions have been defined and stored in the computer for ready use. They are sometimes called "library functions." Here are some of them.

EXP(X)   Calculates e^x where "e" is the base of the natural logarithm system. ("e" is an irrational number approximately equal to 2.7183.)

LØG(X)   Finds the natural (base e) logarithm of x. This expression is often written "In x" in mathematics texts.

SGN(X)   Determines the sign of a real variable or formula. If the value of the expression "x" is positive, SGN(X) = 1; if the value is negative, SGN(X) = −1; if the value is zero, SGN(X) = 0.

Here are examples of BASIC statements involving these functions.

```
10 LET Y = EXP(X↑2 - 3)
97 IF LØG(X) > 2.7183 THEN 150
65 PRINT SGN(Z*Y);LØG(ABS(Z*Y))
110 DEF FNA(X) = EXP(-X↑3)
```

EXERCISES 7-7

B   **1.** Write a program to compute e^x using the following series.

$$e^x = 1 + x + \frac{x^2}{2!} + \frac{x^3}{3!} + \ldots$$

Compare the results with BASIC's EXP(X) function.

2. Write your own program to accomplish the same results as the SGN function.

3. Two functions sinh x ("hyperbolic sine") and cosh x ("hyperbolic cosine") are graphed below and are defined by

$$\sinh x = \frac{e^x - e^{-x}}{2} \qquad \cosh x = \frac{e^x + e^{-x}}{2}$$

Write a program to compute sinh x and cosh x.

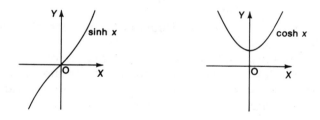

7-8 "ØN" STATEMENTS

The ØN statement provides a means of combining several equality-type
IF . . . THEN statements into one. Thus the sequence of statements

```
60 IF X = 1 THEN 200
70 IF X = 2 THEN 170
80 IF X = 3 THEN 215
```

can be condensed to the following ØN statement.

```
60 ØN X GØ TØ 200, 170, 215
```

"X" may be a variable or a formula. Any number of line numbers may
follow GØ TØ as long as the entire statement fits onto one teletype line.
Here is another example.

```
35 ØN A*B - C GØ TØ 100,110,60,135,10
```

Execution of this statement will proceed as follows.

1. INT(A*B — C) is computed.
2. If INT(A*B — C) = 1, execution branches to line 100.
3. If INT(A*B — C) = 2, execution branches to line 110.
4. If INT(A*B — C) = 3, execution branches to line 60.
5. If INT(A*B — C) = 4, execution branches to line 135.
6. If INT(A*B — C) = 5, execution branches to line 10.
7. If INT(A*B — C) < 1 or if INT(A*B — C) > 5, an error message is printed
   and execution is terminated.

The programmer must know in advance the range of possible values the
formula might take so as to provide an appropriate number of transfers.

EXERCISES 7-8

A   Consider the following statement.

```
50 ØN X/Y GØ TØ 100, 120, 140, 10
```

To what statement will the program branch if X and Y are given as
shown below.
1. X = 4 and Y = 4.   2. X = 5 and Y = 2.
3. X = 12 and Y = 3.   4. X = 1 and Y = 2.

B   5. Recall Exercise 8 on page 231. Use an ØN statement in a program to generate 1000 random digits (0 to 9) and count the
number of times each digit occurs.
6. Simulate the game of "pick a card." That is, when the program
is run, the computer prints the name of one card randomly
selected from a deck of 52 cards.

7-9 "GØSUB", "RETURN", AND "STØP" STATEMENTS

When a particular portion of a program is to be performed more than once at several different places in the overall program, it could be written as a *subroutine*. A **subroutine** is a self-contained program incorporated into a main program. The only restriction is that the last instruction executed in the subroutine must be RETURN.

The subroutine may be entered from any point in the main program by a GØSUB instruction. The subroutine is then executed and computation returns to the main program where it was left off.

As a simple example consider the following program.

```
10 LET X = 1.4
20 GØSUB 200
30 LET X = 2.71
40 GØSUB 200
50 LET X = 4.12
60 GØSUB 200
70 STØP
200 LET Y = 5*X
210 LET Z = 3.14159*LØG(Y)
220 LET M = SQR(Z↑3)
230 PRINT X; M
240 RETURN
500 END
```

The statements of this program would be executed in the following order.

10-20, 200-240, 30-40, 200-240, 50-60, 200-240, 70, 500.

The statement   70 STØP   is necessary to prevent an extra execution of the subroutine.   70 GØ TØ 500   would accomplish the same result.

Caution must be exercised when subroutines contain decisions. A decision may cause a branch to the RETURN statement or to END or STØP. It may also produce a branch to another statement within the subroutine. It may not, however, branch back to any statement in the main program. (This rule is not universal; it is a good idea to check the BASIC manual for your system.)

Such a procedure would usually produce an error message like the one that appears below.

GØSUBS NESTED TØØ DEEPLY AT LINE # ---

EXERCISES 7-9

A   **1.** Show the output of the following program.

```
10 READ A,B,C
20 GØSUB 200
30 IF L = 1 THEN 70
40 LET R = A*B/2
50 PRINT "AREA = " R; " PERIMETER =" A+B+C
60 GØ TØ 10
70 PRINT "NØT A RIGHT TRIANGLE"
80 GØ TØ 10
90 DATA 3,4,5,0,1,1,2,2,2,12,5,13
200 LET L = O
210 IF A + B <= C THEN 250
220 IF A + C <= B THEN 250
230 IF B + C <= A THEN 250
240 IF A↑2 + B↑2 = C↑2 THEN 260
250 LET L = 1
260 RETURN
900 END
```

2. Explain the function of the variable L in the program above.

CHAPTER REVIEW

Write *Yes* or *No* to show whether each of the following is a valid statement for your system.

1. 10 INPUT A,B   **2.** 25 MAT INPUT X   **3.** 15 INPUT A$
4. 10 RANDØMIZE   **5.** 70 GØSUB 200   **6.** 150 STØP
7. 40 DEF FNA = 4*RND(X)   **8.** 35 PRINT Z;TAB(I);
9. 60 MAT PRINT TAB(25);A   **10.** 30 INPUT:SØURCE: X,Y,Z

Write *Yes* or *No* to show whether each of the following is a valid string variable for your system.
11. SMITH   **12.** "SMITH"   **13.** A   **14.** A(I)
15. A$ **16.** A$(I)   **17.** A1$ **18.** A$(I,J)

19. Write a program that accepts a positive integer x from the terminal (rather than from a DATA statement) and prints x random numbers, sorted into ascending order.

Show the output line produced by each statement if $J = -7$ and $K = 3$. Identify key columns.
20. 90 PRINT TAB(5);"J =";J;TAB(20);"K =";K
21. 55 PRINT "J/K =";TAB(10);J/K;TAB(20);J*K

Consider the statement   20 ON 2*G/H GO TO 100,200,50,350,900
To which line will the program branch if G and H are given as below.
22. G = 8, H = 8   **23.** G = 2, H = 3   **24.** G = 40, H = 16

ROUND SEVEN: *PROGRAMS FOR STUDENT ASSIGNMENT*

GENERAL INSTRUCTION:

In each exercise on page 236 through 244, write a program that will do what is specified in the exercise.

1. Devise new operations, such as $a \# b = a + b + ab$, and test the operations against the field axioms. (Note: The DEF statement is particularly useful here.)

2. Given a year (past, present, or future) print the calendar for that year.

3. The game "Twenty-three Matches" (a version of "NIM") is played as follows: Two players take turns removing matches from a pile of twenty-three matches. At each turn a player must take one, two, or three matches. He may not pass. The player who takes the last match loses. A strategy exists whereby the player who moves first can win every time. Simulate this game with the computer playing a human opponent.

4. Write a "teaching program" in which the computer provides practice problems to a student to determine his knowledge of the rules for multiplying positive and negative numbers. (This topic is only suggested; with your teacher's permission you may select another topic to teach.) The computer explains the rules and gives practice problems. It congratulates the student when he is right and corrects him when he is wrong, repeating the rule he has violated. The machine keeps track of how many problems the student answers correctly and prints his percent right at the end of the lesson.

5. Determine how many times Friday the 13th occurs in a given year.

An equation of the form $Ax^2 + Bxy + Cy^2 + Dx + Ey + F = 0$ is given for Exercises 6 and 7.

6. Identify the locus (straight line, circle, hyperbola, and so forth).

7. Print the equation of the image resulting from a rotation of the locus through an angle ϕ about the origin.

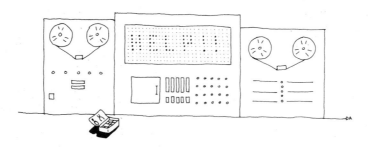

8. A "Monte Carlo" method for calculating π goes as follows: consider a unit square in the *xy*-plane with vertices at (0, 0), (1, 0), (1, 1), and (0, 1). For a circle centered at the origin with radius one (see diagram at right), one quadrant lies within the unit square. The area of this circle is π, and therefore the area of the quadrant shown is $\frac{\pi}{4}$. Imagine randomly choosing

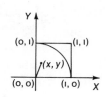

random points within the square. Some of the points will lie within the circle and some will lie outside the circle. Because of the respective areas of the circle quadrant and the square, for a large number of points, approximately $\frac{\pi}{4}$:1 of the points will lie within the circle. Write a program that generates random values for x and y which serve as the coordinates of a point within the square. The distance of this point from the origin is computed. If this radius is less than one, the point lies within the circle. If it is greater than one, it lies outside the circle. Count the number of times the point falls within the circle. The ratio of the number of points falling within the circle to the total number of points generated will be an approximation of $\frac{\pi}{4}$. Multiplying this ratio by four therefore yields an approximation of π itself.

For Exercises 9 and 10 write a program whereby the computer plays tic-tac-toe with a human opponent. Use this numbering system for the board.

1	2	3
8	9	4
7	6	5

9. First have the computer always move first to the center square. This reduces the program strategy to offensive moves. An algorithm can be developed whereby the computer either wins or ties every game.

10. Expand the program so that either the machine or the human opponent moves first (depending, say, on a RND generation). It is more difficult than in Exercise 9 but here too a nonlosing algorithm can be developed.

11. A Latin square is an $n \times n$ array of n numbers such that each number appears in every row and every column. See the example at the right. Write a program to print all Latin squares of order n for $n = 2, 3, \ldots, 9$.

```
1 2 3 4 5
2 3 4 5 1
3 4 5 1 2
4 5 1 2 3
5 1 2 3 4
```

12. A magic square is an $n \times n$ array of the integers 1 to n^2 placed in such a way that the sum of each row, each column, and each diagonal is the same. See the example below.

$$
\begin{array}{ccc}
2 & 9 & 4 \\
\\
7 & 5 & 3 \\
\\
6 & 1 & 8
\end{array}
$$

Print a magic square of order n.

13. Eight queens can be arranged on a chessboard so that none is under attack from any of the others; determine three such arrangements.

14. Create a data file and scan the file and print the names and addresses of those people in the file who are (a) male, between 30 and 40 in age, married, not a home owner, and with a car costing over $2500, (b) less than 25 years old and divorced, and (c) over 60 years of age, do not own a home, and have a car costing less than $2000.

15. Scan a file of employees' Social Security numbers, names, and birthdates. The company's mandatory retirement age is 65. Print a list of those employees who must retire within the next year, within two years, three, four, and five years. Print the retirement lists in order of birthdays.

16. Design a questionnaire to be administered to your fellow students and a computer program to compile and analyze the results.

17. Simulate the dice game of "craps."

18. Prepare a checkbook-balancing program. Given the previous balance and the deposits and withdrawals for the month, print a list of the monthly transactions and the balance at the end of the month.

19. Simulate the batting of one side in a nine-inning baseball game, taking into account the batting statistics of the players. Print a batter-by-batter summary of each inning. Choose a real team and use their latest statistics to create the data file.

20. Plot two-dimensional graphs in table or chart form (months-sales, time-distance, temperature-volume, and so forth). That is, given the ordered pairs of data (in no special order), the program will establish axes and print a bar or line graph.

21. Plot the graph of any function. Allow the user to input the function, the domain, and the increment between *x*-values. Here is a sample plot of a portion of *y* = sin *x*. Turn it sideways to get the proper orientation.

```
FØR X:    TØP  =  0  BØTTØM =  6.2832   INCREMENT =  .5
FØR Y:    LEFT = -1  RIGHT =  1  INCREMENT =  3.33333E-2

   I.........I.........I.........I.........I.........I.........I
 -                              +                            -
 .                                    +
 .                                              +
 .                                                   +.
 .                                          +
 .                                  +
 .                              +
 .                  +
 .         +
 . +
 - +                                                         -
 .        +
 .              +
   I.........I.........I.........I.........I.........I.........I
```

22. From a file of adjectives and nouns, generate random similes of the form ::adjective:: AS A ::noun:: For example, SLØW AS A TURTLE.

23. Generate random four-word sentences.

24. Modtown has five candidates for mayor. You are hired by the city to construct a computer program to tally the election results. As DATA you will have the names of the five candidates in alphabetical order (as they will appear on the ballot), then lists of numbers 1, 2, 3, 4, or 5, indicating which candidate received each person's vote. Count the votes and print the results in the order of finish.

25. Devise a program to decode messages written in a code you create. To test the program teach a friend (or an enemy) your encoding scheme and have him or her encode a message without showing it to you. The program should decode this message correctly.

26. Teach the computer to write four-part harmony for a given melody.

27. Convert Arabic numerals to Roman numerals.

28. Convert Roman numerals to Arabic.

Playpen Magazine has a file listing each subscriber's name, address, and subscription expiration date (month/year). (Exercises 29 and 30)

29. Write a program which, given a month and year, prints the names and addresses of all subscribers whose subscription expires that month.

30. Write a program which, given the current month and year, erases the names and addresses of all subscribers whose subscription expires this month. Print on the terminal the resulting condensed file and also write it back to the external file. "Condensed" means that there are no gaps: the information about the remaining subscribers have been pushed forward to fill vacated space in the array.

31. Given the names of the teams and their won-lost records, print up-to-date National or American League baseball standings. The output should list the teams in descending order of winning percentage, giving in columns the wins, losses, percentage, and games-behind. Do not assume that all teams have played the same number of games.

32. Translate dollar-cents amounts into words. Handle values up to ØNE MILLION DØLLARS AND NØ CENTS.

33. A **palindrome** is a word that is spelled the same backwards or forwards, such as "radar", "level", and "pop". Decide whether a given word is a palindrome.

34. The Rhine Test for extra-sensory perception involves a deck of 25 cards: five identical cards from each of five suits. The "deck" can be represented by 1111122222333334444455555 where the numbers refer to the suits. The deck is shuffled and the subject is asked to name the suit of each card in turn without seeing the card. Guessing at random, a person should correctly identify the suits of five of the 25 cards. If he guesses more than five, he is a candidate for having ESP. Simulate the experiment a large number of times.

35. Program the computer to "draw" a picture on the terminal.

36. Given the master file of cumulative individual statistics for past games of a basketball team and the statistics from the latest game, print the updated team and individual statistics of the team.

37. Program the computer to play blackjack against human opponents with the computer being the dealer.

38. Given each senior's code number, name, total number of subjects, and total quality points, compute each graduate's grade-point average and print a ranked list of the graduating class in order of GPA.

39. Deal and analyze a poker hand. Possible outputs include "pair of eights," "full house," and "2–6 straight."

40. Simulate the trip of a mouse through a maze in search of cheese. In the diagram on the right, each intersection point of the maze has been given x and y coordinates. The mouse starts at (1, 0). At an interior intersection point such as (1, 1), assume that the probability the mouse goes in any direction is $\frac{1}{4}$. For a corner point such as (3, 0), assume that the probability is $\frac{1}{2}$ for either direction. For other border points such as (0, 2) the probability is $\frac{1}{3}$ for any direction. The mouse's trip ends when he reaches the cheese. Find the number of moves in each trip.

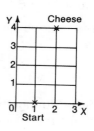

41. Determine the date of Easter in a given year.

42. Write a program to deal a hand of bridge and make an opening bid.

There are several methods for approximating an irrational zero of a polynomial function. One is Newton's Method (see Ex. 57, p. 172). Here are two more methods briefly explained in Exercises 43 and 44.

43. The Bisection Method: Suppose it is known (by substitution) that $P(a) < 0$ and $P(b) > 0$ (see the diagram at the right). Then P, being continuous, must cross the x-axis between a and b. To estimate the x-value of the crossing point, find the midpoint x_1 of the interval (a, b). If $P(x_1) > 0$, the root lies in the left half of the interval (a, b); if $P(x_1) > 0$, the root lies in the right half (for the diagram shown). In either case half the original interval can be discarded. Now bisect this new, smaller interval and repeat the analysis. By successive bisections the intervals in which the root is "trapped" become smaller and smaller and the root can be approximated to any desired accuracy.

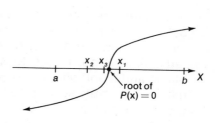

Write a program that accepts a polynomial function, finds two consecutive integers between which a real root lies, and then uses the Bisection Method to approximation the root.

44. The Method of Chords ("Method of False Position"): In the diagram at the right, chord AB crosses the x-axis "close" to the root of $P(x)$. The slope of AB is $\dfrac{P(x_2) - P(x_1)}{x_2 - x_1}$. By the point-slope form, the equation of AB is

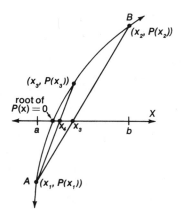

$$y - P(x_1) = \frac{P(x_2) - P(x_1)}{x_2 - x_1}(x - x_1)$$

Substituting the coordinates of the point $(x_3, 0)$ into this equation and solving for x_3, we obtain

$$x_3 = x_1 + \frac{P(x_1)(x_1 - x_2)}{P(x_2) - P(x_1)}.$$

Now iterate the technique, first using the chord from $(x_1, P(x_1))$ to $(x_3, P(x_3))$ to gain a closer approximation x_4, then using the chord from $(x_1, P(x_1))$ to $(x_4, P(x_4))$ to gain a still closer approximation x_5, and so forth. Write a program that uses the Method of Chords to approximate a zero of a polynomial function.

Simulate the game of roulette and two systems of betting. Each part of the process is explained in Exercises 45–47.

45. A roulette wheel contains 38 numbers: 0–36, and 00. A player may bet on (**a**) a particular number; (**b**) even or odd; (**c**) red or black where 1, 3, 5, 7, 9, 12, 14, 16, 18, 19, 21, 23, 25, 27, 30, 32, 34, 36 are red, 2, 4, 6, 8, 10, 11, 13, 15, 17, 20, 22, 24, 26, 28, 29, 31, 33, 35 are black, and 0 and 00 are colorless; (**d**) the number falling in the first half (1–18) or the second half (19–36), and (**e**) the number falling in the low (1–12), middle (13–24), or high (25–36) range. Write a program to accept a number from 0 to 37 (37 represents 00) and print its characteristics (even-odd, red-black, 1st-2nd half, low-middle-high).

46. Under the "Martingale" betting system, a player begins with a basic bet. Then whenever he wins, he repeats the basic bet. If he loses, his next bet is double the previous amount (unless his money is insufficient, in which case he bets the remainder of his funds). A sample sequence is the following: bet $10—win, bet $10—lose, bet $20—lose, bet $40—win, bet $10—lose, and so forth. The player continues until he either exhausts his capital or reaches a predetermined upper limit. Expand the roulette program to test this system.

47. The "progressive" system of gambling can be used for any bet that is close to even-money (such as "even-odd" or "high-low" in roulette). The player begins with a sequence of numbers, say 1, 2, 3, 4, 5. For each play he bets the sum of the first and last terms ($6 for the first bet using the sample sequence). If he wins, he crosses off the first and last terms; if he loses, he appends the amount just bet to the end of the list. Thus if the first play wins, the sample list becomes 2, 3, 4 and the next bet is $6. If he loses, the list becomes 1, 2, 3, 4, 5, 6 and the next bet is $7. The sequence should eventually disappear, at which point (theoretically) the player has won the sum of his original sequence. Test this approach for roulette.

Briefly explained below are four methods for finding the area under a curve, as shaded in the figure on the right. In each case write a program to compute the area of a given function over a given interval by the method explained.

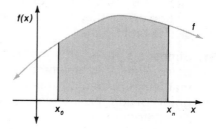

48. Rectangular Rule: Divide the interval (x_0, x_n) into n equal parts and use each interval as the base of a rectangle that has one vertex on the curve f, as in the figure on the right. The sum of the areas of the rectangles approximates the total area under the curve. To obtain a better approximation, increase (for example, by doubling) the number of rectangles.

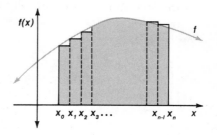

49. Trapezoidal Rule: This technique is similar to the Rectangular Rule except that trapezoids replace the rectangles (see the figure on the right). Again the approximation can be improved by increasing the number of trapezoids.

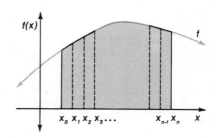

50. Midpoint Rule: Rectangles are used, as in Exercise 48, but the midpoint of the top side of each rectangle rests on the curve f (see the figure on the right). Note that a portion of each rectangle lies above the curve to counterbalance the small areas under the curve that are not covered by the rectangles. (This last fact helps explain why this method gives a better approximation than either the rectangle or trapezoid rules.)

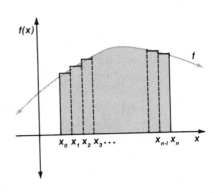

51. Simpson's Rule: This method, even more accurate than the Midpoint Rule, was invented by Thomas Simpson (1710–1761). The mathematics behind this method cannot be summarized in a diagram. Divide the interval (x_0, x_n) into an *even* number of segments and determine $y_0, y_1, y_2, \ldots, y_n$ where $y_i = f(x_i)$. Then

$$\text{area} = \frac{h}{3}(y_0 + 4y_1 + 2y_2 + \cdots + 2y_{n-2} + 4y_{n-1} + y_n)$$ where h is the width of each interval $(x_0, x_1), (x_1, x_2), \ldots, (x_{n-1}, x_n)$. Again a better approximation can be obtained by increasing n.

INDEX